MAIL/FAX BID SHEET

Heritage Auction Galleries
Direct Customer Service Line—Toll Free:
866-835-3243
HA.com
3500 Maple Avenue, 17th Floor
Dallas, Texas 75219-3941

(All information must be completed.)

HERI

Auction #652
Submit Your Bids By Fax
FAX HOTLINE: 214-443-8425

NAME ______________________ CUSTOMER # (if known) ______________________

ADDRESS ______________________ E-MAIL ADDRESS ______________________

CITY/STATE/ZIP ______________________

DAYTIME PHONE (A/C) ______________________ EVENING PHONE (A/C) ______________________

Would you like a FAX or e-mail confirming receipt of your bids? If so, please print your FAX # or e-mail address here: ______________

REFERENCES: New bidders who are unknown to us must furnish satisfactory industry references or a valid credit card in advance of the sale date.

Dealer References (City, State) and/or Credit Card Information

____

____

____

____

____

You are authorized to release payment history information to other dealers and auctioneers so that I may establish proper credit in the industry. (Line out this statement if you do not authorize release.)

Non-Internet bids (including but not limited to, podium, fax, phone and mail bids) may be submitted at any time and are treated similar to floor bids. These types of bids must be on-increment or at a half increment (called a cut bid). Any podium, fax, phone or mail bids that do not conform to a full or half increment will be rounded up or down to the nearest full or half increment and will be considered your high bid.

Current Bid	Bid Increment	Current Bid	Bid Increment
< $10	$1	$3,000 - $4,999	$250
$10 - $29	$2	$5,000 - $9,999	$500
$30 - $59	$3	$10,000 - $19,999	$1,000
$60 - $99	$5	$20,000 - $29,999	$2,000
$100 - $199	$10	$30,000 - $49,999	$2,500
$200 - $299	$20	$50,000 - $99,999	$5,000
$300 - $499	$25	$100,000 - $249,999	$10,000
$500 - $999	$50	$250,000 - $499,999	$25,000
$1,000 - $1,999	$100	$500,000 - $1,499,999	$50,000
$2,000 - $2,999	$200	> $1,500,000	$100,000

(Bid in whole dollar amounts only.)

LOT NO.	AMOUNT	LOT NO.	AMOUNT	LOT NO.	AMOUNT	LOT NO.	AMOUNT

PLEASE COMPLETE THIS INFORMATION:

1. IF NECESSARY, PLEASE INCREASE MY BIDS BY:
   ☐ 10% ☐ 20% ☐ 30%
   Lots will be purchased as much below bids as possible.

2. ☐ I HAVE BOUGHT COINS FROM YOU BEFORE (references are listed above)

I have read and agree to all of the Terms and Conditions of Auction: inclusive of paying interest at the lesser of 1.5% per month (18% per annum) or the maximum contract interest rate under applicable state law from the date of sale (if the account is not timely paid), and the submission of disputes to arbitration.

____

(Signature required) Please make a copy of your bid sheet for your records.

SUBTOTAL ________

TOTAL from other side ________

TOTAL BID ________

FAX HOTLINE: 214-443-8425

LOT NO.	AMOUNT	LOT NO.	AMOUNT	LOT NO.	AMOUNT	LOT NO.	AMOUNT
						TOTAL this side	

Please make a copy of your bid sheet for your records.

FINE AMERICAN & EUROPEAN PAINTINGS & SCULPTURE

HERITAGE SIGNATURE AUCTION #652

May 24-25, 2007 | DALLAS, TEXAS

Heritage Auction Galleries — 10th Floor Auction Room 3500 Maple Avenue | Dallas, Texas 75219

LOT VIEWING
3500 Maple Avenue, 10th Floor Gallery
Dallas, Texas 75219
May 12 – 23, 2007
Monday through Friday 9:00 AM – 6:00 PM CT
Saturday 10:00 AM – 5:00 PM CT
Sunday 12:00 – 5:00 PM CT

CUSTOMER SERVICE
Heritage Auction Galleries
3500 Maple Avenue, 17th floor
Dallas, Texas 75219
Direct Client Services Line: 866.835.3243

ABSENTEE BIDS BY FAX
Deadline, Wednesday, May 23, by 6:00 PM CT
Fax: 214.443.8425

ABSENTEE BIDS BY INTERNET
HA.com/FineArt
Bid@HA.com
Bidding closes at 10:00 PM CT the evening before each session

LIVE TELEPHONE BIDDING
Customer Service: 866.835.3243
Must be arranged on or before
Wednesday, May 23, by 5:00 PM CT

VIEW LOTS ONLINE AT: HA.COM/FINEART

AUCTION SESSIONS

Session I – American Art
Thursday, May 24, 1:00 PM CT
Lots 23001 – 23242

Session II – Western Art *(see separate catalog)*
Thursday, May 24, 6:00 PM CT
Lots 24001 – 24073

Session III – European Art
Friday, May 25, 10:00 AM CT
Lots 25001 – 25235

Session IV – Photography
Friday, May 25, 2:00 PM CT
Lots 26001 – 26081

Lots are sold at an approximate rate of 75 lots per hour.
This auction is subject to a 19.5% Buyer's Premium.

AUCTIONEERS
Kathleen Guzman, TX 16142
John Petty, TX license #00013740

AUCTION RESULTS
Immediately available at: HA.com/FineArt

LOT PICK UP
Available immediately following each session or Tuesday, May 29, 2007, 9:00 AM – 5:00 PM CT by appointment only. Third party shipping applies after this date; contact client services at (866) 835-3243.

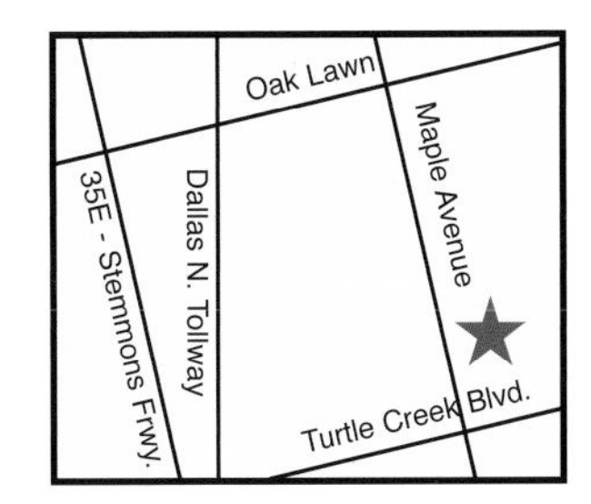

HERITAGE HA.com
Auction Galleries

Direct Client Service Line: Toll Free 866.835.3243
3500 Maple Avenue, 17th Floor, Dallas, Texas 75219-3941
214.528.3500 | 800.872.6467 | 214.443.8425 (fax)

THIS AUCTION IS PRESENTED AND CATALOGUED BY HERITAGE AUCTIONS, INC.

Catalogued by: Marianne Berardi, Christine Carmody, Courtney Case, Lindsay Davis, Bridget McWilliams, and Melynda Seaton
Edited by: Courtney E. Kennedy, Lindsay Davis, and Christine Carmody
Production and Design by: Cindy Brenner, Kelley Norwine, Matt Pegues, and Michael Puttonen
Catalogue and Internet Imaging by: Nina Castro, Lucas Garritson, Lori McKay, Ray Proska, Roy Richardson, Terry Thibeau, and Tony Webb
Operations support by: Jant Brown, Royce Cornelison, Ralph Jubera, Erin Murphy, Perry Nichols, Randy Rinestine, Lindsay Walton, and Monica Wilkins

6756

Steve Ivy
CEO
Co-Chairman of the Board

Jim Halperin
Co-Chairman of the Board

Greg Rohan
President

Paul Minshull
Chief Operating Officer

FINE AND DECORATIVE ART DEPARTMENT

Edmund P. Pillsbury, Ph.D.
Chairman of Fine and Decorative Arts

Kathleen Guzman
Senior Auctioneer

Michael Wolf
Deputy Managing Director

Gary Hendershott
Director, Civil War Memorabilia

Courtney E. Kennedy
Associate Managing Director

Janet Brown
Director of Operations

Ed Jaster
Vice President

Lindsay Davis
Consignment Director

Christine Carmody
Consignment Director

Courtney Case
Consignment Director

Larry Boettigheimer
Consignment Director

HERITAGE HA.com
Auction Galleries

3500 Maple Avenue, 17th Floor
Dallas, Texas 75219-3941
214.528.3500 • 800.872.6467
214.443.8425 (fax)

SESSION I
AMERICAN ART

23001

AMERICAN SCHOOL (Nineteenth Century)
Early American Regional Folk Art Portraiture
Young Child Clutching A Wheeled Toy Dog
Oil on canvas
29-1/4 x 23-1/4 inches (74.3 x 60.3 cm)
Inscribed verso: *painted by W. Bazin*

Provenance:
Private collection (Philadelphia, Pennsylvania)

Estimate: $14,000-$18,000

This lot is being sold without reserve. Unreserved lots generally open at 50% of the low estimate.

23002

LAWRENCE H. LEBDUSKA
(American 1894-1966)
The Wolf And The Hare
Oil on artist's palette
12 x 15-3/4 inches (30.5 x 40 cm)
Signed lower left: L. H. Lebduska

Estimate: $1,200-$1,800

The reserve for this lot is available at HA.com/FineArt.

23003

LAWRENCE H. LEBDUSKA (American 1894-1966)
The Rider And His Dog
Oil on canvasboard
20 x 16 inches (50.8 x 40.6 cm)
Signed lower right: *L.H. Lebduska*

Estimate: $1,200-$1,800

The reserve for this lot is available at HA.com/FineArt.

23004

Attributed to (CHARLES) CHESTER HARDING
(Early Nineteenth Century)
Portrait Of A Gentleman
Oil on canvas
15 x 11 inches (38.1 x 27.9cm)
With label: *Daniel Webster life painted by Chester Harding*
Depicting a bust-length portrait of the American statesman, Daniel Webster (1782-1852).

Estimate: $2,000-$3,000

The reserve for this lot is available at HA.com/FineArt.

23005

AMERICAN SCHOOL (Nineteenth Century)
Early Folk Art
Portrait Of Two Sisters
Oil on canvas
34 x 43 inches (86.4 x 109.2 cm)
Unsigned

Estimate: $9,000-$11,000

The reserve for this lot is available at HA.com/FineArt.

23006

Attributed to ALVAN FISHER (American 1792-1863)
Napoleon's Horse, circa 1818-25
Oil on canvas
24-3/4 x 30-1/4 inches (62.9 x 76.8 cm)
Signed verso in pencil: *Painted by Alvan Fisher*
With a paper label: *Purchased from Victor Sparks, N.Y. / on back of original canvas, Alvan Fisher / "Napoleon's Horse" 1818(?) / relined circa 1940 / exhibited in shows of early American painting / various cities and dates (museum or museum sponsored exhibitions) Hartford, Providence, Chicago, San Francisco, etc. / .....*

Estimate: $6,000-$9,000

The reserve for this lot is available at HA.com/FineArt.

23007

JAMES J. McAULIFFE
(American 1848-1921)
Molly
Oil on canvas
20 x 24 inches (50.8 x 61 cm)
Signed lower left: *J. McAuliffe*

Provenance:
H.V. Allison Galleries, Inc. (New York);
Hirschl & Adler Galleries, Inc. (New York)

Estimate: $15,000-$20,000

This lot is being sold without reserve. Unreserved lots generally open at 50% of the low estimate.

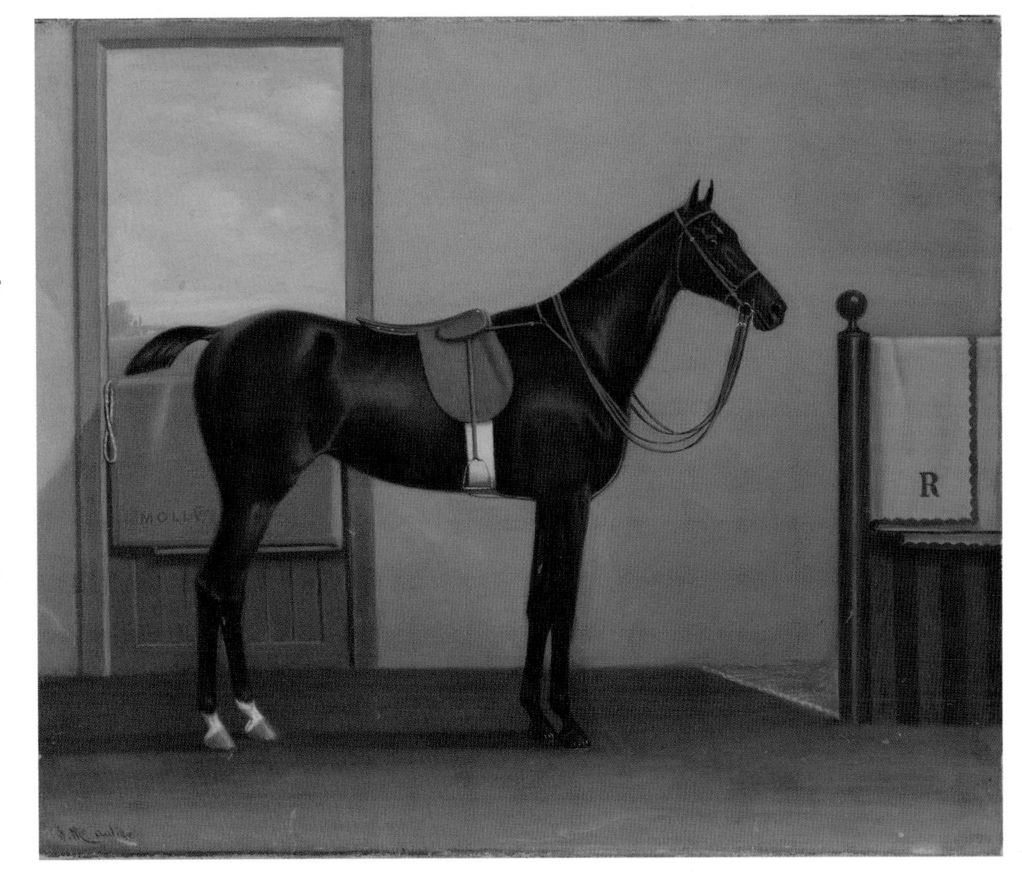

23008

EDGAR TAYLOR (American b.1862)
The Horse Traders, 1893
Gouache en grisaille on paper
19 x 21-1/4 inches (48.3 x 54 cm)
Signed and dated lower left: *Edgar Taylor 93*

Edgar Taylor studied at The Brooklyn Art Guild under Thomas Eakins.

Estimate: $2,000-$3,000

The reserve for this lot is available at HA.com/FineArt.

23009

JOHN WILLIAMSON (American 1826-1885)
Snow Peaks
Oil on canvas
13-1/2 x 10-1/2 inches (34.3 x 26.7 cm)
Initialed lower left: *JW*
Inscription verso: *Snow Peaks, J.W.*

Provenance:
Alexander Gallery (New York)

In the 1850s, Williamson established a reputation as a painter of mountain views of the Catskills and the Hudson Valley. During his career, he also was active in the Adirondacks, the Berkshires, and the White Mountains. Williamson's paintings focus more on the impression of the scene than on topographical accuracy.

Estimate: $12,000-$18,000

This lot is being sold without reserve. Unreserved lots generally open at 50% of the low estimate.

23010

AMERICAN SCHOOL (Nineteenth Century)
Landscape
Oil on canvas laid on board
7 x 5 inches (17.8 x 12.7 cm)

A small, but exceptionally detailed landscape with giltwood frame.

Estimate: $300-$500

This lot is being sold without reserve. Unreserved lots generally open at 50% of the low estimate.

23011

THOMAS CORWIN LINDSAY (American 1838-1907)
Autumn
Oil on canvas
22 x 18 inches (55.9 x 45.7 cm)
Signed lower left: *T.C. LINDSAY*

Provenance:
Private collection (Dallas, Texas)

Estimate: $2,500-$5,000

The reserve for this lot is available at HA.com/FineArt.

23012

RANSOM GILLET HOLDREDGE
(American 1836-1899)
Indians Fishing The Klamath,
circa 1875
Oil on canvas
21 x 36 inches (53.3 x 91.4 cm)
Signed lower left: *Holdredge*

Provenance:
Private collection (Washington)

Estimate: $4,000-$6,000

The reserve for this lot is available at HA.com/FineArt.

23013

JOHN ADAMS PARKER
(American 1829-1905)
On The Upper Hudson
Oil on canvas
20-1/4 x 30-1/8 inches
(51.4 x 76.5 cm)

Estimate:
$8,000-$12,000

The reserve for this lot is available at HA.com/FineArt.

23014

JAMES REID LAMBDIN (American 1807-1889)
Portrait Of George Washington (after Gilbert Stuart)
Oil on canvas
30-1/4 x 24-3/4 inches (76.8 x 62.9 cm)
Inscribed verso: *Washington / the original / by Stuart / J. R. Lambdin*

Estimate: $2,500-$4,500

The reserve for this lot is available at HA.com/FineArt.

23015

GEORGE PETER ALEXANDER HEALY (American 1813-1894)
Portrait Of Margaret Gail Moore, 1804-1893
Oil on canvas
30 x 24-1/2 inches (76.2 x 62.2 cm)
Inscribed on the back of the relining in a handwriting that appears to mimic an original inscription: *Margaret Gail Moore born 1804 - died 1893 painted by George P.A. Healy*

Estimate: $2,000-$5,000

The reserve for this lot is available at HA.com/FineArt.

23016

HIRAM POWERS (American 1805-1873)
Proserpine, modeled 1844
Marble
24 inches, high (61 cm)
Inscription on front of base: *Hiram Power*

Literature:
Richard P. Wunder, *Hiram Powers Vermont Sculptor, 1805 -1873* (Newark, Delaware: University of Delaware Press, 1990), II:187-204

Proserpine was Powers's most popular sculpture. He carved 147 busts of the goddess of flowers in five different versions. The first version was completed in 1843 and shows the figure emerging from an elaborate wicker basket filled with a corsage of spring flowers. The second, the present example, was modeled a year later and features the goddess emerging from a basket filled with acanthus leaves. In the other versions Powers substituted a simple fringe of beads around the base, omitted the molding altogether, and depicted only the goddess's head and neck. Proserpine was originally intended to be a companion piece for Powers's bust Ginerva, which was executed in 1838, shortly after the sculptor's arrival in Florence.

In his description of this sculpture, Hiram Powers recounted the story of Proserpine (the Roman equivalent of Persephone) and explained his specific presentation of the goddess: "She was the daughter of Jupiter and Ceres and while gathering flowers when very young and exceedingly beautiful, was discovered by Pluto who seized her in his arms and bore her down through a neighboring lake to his own infernal dominions. Her mother sought her a long time in vain, but at last found out her fate and besought Jupiter to release her, which request was granted on condition that 'Proserpine' had eaten nothing while with Pluto. But unhappily she had eaten a pomegranate in his garden so a compromise was made, viz., she should come back to earth half the year and remain with her husband the other half. And so she appears in the bust with a wreath of wheat in bloom on her head and rising out of an acanthus (emblem of immortality) around her waist" (Richard P. Wunder, Hiram Powers: Vermont Sculptor, 1805-1873, University of Delaware Press, Newark, Delaware, 1990, II, p. 189).

Proserpine is one of a number of heads of female mythological characters Powers sculpted. He also executed busts of Diana, Psyche and Clytie. Several of Powers's female sitters, including Martha Endicott Peabody of Salem, Massachusetts (1847 or 1848, Essex Institute), chose to be portrayed in the guise of Proserpine, a popular subject in Romantic and Victorian poetry. Percy Bysshe Shelley, Walter Savage Landor, Robert Browning, and Algernon Charles Swinburne all wrote verse about the goddess of Springtime. The American sculptor Joel Tanner Hart was greatly moved by Powers's sculpture and remarked: "I defy Antiquity to surpass – I doubt its ability to rival – Powers's Proserpine" (Cecilia Cleveland, The Story of a Summer or, Journal Leaves from Chappaqua, G.W. Carleton & Co., New York, 1874, p. 120).

Estimate: $60,000-$80,000

This lot is being sold without reserve. Unreserved lots generally open at 50% of the low estimate.

23017

GEORGE INNESS (American 1825-1894)
Landscape, 1857
Oil on canvas-faced academy board
7-3/8 x 10-5/8 inches (18.7 x 27 cm)
Signed at lower left: *G. Inness 1857*

Provenance:
M. Giblin;
Mrs. Louis Wilson (Washington, DC);
Mrs. Graham B. Peake, to 1952 (New York);
With Grand Central Art Galleries, 1952 (New York);
Private collection (Dallas, Texas)

The painting depicts a peaceful countryside filling with soft light from the right with beautifully colored clouds in the lower sky. The foreground is shaded by trees on the right. A stream with cows wading, flows out from the left of the canvas to the right and then curves back again to the left. The stream passes back through high banks to the left and center, decorated with mature trees and a house at center. The background depicts a rolling landscape and a sloping mountain. An exceptionally detailed example of the period, this *Landscape* is part of a group of three paintings that passed through the market in 1952. Each painting in the series depicts a different time of day. The other two paintings *The Meadows* and *The Sunset* are currently in the collection of the Worcester Art Museum. This particular painting will be included in the supplement to Michael Quick's, *George Inness: A Catalogue raisonné* (2006).

Estimate: $40,000-$60,000

The reserve for this lot is available at HA.com/FineArt.

23018

WILLIAM HOLBROOK BEARD

(American 1824-1900)

It Rains It Shines, The Devil Whipping His Wife

Oil on canvas

24 x 20 inches (61 x 50.8 cm)

Provenance:

Private collection;

Adelson Galleries, label verso (New York);

Questroyal Fine Art, label verso (New York)

The author of this provocative nineteenth-century painting, William Holbrook Beard, was born into a family of portrait, animal, landscape, and genre painters in the small town of Painesville, Ohio, near Cleveland. He is best known for his satiric genre scenes featuring animals as stand-ins for human beings behaving badly. He frequently used bears as protagonists. The present work is less anecdotal, and more hauntingly compelling than many of his satirical works. In the upper scene, an innocent child has happened upon a peculiar wooden grate on the ground in a clearing of a misty field. Noises from below the strange construction attracted the child's attention and led him to kneel down and listen. In the lower, underground scene, which is rendered in an entirely different palette of earth tones and fiery furnace reds, Beard has painted a scene of a devil flogging his wife. Reminiscent of the work of Salvator Rosa, the subject is doubtless related to a literary source, but has a painterly rather than illustrational quality.

Basically self-taught, the young artist began his career painting with his older brother James Henry Beard, and then worked for several years as an itinerant portraitist in his home state. He moved to New York City in 1845, but by 1850 left the larger metropolis for Buffalo. There he established a studio and became close to a group of successful artists including portraitist Thomas LeClear (whose daughter he married) and Swedish-born landscapist Lars Gustave Sellstedt, Buffalo's principal mid-century painter. Beard remained in Buffalo until 1856, the year he left for a two-year tour of Europe. He traveled extensively, and met and painted with many American artists including Emanuel Leutze, Sanford Gifford, Worthington Whittredge, and Albert Bierstadt. Upon his return to the United States, he spent two more years in Buffalo before settling into apartments in the Tenth Street Studio Building in New York, home to many of the nation's most celebrated painters. After his return from Europe, Beard concentrated upon satirical animal subjects. As William Gerdts has noted, "One of his most characteristic and controversial of such paintings was his *March of Silenus* (Albright-Knox Art Gallery, Buffalo, New York), a classical theme reinterpreted with a drunken bear attended by an entourage of goats, which led to the artist's election as National Academician in 1862."

In 1866, he traveled West by train to explore the landscape, and in Colorado his companion was Bayard Taylor, a writer and lecturer. During the trip, he wrote home to his wife that the landscape was monotonous, that he was disappointed in seeing so few buffalo, and the life out West was too hard. As a result of the trip, his wanderlust was sated, and he turned increasingly to his imagination as the source of inspiration for the habits and environments of his wildlife subjects. Many of his later paintings showed animals as physically realistic but atypical in terms of their behavior.

Estimate: $15,000-$25,000

The reserve for this lot is available at HA.com/FineArt.

23019

CHARLES CARYL COLEMAN
(American 1840-1928)
River Landscape With Mist, 1861
Oil on panel
7 x 17-3/4 inches (17.8 x 45 cm)
Signed and dated lower left: *C.C. Coleman 1861*

Provenance:
Private collection

Charles Caryl Coleman was born in Buffalo, New York, and was briefly under the tutelage of William Holbrook Beard (1824-1900) before seeking instruction under Thomas Couture in Paris in 1856. By 1860, Coleman, along with lifelong friend and fellow painter Elihu Vedder, traveled to Florence where he was introduced to the expatriate lifestyle. Before he could settle in Italy, Coleman returned to the United States to serve in the Union army during the Civil war. He subsequently settled in New York City in 1863 after receiving an honorable discharge from the army. By 1866, Coleman had returned to Italy where he became a full-time resident of the city of Rome and eventually permanently settled on the island of Capri in the 1880s, a place that became a popular subject for Coleman's paintings.

Best known for his studio compositions executed in the late 1870s-1900s, this work, created while the artist was no more than 21 years of age, is a fine example of his early career in painting.

The present work will be included in Adrienne Baxter Bell's forthcoming *catalogue raisonné* of Coleman's work.

Estimate: $6,000-$8,000

This lot is being sold without reserve. Unreserved lots generally open at 50% of the low estimate.

23020

NINETEENTH CENTURY SCHOOL
Landscape, Possibly American
Oil on board
21 x 28-1/2 inches
(53.3 x 72.4 cm)

Estimate: $1,000-$2,000

This lot is being sold without reserve. Unreserved lots generally open at 50% of the low estimate.

23021

JOHN WILLIAM HILL (Amercian 1812-1879)
Lilacs, circa 1865-1870
Watercolor on paper
13 x 11-1/2 inches (33 x 29.2 cm)
Signed lower left: *J.W. Hill*

Hill often painted watercolors featuring flowers growing in a natural setting. Generally intimate in scale, the artist uses the stipple technique advocated by Ruskin to achieve a gem-like luminosity of tone. Hill was extraordinarily sensitive to form and detail, and achieved a stunning subtlety of effect similar to the work of painters associated with the Pre-Raphaelite Brotherhood in England.

Estimate: $15,000-$25,000

This lot is being sold without reserve. Unreserved lots generally open at 50% of the low estimate.

23022

PAUL LACROIX (American 1827-1869)
Two Tier Still Life With Fruit, circa 1863-68
Oil on canvas
12 x 16-7/8 inches (30.5 x 42.9 cm)
Signed lower right: *P. Lacroix*

Provenance:
The Robert P. Coggins Collection (Marietta, Georgia)

Exhibitions:
Memorial Art Gallery of the University of Rochester, New York, *Selections for the Robert P. Coggins Collections of American Painting,* February 25 - April 10, 1977, catalogue p.58 (reproduced); traveled to: The High Museum of Art, Atlanta, Georgia, December 3, 1976 - January 16, 1977; Herbert E. Johnson Museum of Art, Cornell University, Ithaca, New York, May 4 - June 12, 1977

Estimate: $30,000-$50,000

This lot is being sold without reserve. Unreserved lots generally open at 50% of the low estimate.

23023

JOHN F. FRANCIS (American 1808-1886)
Still Life With Fruits And Nuts, 1865
Oil on panel
14-3/4 x 19 inches (36.2 x 48.3 cm)
Signed and dated lower right: *J F Francis pt. 1865*
Signed verso: *J. F. Frances 1865*

Exhibitions:
The Packwook House Museum, Lewisburg, Pennsylvania, *A Suitable Likeness: The Paintings of John F. Francis 1832-1879,* June 28 - November 2, 1986, catalogue no. 47;
Berry-Hill Galleries, New York, *John F. Francis: Not Just Desserts,* November 19, 1990 - January 5, 1991

Literature:
Bernard S. Dean Levy, Inc., *American Paintings,* 1980, reproduced, n.p.;
"A Suitable Likeness: The Paintings of John F. Francis at the Packwood House Museum", *Antiques and the Arts Weekly,* September 12, 1986, pp. 1, 62 (reproduced);
John F. Francis: Not Just Desserts, New York Berry-Hill Galleries, 1990, pp. 3, 7.

John F. Francis and Severin Roesen are recognized as the two most important American still life painters of the mid-nineteenth century. Whereas Roesen specialized in fruit pieces and bouquets of flowers, Francis concentrated upon his luncheon and dessert still lifes in which oranges, nuts, glasses of wine, compotes and pitchers are arranged both artfully and casually upon a tabletop covered with a white cloth. The dessert picture connotes not only an extended, multiple-course meal, but also abundance and the leisure to enjoy it, thus making such still lifes paradigms of Victorian middle-class prosperity.

Estimate: $30,000-$50,000

This lot is being sold without reserve. Unreserved lots generally open at 50% of the low estimate.

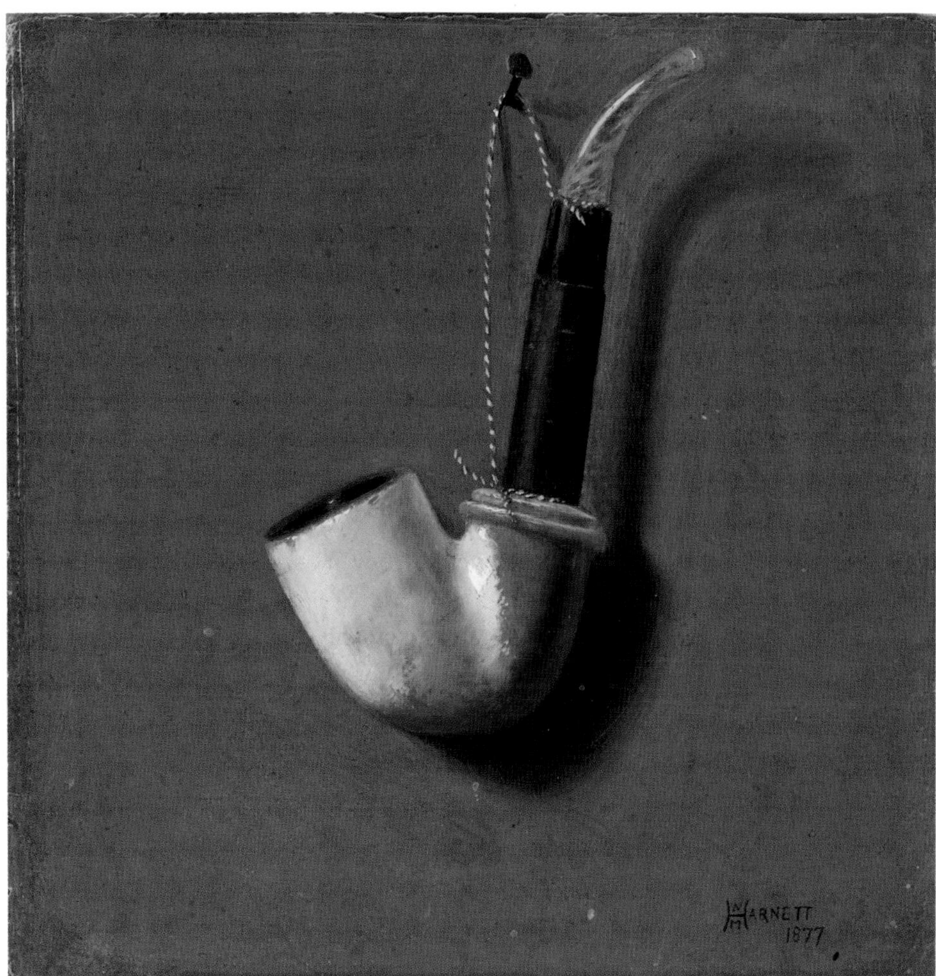

23024

WILLIAM MICHAEL HARNETT
(American 1848-1892)
The Pipe Rack (The Artist's Pipe Rack), 1877
Oil on panel
7-3/4 x 7-1/4 inches (19.7 x 18.4 cm)
Signed and dated lower right: *WM (within H) 1877*
Inscription verso: *Presented to Mr. George Y. Browne/by Frank lavaud of Rossville/Staten Island 1884./ This picture hung on the wall of the hotel several years before it was presented to Mr. Browne.*

Provenance:
Thomas Lavaud [also known as Lavand], about 1877 (Staten Island, New York);
George Y. Browne, 1884;
Mrs. Mimi Bloch (New York);
Coe Kerr Gallery (New York);
Private collection, about 1981 (New York)

Exhibition:
Adelson Galleries, *American Still Life Paintings 1860-1900,* November 4 - 30, 1968, no. 114

Literature:
American Still Life Painting, 1860-1900 (Boston: Adelson Galleries, Inc. 1968), p. 12, 14 (reproduced)

The Pipe Rack, painted in Philadelphia in 1877 was originally owned by Thomas Lavaud, the owner of the Rossville Hotel in Staten Island, where the work was displayed for several years. The picture relates to Harnett's "smoking scenes" of the late 1870s, which commonly include a pipe, beer stein, tobacco holder, matches, biscuits, and a folded newspaper. Over the course of his career, Harnett created a number of pictures which focus on a single object that appears to be hanging on a wall or door.

Alfred Frankenstein noted that the specific pipe that appears in Harnett's trompe l'oeil still lifes of this time usually has "a richly stained bowl, a cherry-wood stem, and a rubber but, and there are bright brass fittings at the point where the bit fits into the stem and around the upper end of the bowl" (After the Hunt, William Harnett and Other American Still Life Painters 1870-1900, University of California Press, Berkeley and Los Angeles, 1953, p. 42). Harnett's ability to render such meticulous details earned him a strong clientele, not merely among art lovers but particularly among business types who prized the keen observation which lay behind the verisimilitude.

Estimate: $100,000-$150,000

This lot is being sold without reserve. Unreserved lots generally open at 50% of the low estimate.

23025

ALFRED STEVENS
(American 1823-1906)
Winding The Mantle Clock, circa 1875-1880
Oil on panel
18-1/8 x 11-5/8 inches
(47.8 x 29.5 cm)
Signed lower left: *Alfred Stevens*

Estimate:
$60,000-$80,000

This lot is being sold without reserve. Unreserved lots generally open at 50% of the low estimate.

23026

FRANK DUVENECK (American 1848-1919)
Portrait Of A Gentleman, circa 1876-80
Oil on panel
10-3/4 x 7-1/8 inches (27.3 x 18 cm)
Monogram lower right

Provenance:
Bryan & Scott (Colorado Springs, Colorado);
Mr. and Mrs. F. Howard Walsh (Fort Worth, Texas);
Walsh Family Art Trust

Frank Duveneck was born from German stock in Covington, Kentucky. He trained in Munich during the 1870s, when artists were taught the kind of bravura brushwork against very dark backgrounds as seen here. He was greatly influenced by his instructor Wilhelm Leibl, who introduced him to the works of Hals, Velazquez and Goya. Duveneck was a realist whose paintings often reflect the sitter's character through confident brush strokes, design and color. His focus on light and shadow together with form suggest a vitality of movement. The legacy of Duveneck's work and teachings place him squarely as a significant artist in the history of American art.

Estimate: $3,000-$5,000

The reserve for this lot is available at HA.com/FineArt.

23027

LAWRENCE CARMICHAEL EARLE
(American 1845-1921)
Still Life Of Game Birds
Oil on canvas
25 x 30 inches (63.5 x 76.2 cm)
Signed lower right: L. C. Earle

Estimate: $1,200-$1,800

The reserve for this lot is available at HA.com/FineArt.

23028

GRIMM (Nineteenth Century)
Soldier On Duty, 1881
Gouache and ink on paper
Signed lower right: *Grimm / Paris 81.*

Estimate: $1,000-$2,000

The reserve for this lot is available at HA.com/FineArt.

23029

H. T. CARISS (American 1840-1903)
Untitled (Couple In A Field)
Oil on canvas
19-1/2 x 15-1/2 inches (49.5 x 39.4 cm)
Signed lower left: *H.T. Cariss*

Estimate: $4,000-$6,000

This lot is being sold without reserve. Unreserved lots generally open at 50% of the low estimate.

23030

ROBERT FREDERICK BLUM (American 1957-1903)
Woman In A Shawl Holding A Fan, circa 1878-80
Watercolor on paper
17 x 11 inches (43.2 x 27.9 cm)
Unsigned

Blum's watercolors from the late 1870s, are generally characterized by an emphasis on texture and brushwork, exaggerated effects of light and dark, and an application of fluid washes which merely hint or suggest the shape and character of forms. To achieve these results, Blum regulary worked on grained paper which broke up the brushwork and gave it an extremely fluid appearance. Both in subject and style *Woman In Shawl Holding A Fan* reflects the strong influence of the Spaniard Mariano Fortuny. In certain passages, however, Blum went beyond his mentor with his daringly expressive application of the watercolor medium, seen here in his treatment of the woman's shadow.

Estimate: $20,000-$30,000

This lot is being sold without reserve. Unreserved lots generally open at 50% of the low estimate.

23031

ERNEST WADSWORTH LONGFELLOW
(American 1845-1921)
House On The Shore
Oil on canvas
12-3/8 x 18-1/4 inches (31.4 x 46.4 cm)
Signed lower left:
Ernest Longfellow

Estimate: $1,500-$3,000

The reserve for this lot is available at HA.com/FineArt.

23032

GRANVILLE PERKINS
(American 1830-1895)
Village Coast, pair,
circa 1875-1900
Oil on canvas
10 x 16 inches, each (25.4 x 40.6 cm)
Signed lower left, each:
Granville Perkins

Estimate: $4,000-$6,000

The reserve for this lot is available at HA.com/FineArt.

23033

ARTHUR PARTON
(American 1842-1914)
Pumpkins In A Field, circa 1880s
Oil on canvas
13 x 20-1/2 inches (33 x 52.1 cm)
Signed lower right: *Arthur Parton NA*

Born in Hudson, New York, Arthur Parton became a successful nineteenth-century landscape painter – first in the meticulous tradition of William Trost Richards with whom he trained in Philadelphia, and later in a freer *plein-air* manner inspired by exposure to the work of the Barbizon painters during an 1869 trip to Europe. In 1872, Parton's view of the Shenandoah River (Virginia) was published in Bryant's *Picturesque America* and catapulted him to national recognition. The artist became an Associate of the National Academy of Design in 1871, and a full National Academician in 1884. He was a leading member of both the American Water Color Society and the Artist's Fund Society, and exhibited widely. His work was shown at the annual National Academy exhibitions from 1862 to 1914; the Corcoran Gallery, Washington, DC (1907, 1908, 1910); Brooklyn Art Association (1866-1885); Philadelphia Centennial Exhibition, 1876; and the Boston Art Club (1882-1909). His work is represented in the permanent collections of the Brooklyn Museum, the Indianapolis Museum of Art, and the Metropolitan Museum of Art, New York.

Parton painted throughout his home state, recording scenes in the Catskill and Adirondack mountains upon which he built his artistic reputation. From 1874 to 1893, the artist maintained an atelier in the Tenth Street Studio at 51 West 10th Street in New York, alongside William Merritt Chase whose impressionistic views of Shinnecock doubtless influenced Parton's work from the same period. The present scene of pumpkins dotting a rural field combines Parton's awareness of Barbizon painting in the silvery, cloud tousled sky with Chase's brushy manner. The painting has the freshness of an oil sketch made on-the-spot outdoors.

Estimate: $2,000-$3,000

The reserve for this lot is available at HA.com/FineArt.

23034

EDMUND HENRY OSTHAUS
(American 1858-1928)
Hunting Dogs
Watercolor on paper
24 x 32 inches
(61 x 81 cm)
Signed lower left: *Edm.H.Osthaus*

Estimate: $15,000-$20,000

This lot is being sold without reserve. Unreserved lots generally open at 50% of the low estimate.

23035

L.A. HUFFMAN
(American 1879 - 1931)
Grazing Cattle
Handcolored Printing-Out Paper mounted on board
20 x 16 inches (50.8 x 40.6 cm)
Stamped verso: *L.A. Huffman/All rights reserved/Coffrin's Old West Gallery/1600 Main St.-Miles City, Mt. 59301*

Estimate: $700-$900

This lot is being sold without reserve. Unreserved lots generally open at 50% of the low estimate.

23036

CHARLES SPRAGUE PEARCE
(American 1851-1914)
Home From The Fields, circa 1880-84
Oil on canvas
18 x 11-1/2 inches (45.7 x 29.2 cm)
Signed and inscribed lower left: *Charles Sprague Pearce/Paris*
Stamped with artist's monogram on stretcher

Literature:
Julia Rowland Myers, "The American Expatriate Painters of the French Peasantry, 1863-1893," Ph.D. Dissertation, University of Maryland, College Park, 1989, p 239, ff 3

Together with Daniel Ridgeway Knight, Charles Sprague Pearce was regarded during the 1880s and 1890s as the finest and most poetic American painters of French peasant subjects. In 1888 George Sheldon remarked that Pearce and Knight 'each has made a study of the Brittany peasant-woman in her relations to the landscape that environs her, each has sought the essential and found it, and each has remained steadfast to the truth without degrading himself with the trivialities of prose' (Recent Ideals of American Art, D. Appleton and Company, New York and London, 1888, p. 23).

Pearce was born and raised in Boston. His grandfather and namesake was the noted poet and banker Charles Sprague, who was a participant in the "Boston Tea Party." After graduating from the Boston Latin School Pearce worked for five years as a merchant in the China trade. During this period he was also actively painting and in 1872 gained some local renown for his early efforts. In 1873 Pearce followed the advice of William Morris Hunt and went to Paris, where he spent three years studying in the private atelier of Leon Bonnat.

In Europe Pearce quickly established his reputation and became one of the most highly regarded American artists. In the early 1880s he began painting in the small village of Auvers-sur-Oise in Picardy and settled there permanently in 1885. He was a regular and popular exhibitor at the Paris Salon and received many distinguished honors including the French Legion of Honor. Pearce maintained close ties with the United States and served as chairman of the Parisian jury for the Chicago Exposition of 1893 and the St. Louis Exposition of 1904. In the 1890s Pearce executed a mural decoration for the Library of Congress in Washington, D.C.

Home from the Field was painted in the early 1880s when Pearce fell under the sway of Jules Bastien-Lepage, whose figurative paintings of peasants in nature attracted many young Americans with their original synthesis of realism and naturalism. Following the Frenchman's example, Pearce depicted the peasant life of northern France, favored a cool gray-green palette, painted landscape elements in a loose and blurry fashion to convey the presence of atmosphere, and employed a high horizon. Pearce's pictures of Breton women attired in patchwork clothing standing in a contemplative pose were regarded by American, French and English critics alike. He was commended for the beauty of his figures, sympathetic treatment of character, and soft and evocative depiction of light and atmosphere.

Estimate: $60,000-$80,000

This lot is being sold without reserve. Unreserved lots generally open at 50% of the low estimate.

23037

WILLIAM BAPTISTE BAIRD
(American 1847-1899)
Untitled (Rooster And Hen)
Oil on canvas laid on board
9-1/4 x 15-1/2 inches (23.5 x 34.9 cm)
Signed verso: *W.B. Baird*

Estimate: $2,000-$3,000

This lot is being sold without reserve. Unreserved lots generally open at 50% of the low estimate.

23038

ARTHUR HOEBER
(American 1854-1915)
Through The Fields
Oil on canvas
16 x 20 inches (40.6 x 50.8 cm)
Signed lower right:
Arthur Hoeber

Provenance:
The Anderson Galleries

Estimate: $2,500-$5,000

The reserve for this lot is available at HA.com/FineArt.

23039

ARTHUR FITZWILLIAM TAIT
(American 1819-1905)
Barnyard Scene, 1866
Oil on board
10 x 12 inches (25.4 x 30.48 cm)
Signed and dated lower right in red paint: *A. F. Tait / N.Y. 1866*
Inscribed verso: *No 493 / A.F. Tait / Morrisania / N.Y. / 1866 / Copyright reserved / A.F.T.,* with a paper label for Winsor & Newton; and a paper label numbered: *Painting #5 / $600.00/ H82.7 / 8A.152A*

Provenance:
Bessie Heard (McKinney, Texas);
Bessie Heard Trust

Estimate: $8,000-$12,000

This lot is being sold without reserve. Unreserved lots generally open at 50% of the low estimate.

23040

ARTHUR FITZWILLIAM TAIT
(American 1819-1905)
Spring Pets, 1901
Oil on panel
8 x 12 inches (20.3 x 30.5 cm)
Signed and dated lower right: *A. F. Tait / N.Y. 1901*
Inscribed verso: *(CL) 1901 / "Spring Pets" / A.F. Tait, N.A. / Ludlow Park / N.Y.;* and with a label numbered: *H82.7 / 8A.152B*

Provenance:
Bessie Heard (McKinney, Texas);
Bessie Heard Trust

Estimate: $8,000-$12,000

This lot is being sold without reserve. Unreserved lots generally open at 50% of the low estimate.

23041

MILNE RAMSEY
(American 1847-1915)
Champagne And Apples, 1880
Oil on canvas
21 x14-1/2 inches (53.3 x 36.8 cm)
Signed lower right: *Milne Ramsey/ Paris 1.80*

Exhibition:
The Apple of America - The Apple in Nineteenth Century Amercian Art, May 6 - June 8, 1993, Berry Hill Galleries (New York)

Literature:
Bruce Weber, *The Apple of America: The Apple in Nineteenth century American Art* (New York: Berry-Hill Galleries, 1993) pp. 15, 27, pl. 17 (reproduced)

Ramsey studied painting at the Pennsylvania Academy of Fine Arts from 1863 to 1867, before traveling to Paris and entering the atelier of Leon Bonnat. While in Paris, Ramsey painted a number of still lifes featuring apples paired with champagne and established a reputation as a painter of floral, fruit, and kitchen still lifes.

Estimate: $20,000-$30,000

This lot is being sold without reserve. Unreserved lots generally open at 50% of the low estimate.

23042

ROBERT SPEAR DUNNING (American 1829-1905)
Tabletop Still Life With Fruit, circa 1884
Oil on canvas
18-1/4 x 24-1/4 inches (46.4 x 61.6 cm)
Signed verso: *R.S. Dunning*

Provenance:
Family of the artist

Literature:
Berry-Hill Galleries, *American Paintings V,* New York, 1988, pp. 48-49 (reproduced)

Robert Spear Dunning, one of the masters of American still life painting of the late nineteenth century, was the founder and leader of the "Fall River School," of Fall River, Massachusetts. Under his guidance Dunning's school produced a small but important corps of still-life painters who remained active well into the twentieth century, including Abbie Zuill, Bryant Chapin, Albert E. Munroe, and Franklin H. Miller.

Dunning was born in Brunswick, Maine and first moved to Fall River in 1834. He trained with James Roberts of Thomaston, Maine, and then with Daniel Huntington at the National Academy of Design in New York City. In 1853, Dunning returned to Fall River where he initially specialized in portraiture. By 1865, however, he had turned increasingly to the painting of still-lifes. During the late 1860s and early 1870s, his style became more polished, with carefully differentiated textures, a bright palette, and unusual outdoor settings. By the early 1880s, however, he shifted to more complex designs, warmer tonalities and softer pictorial effects.

A Tabletop Still Life with Fruit represents Dunning's later manner. The polished tabletop onto which the softly textured fruit spill out and by which they are mirrored, the ornately carved table edge, and the warm hues are all Dunning trademarks.

Estimate: $80,000-$120,000

This lot is being sold without reserve. Unreserved lots generally open at 50% of the low estimate.

23043

JEAN LEON GEROME FERRIS (American 1863-1930)
The Chess Match
Oil on canvas
24 x 20 inches (60.9 x 50.8 cm)
Signed at upper right: *J.L.G.Ferris*

Estimate: $1,500-$2,500

This lot is being sold without reserve. Unreserved lots generally open at 50% of the low estimate.

23044

PERCY MORAN (American 1862-1935)
Senorita
Watercolor on paper
19-3/4 x 13-1/2 inches (50.2 x 33.5 cm)
Signed lower left: *Percy Moran*

Estimate: $2,000-$4,000

This lot is being sold without reserve. Unreserved lots generally open at 50% of the low estimate.

23045

ROBERT WILTON LOCKWOOD (American 1861-1914)
Portrait Of A Gentleman
Oil on canvas
38 x 30 inches (96.5 x 76.2 cm)
Unsigned
Label verso: *Goster Bros. / 4 Park Sq. / Boston / Pictures and Frames*

This half-length likeness of a gentleman is a fine example of Lockwood's sensitive, painterly manner, which earned him distinction both as a portraitist and as an accomplished flower painter. The Boston Museum of Fine Arts owns one of Lockwood's finest likenesses-his 1891 portrait of John La Farge, the American painter and stained glass artist with whom he trained and served as a longtime assistant. Born in Wilton, Connecticut, Lockwood studied in Paris following his initial tutelage under La Farge. Once he became an established painter, he became a member of the Society of American Artists (1898), of the Copley Society, Boston, and an associate of the National Academy of Design in New York. His most notable sitters were President Grover Cleveland and Justice Oliver Wendell Holmes, Jr.

Estimate: $2,000-$4,000

The reserve for this lot is available at HA.com/FineArt.

23046

DANIEL HUNTINGTON (American 1816-1906)
Portrait Of Cornelius Vanderbilt, 1896
Oil on canvas
30 x 25 inches (76.2 x 63.5 cm)
Signed and dated lower left: *D. Huntington / 1896*

Estimate: $3,000-$5,000

The reserve for this lot is available at HA.com/FineArt.

23047

AMERICAN SCHOOL
(Nineteenth Century)
River Scene
Oil on canvas
22-1/8 x 32 inches (56.2 x 81.3 cm)
Unsigned

Estimate: $1,500-$2,500

The reserve for this lot is available at HA.com/FineArt.

23048

GEORGE WASHINGTON NICHOLSON
(American 1832-1912)
The Village Fleet
Oil on canvas
20 x 36 inches (50.8 x 91.4 cm)
Signed lower right:
G. W. Nicholson

Estimate: $800-$1,600

This lot is being sold without reserve. Unreserved lots generally open at 50% of the low estimate.

23049

JAMES HAMILTON
(Irish/American 1819-1878)
A Light Breeze
Oil on canvas
30-1/2 x 45 inches (77.5 x 114.3 cm)
Signed lower right

Provenance:
McClees Galleries, 1507 Walnut Street, label verso (Philadelphia, Pennsylvania);
Mrs. J. Best

Estimate: $9,000-$15,000

The reserve for this lot is available at HA.com/FineArt.

23050

GIDEON JACQUES DENNY
(American 1830-1886)
Evening Landscape
Oil on sheet metal laid on masonite
14-1/4 x 43 inches (36.19 x 109.22 cm)
Signed and dated lower left: *G.J. Denny 1878*
Inscribed lower right: *55*

Provenance:
Private collection (Washington)

Estimate: $3,000-$5,000

The reserve for this lot is available at HA.com/FineArt.

23051

GIDEON JACQUES DENNY
(American 1830-1886)
Seascape With Ship
Oil on canvas
20 x 36 inches (50.8 x 91.4 cm)
Signed and dated lower left: *G.J. Denny 1880*

Provenance:
Private collection (Washington)

Estimate: $3,000-$5,000

The reserve for this lot is available at HA.com/FineArt.

23052

WILLIAM FREDERICK DE HAAS
(American 1830-1880)
A Fine Day On The Cliffs Of Star Island, Isles Of Shoals, NH,
1878
Oil on canvas
20-1/8 x 36-1/4 inches
(51.1 x 92.1 cm)
Signed and dated lower right:
William F. De Haas 78

Provenance:
Plaza Art Galleries, Inc. (New York)

Estimate:
$20,000-$30,000

The reserve for this lot is available at HA.com/FineArt.

23053

MILTON JAMES BURNS (American 1853-1933)
Old Whaler, A Forty-Niner
Oil on board
18 x 13 inches (45.7 x 33 cm)
Signed lower left: *Burns*
Inscribed verso: *Old Whaler - A "Forty-Niner" / -1849- / M.J. Burns -* ,
and with further illegible inscriptions in pencil

Provenance:
Bradford Trust Fine Art (Cape Cod, Massachusetts);
Private collection (Houston, Texas)

The great American gold rush struck in 1849, creating a frenzy of travel to California for those who had caught the "gold fever". As a result ships of all sorts were utilized for the transport of passengers to the west, including old Whale boats such as the one depicted in the present lot.

Estimate: $4,000-$6,000

The reserve for this lot is available at HA.com/FineArt.

23054

WARREN W. SHEPPARD
(American 1858-1937)
Shipwreck On The Beach At Sunrise
Oil on canvas
14 x 24-1/4 inches (35.6 x 61.6 cm)
Signed lower right: *W.W. Sheppard*
Auction house stencil verso: *456TA*

Estimate: $8,000-$12,000

The reserve for this lot is available at HA.com/FineArt.

23055

School of WARREN SHEPPARD
(American 1858-1937)
Fisherman On A Rocky Coast
Oil on canvas
20 x 30 inches (50.80 x 76.20 cm)
Signed lower right: *Warren Sheppard*

Provenance:
Cotai Fine Arts (Quebec, Canada);
Private collection (Houston, Texas)

Estimate: $2,000-$3,000

The reserve for this lot is available at HA.com/FineArt.

23056

HARRY HARLOW HOWE, also known as **WILLIAM FREDERICK PASKELL**
(American 1866-1951)
Clipper Ship
Oil on canvas
16 X 21 inches (40.6 x 53.3 cm)
Signed lower right: *HHowe*

Estimate: $600-$1,200

This lot is being sold without reserve. Unreserved lots generally open at 50% of the low estimate.

23057

THOMAS MORAN (American 1837-1926)
Vera Cruz Harbor, 1885
Oil on canvas
16-1/4 x 27-5/8 inches (41.3 x 70.2 cm)
Signed and dated lower right: *TMoran./1885.*

Provenance:
Purchased by Dr. P.J. Koonz (New Jersey);
Acquired by descent from the above to son, Dr. and Mrs. Harold Addison, 1912 (New Jersey);
Acquired by descent from the above to Mr. and Mrs. John Carver Koonz, mid-1960s to 1993 (New Jersey);
Thus by descent to Mrs. (John Carver) Delores Koonz, 1993 to present (Texas)

Exhibition:
McNay Art Museum, San Antonio, Texas, 1987-1988

Literature:
To be included in Stephen Good's forthcoming catalogue raisonné

Estimate: $100,000-$140,000

The reserve for this lot is available at HA.com/FineArt.

23058

ANTONIO JACOBSEN
(American 1850-1921)
Sailing Ship St. Mary
Oil on canvas
22 x 36 inches (55.9 x 91.4 cm)

Estimate:
$15,000-$25,000

The reserve for this lot is available at HA.com/FineArt.

23059

ANTONIO JACOBSEN
(American 1850-1921)
Steamship Seguranca, 1902
Oil on canvas
Inscribed lower right:
Antonio Jacobsen / 1902 / 31 Palisade Ave. West Hoboken NJ

Estimate:
$15,000-$25,000

The reserve for this lot is available at HA.com/FineArt.

23060

ANTONIO JACOBSEN
(American 1850-1921)
U.S. Army Transport "Terry", 1901
Oil on canvas
22 x 36 inches (55.9 x 91.4 cm)
Inscribed lower right: *Antonio Jacobsen 1901, 31 Palisade Ave. West Hoboken N.J.*

Estimate: $4,000-$6,000

The reserve for this lot is available at HA.com/FineArt.

23061

ANTONIO JACOBSEN (American 1850-1921)
U.S. Army Transport "Warren", 1900
Oil on canvas
22 x 36 inches (55.9 x 91.4 cm)
Inscribed lower right: *A. Jacobsen 1900 West Hoboken NJ*

Estimate: $12,000-$16,000

The reserve for this lot is available at HA.com/FineArt.

23062

EDWARD HENRY POTTHAST (American 1857-1927)
Lawn Tennis, St. Ives circa 1885-1890
Oil on panel
5-5/8 x 9-1/16 inches (14.2 x 23 cm)
Signed lower left: *E. Potthast*

Literature:
To be included in Mary Ran's forthcoming catalogue raisonné of the works of Edward Potthast.

Lawn Tennis, St. Ives was likely painted during the course of Potthast's stay abroad in the late 1880s and early 1890s. Potthast is known to have traveled extensively in Europe at this time. As in many of Potthast's works, faces are featureless or concealed from the viewers gaze. The artist commonly created small outdoor sketches of this type, and then worked them up into larger paintings in his studio.

Estimate: $40,000-$60,000

This lot is being sold without reserve. Unreserved lots generally open at 50% of the low estimate.

23063

CHILDE HASSAM
(American 1859-1935)
Banks Of The Seine,
1888
Oil on canvas
8-3/4 x 11 inches (22.2 x 27.9 cm)
Signed and dated lower left: *Childe Hassam 1888*

Provenance:
Hirschl and Adler Galleries, early 1960s (New York);
Bernard Danenberg Galleries, Inc.;
Carola Warburg Rothschild, circa 1970s (purchased from Danenberg Galleries);
Sale, Doyle's, New York, Property from the Estate of Carola Warburg Rothschild, 1987, Lot 71;
Private collection (Dallas, Texas)

The present work by the celebrated American Impressionist, Childe Hassam, records a view along the Seine, which he painted in the spring of 1888—approximately halfway through his second of four sojourns to Paris. The Massachusetts-born painter had first visited the French capital in the summer of 1883 with the Boston artist Edmund H. Garrett. In the autumn of 1886, he returned there with his wife, Maud, and this time stayed for three years. Prior to this extended stay in France, Hassam had had very little formal art training, and quickly sought to remedy that situation by enrolling at the Académie Julian by the end of 1886. There he trained under Gustave Boulanger and Jules-Joseph Lefebvre (whose work is represented in the current auction.) By the spring of 1888, Hassam decided to quit his academic training in order to concentrate on painting urban subjects, such as the present scene, and sunlit garden views which earned him major critical acclaim. The rather spare composition of this work, together with its blond tonality, pay tribute to the radical compositions of Edgar Degas, which drew inspiration from Japanese prints.

A work closely related in subject and composition to the present painting is Hassam's *Along the Seine, Winter* of 1887 in the Dallas Museum of Art (oil on wood, 8 x 11 in., bequest of Joel T. Howard), which was included in the recent exhibition, *Americans in Paris 1860-1900,* organized by the National Gallery, London, and the Museum of Fine Arts, Boston, in association with The Metropolitan Museum of Art, New York.

Banks of the Seine will be included in the forthcoming Childe Hassam *catalogue raisonné* now being prepared by Stuart P. Feld and Kathleen Burnside.

Estimate: $160,000-$200,000

This lot is being sold without reserve. Unreserved lots generally open at 50% of the low estimate.

23064

ROBERT HENRI (American 1865-1929)
Coastal Scene
Oil on panel
8 x 10 inches (20.3 x 25.4 cm)

Provenance:
The Robert Henri Estate;
Chapellier Gallery (New York);
Mr. and Mrs. Edgar E. Townes, 1967 (Houston, Texas)

Literature:
Robert Henri Record Book, 45B

Estimate: $5,000-$7,000

The reserve for this lot is available at HA.com/FineArt.

23065

ROBERT HENRI
(American 1865-1929)
Place In Paris (Place de Breteuil), circa 1895-1897
Oil on panel
10-1/2 x 13-3/4 inches
(26.7 x 34.9 cm)
Signed lower left:
Robert Henri

Literature:
Robert Henri Record Book, 257A

During the period 1890-1903, Henri principally painted cityscapes, landscapes and marine paintings. His interest in painting outdoors began in the late 1880s when he became enamored with sketching outdoors during his summer months he spent in France. The experience led him to experiment with Impressionism and to paint broadly brushed landscapes which recorded the rich effects of color and the transient effects of light. By 1895, Henri began to adopt a style that was equally bold in paint handling but which emphasized chiaroscuro effects and depended upon a more somber range of color. This approach reflects his admiration for the works of Manet, Hals, Velasquez and Rembrandt as well as seventeenth-century Dutch landscape painting and the nineteenth-century Barbizon School.

Place in Paris was painted sometime between the summer of 1895 and the autumn of 1897 while Henri was living at 49 Boulevard du Montparnasse. It was during this time that he formed a close association with the Canadian artist James Wilson Morrice. They would often go on sketching excursions together in Paris, in the surrounding suburbs of Saint Cloud and Charenton, and to Bois-le-Roi near Fontainebleau. They would sketch on small wood panels, or *pochades*, spontaneously recording the passing scene. Henri referred to these works as memory sketches or mental sketches, and carried the panels together with brushes, palette, and a few tubes of oil in a small box that fit into his pocket. When creating such works in Paris he often situated himself at the table of an outdoor cafe (especially the Cafe Versailles in the Place de Rennes), and painted views featuring the surrounding street and crowd. He would cover the entire surface with a single tone, then freely work the subject into it. He generally favored a palette consisting of greens, grays, blacks, and ochre, and emphasized vertically-oriented elements such as lamp posts, columns or churches. The monument featured in this view of the Place de Breteuil near the Invalides was a temporary one that was subsequently replaced by a monument honoring Louis Pasteur. Henri's Parisian *pochades* led directly to his important New York cityscapes of the first years of the twentieth century.

Estimate: $60,000-$80,000

The reserve for this lot is available at HA.com/FineArt.

23066

FREDERICK JAMES BOSTON
(American 1855-1932)
Landscape
Oil on board
11-1/2 x 15-1/2 inches (29.2 x 39.4 cm)
Signed lower right: *Fed. Boston*

Estimate: $2,000-$3,000

This lot is being sold without reserve. Unreserved lots generally open at 50% of the low estimate.

23067

WORTHINGTON WHITTREDGE
(American 1820-1910)
Seascape At Barnegat Bay, Bay Head, New Jersey, 1900
Oil on canvas
Signed lower right: *W. Whittredge N.A.*
Partial pencil inscription identifying site and date on stretcher (verso)

Provenance:
Questroyal Fine Art label verso (New York);
Private collection

In this late seascape by the Ohio-born painter Worthington Whittredge, the meticulous description of his earlier Hudson River School manner has given way to a much softer tonalism favored by American landscape painters of the later nineteenth century. Indebted both to the *plein-air* painting of the Barbizon masters and the atmospheric "arrangements" of Whistler, this view of the surf near Bay Head, New Jersey evokes the sense of wind on sand and water through a palette of soft blues, silvers and browns. During the final decade of his life, Whittredge lived at his home "Hillcrest" near Summit, New Jersey. The site of the present scene at the head of Barnegat Beach Island is approximately 60 miles from New York, Philadelphia, and Atlantic City.

During his long career, Worthington Whittredge served two terms as president of the National Academy of Design and was intimately involved with both the Philadelphia Centennial Exhibition and the founding of The Metropolitan Museum of Art.

Anthony Janson has kindly confirmed the authenticity of this work.

Estimate: $25,000-$40,000

The reserve for this lot is available at HA.com/FineArt.

23068

After ASHER B. DURAND
(Early Twentieth Century)
River Stream
Oil on canvas
17 x 21 inches (43.2 x 53.3 cm)
Unsigned

Estimate: $1,500-$2,500

This lot is being sold without reserve. Unreserved lots generally open at 50% of the low estimate.

23069

CHRISTOPHER H. SHEARER
(American 1840-1926)
Romantic Woodland Landscape With Meandering Stream
Oil on canvas
14 x 24 (35.6 x 61 cm)
Signed and dated lower right:
1905. / C.H. Shearer

Estimate: $800-$1,200

The reserve for this lot is available at HA.com/FineArt.

23070

CHAUNCY FOSTER RYDER
(American 1868-1949)
Oil on canvas
12 x 16 inches (30.4 x 40.6 cm)
Signed lower right:
Chauncy F. Ryder

Provenance:
Private collection (Dallas, Texas)

Estimate: $4,000-$6,000

This lot is being sold without reserve. Unreserved lots generally open at 50% of the low estimate.

23071

LOUIS COMFORT TIFFANY
(American 1848-1933)
Architecture Study, Hagia Sofia, Istanbul
Watercolor on paper
8 x 11-3/4 inches (20.3 x 29.8 cm)
Signed lower left: *L.C. Tiffany*

Estimate: $4,000-$6,000

The reserve for this lot is available at HA.com/FineArt.

23072

HAYLEY LEVER
(American 1876-1958)
The Red Doorway
Watercolor on paper
10 x 13-1/4 inches (25.4 x 33.7 cm)
Signed lower right: *Hayley Lever*

Provenance:
Estate of Leonard Clayton (Lever's longtime dealer and supporter)

Estimate: $2,000-$3,000

The reserve for this lot is available at HA.com/FineArt.

23073

HAYLEY LEVER
(American 1876-1958)
Old Farm, Devon
Watercolor on paper
10 x 14 inches (25.4 x 35.6 cm)
Initaled lower left: *HL*

Provenance:
Estate of Leonard Clayton (Lever's longtime dealer and supporter)

Estimate: $2,000-$3,000

The reserve for this lot is available at HA.com/FineArt.

23074

HAYLEY LEVER (American 1876-1958)
Tree Study
Ink wash and graphite on paper
7-1/2 x 7-1/2 inches (19.1 x 19.1 cm)
Initialed lower right: *HL*

Estimate: $600-$1,200

This lot is being sold without reserve. Unreserved lots generally open at 50% of the low estimate.

23075

HAYLEY LEVER
(American 1876-1958)
Stowe, VT, 1933
Watercolor on paper
10-3/4 x 15 inches (27.3 x 38.1 cm)
Initialed lower left: *HL*

Provenance:
Estate of Leonard Clayton (Lever's longtime dealer and supporter)

Estimate: $2,000-$3,000

The reserve for this lot is available at HA.com/FineArt.

23076

HALEY LEVER
(American 1876-1958)
The Fishing Shacks Of Nantucket
Oil on canvas
10 x 12 inches (25.4 x 30.5 cm)
Signed lower right: *Haley Lever*

Estimate: $5,000-$7,000

The reserve for this lot is available at HA.com/FineArt.

23077

ANNA ALTHEA HILLS
(American 1882-1930)
Pair of Californian landscapes
Watercolor on paper
Untitled (Cityscape), 10 x7-1/2 inches (25.4 x 19.1 cm)
Sunny Fields, 10 x 9 inches (25.4 x 22.9 cm)
Both images signed lower right: *A.A. Hills*

Estimate: $1,500-$2,500

This lot is being sold without reserve. Unreserved lots generally open at 50% of the low estimate.

23078 No Lot

23079

JANE PETERSON (American 1876-1932)
Lilies
Oil on canvas
29 x 23 inches (73.7 x 58.4 cm)
Signed lower right: *JANE PETERSON*

Exhibition:
Pennsylvania Academy of Fine Arts, 148th Annual Exhibition of Painting and Sculpture, January-March, 1953

Estimate: $8,000-$12,000

The reserve for this lot is available at HA.com/FineArt.

23080

JANE PETERSON (American 1876-1965)
Anthuriums
Oil on canvas
40-1/2 x 30-1/2 inches (102.9 x 77.5 cm)
Signed lower left: *JANE PETERSON*

Provenance:
Estate of the artist;
Private collection, (New York)

Estimate: $10,000-$15,000

The reserve for this lot is available at HA.com/FineArt.

23081

JANE PETERSON (American 1876-1965)
Venice Canal Scene
Oil on linen on board
5-3/4 x 6-1/4 inches (14.6 x 15.9 cm)
Signed lower right: *JANE PETERSON*

Estimate: $3,000-$6,000

This lot is being sold without reserve. Unreserved lots generally open at 50% of the low estimate.

23082

ARTHUR WILLIAM BEST
(American 1859-1935)
Half Dome
Oil on canvas
20-1/4 x 30-1/8 inches
(51.4 x 76.5 cm)
Signed lower right: *AW Best*
Inscribed on the stretcher: *#10 Path to Happy Isles / Mural Lake Half Dome Yosemite / Mentioned in Taffs American Pts. Yale University*

Provenance:
Private collection (Washington)

Estimate: $2,000-$4,000

The reserve for this lot is available at HA.com/FineArt.

23083

ALBERT SHELDON PENNOYER
(American 1888-1957)
Shaded Path
Pastel on paper
13-1/4 x 20-3/4 inches (33.7 x 52.7 cm)
Signed lower left: *A. Sheldon Pennoyer*

Estimate: $1,500-$2,500

This lot is being sold without reserve. Unreserved lots generally open at 50% of the low estimate.

23084

WILLIAM DE LEFTWICH DODGE
(American 1867-1935)
Vesuve From Salto Tiberio, Capri (Midday)
Oil on board
6-5/8 x 11 inches (16.8 x 27.9 cm)
Inscribed: *Capri*
Titled and inscribed verso

Estimate: $3,000-$5,000

This lot is being sold without reserve. Unreserved lots generally open at 50% of the low estimate.

23085

MARY DENEALE MORGAN
(American 1868-1948)
Monterey Bay
Oil on canvas
12 x 18 inches (30.5 x 45.7 cm)
Signed lower right: *M. DeNeale Morgan*

Provenance:
Private collection (Washington)

Estimate: $7,000-$9,000

The reserve for this lot is available at HA.com/FineArt.

23086

FRANK MONTAGUE MOORE
(American 1877-1967)
Moon Foam
Oil on panel
27-1/2 x 39-1/2 inches (69.9 x 100.3 cm)
Signed lower right: *F.M. Moore*
Signed and titled verso: *"Moon Foam"/F.M. Moore*

Estimate: $3,000-$5,000

The reserve for this lot is available at HA.com/FineArt.

23087

LOUIS MICHAEL EILSHEMIUS
(American 1864-1941)
The Intruder, 1905
Oil on canvas
24 x 37-1/4 inches (61 x 94.6 cm)
Signed and dated lower left:
Elshemus / 1905
Inscribed on verso: *No.10696 / "The Intruder" / Louis Eilshemius*

Provenance:
Babcock Galleries (New York);
Private collection (Boca Raton, Florida)

Estimate: $2,000-$4,000

The reserve for this lot is available at HA.com/FineArt.

23088

Style of EDGAR ALWIN PAYNE
(American 1883-1947)
Sailboats In The Harbor
Oil on canvas
17 x 24 inches (43.2 x 61 cm)
Signed lower left: *EDGAR PAYNE*

Estimate: $1,000-$2,000

The reserve for this lot is available at HA.com/FineArt.

23089

ALICE BEACH WINTER (American 1877-1970)
Gloucester, 1914
Oil on canvas
19-3/4 x 15-1/2 inches (50.2 x 39.4 cm)
Signed lower right: *Alice-Beach Winter/Gloucester 1914*

Provenance:
"Best of the West", November 16, 2002, Best of the West Art Auction (Colorado Springs, Colorado)

Estimate: $4,000-$6,000

The reserve for this lot is available at HA.com/FineArt.

23090

CHARLES PAUL GRUPPE (Canadian 1860-1940)
Gilly
Oil on board
17 x10 inches (43.2 x 24.5 cm)
Signed lower right: *Gruppe*

Estimate: $2,000-$4,000

This lot is being sold without reserve. Unreserved lots generally open at 50% of the low estimate.

23091

CHARLES PAUL GRUPPE
(American 1860-1940)
Autumn Landscape
Oil on board
11 x 14 inches (23.5 x 30 cm)
Signed lower right: *C.P. Gruppe*

Provenance:
Private collection (Dallas, Texas)

Estimate: $2,000-$4,000

This lot is being sold without reserve. Unreserved lots generally open at 50% of the low estimate.

23092

MARIA ELSA BLANKE (American 1879-1961)
Still Life
Oil on panel
25-1/2 x 21-1/2 inches (64.8 x 54.6 cm)
Signed lower right: *M Blanke*

Estimate: $2,000-$3,000

The reserve for this lot is available at HA.com/FineArt.

23093

ERNEST MARTIN HENNINGS (American 1886-1956)
Man With Beard
Oil on canvas
35 x 29 inches (88.9 x 73.7 cm)

Ernest Hennings was a highly recognized painter of western subjects, particularly his depiction of the New Mexican Native Americans. Born to German immigrants in New Jersey, Hennings studied at the Art Institute of Chicago before venturing west. In 1921, Hennings permanently moved to Taos and in 1924 he was elected into membership of the Taos Society of Artists. Hennings considered himself to be foremost a figure painter, however he excelled as an artist by combining the elements of figure painting with those of the New Mexico landscape painting, thus developing a unique style that distinguished him from the other Taos artists.

Estimate: $6,000-$8,000

The reserve for this lot is available at HA.com/FineArt.

23094

CHARLES W. HAWTHORNE (American 1872-1930)
Untitled (Woman With Hat)
Oil on canvas
19 x 23 inches (48.3 x 58.4 cm)

Provenance:
Mrs. Mildren S. Ruben (Tyler, Texas)

Estimate: $3,000-$5,000

This lot is being sold without reserve. Unreserved lots generally open at 50% of the low estimate.

23095

ELMER LIVINGSTON MACRAE (American 1875-1953)
Sailboat On The Water, Connecticut Coast, 1906
Pastel on paper
18-5/8 x 14-3/4 inches (47.3 x 37.5 cm)
Signed and dated lower right: *EL MACRAE / ...1906*

Estimate: $1,000-$1,500

This lot is being sold without reserve. Unreserved lots generally open at 50% of the low estimate.

23096

HUGH H. BRECKENRIDGE (American 1870 -1937)
The Phlox Garden, circa 1906
Oil on canvas
25 x 30 inches (63.5 x 76.2 cm)
Signed lower right: *Hugh H. Breckenridge*
Inscription verso: *The Phlox Garden by Hugh H. Breckenridge*

Exhibitions:
Worcester Museum of Art, Worcester, Massachusetts, *Exhibtion of Paintings by Hugh H. Breckenridge,* December 8-30, 1907, no. 9;
Albright Art Gallery, Buffalo Fine Arts Academy, *Catalogue of Collection Pictures by Hugh H. Breckenridge,* 1908, no. 9

A native of Virginia, Breckenridge attended the Pennsylvania Academy of Fine Arts, where he eventually taught after traveling and studying abroad. He was one of Philadelphia's leading Impressionist landscape painters of his time, . He once remarked: "I must have been born an Impressionist" (quoted in Gerald L. Carr, "Hugh Henry Breckenridge A Philadelphia Modernist," American Art Review 4 [May 1978]: 95). He believed that Impressionism and artistic freedom were simultaneous developments, and that the Impressionists were the first modern artists. Extremely knowledgeable about color theory and color chemistry, he spoke often of the importance of color "resonance." His landscapes dating from about 1905-1910 verge on Neo-Impressionism and even Fauvism. Indeed, William H. Gerdts has noted that Breckenridge's garden pictures of the early twentieth century are marked by "a rich chromatic scale and a vivacity of brushwork almost Fauve in [their] dynamic expressivity" (Down Garden Paths: The Floral Environment in American Art, Associated University Presses, Cranbury, New Jersey, 1983, p. 102).

The Phlox Garden features the garden of Breckenridge's home in Fort Washington, dubbed "Phloxdale" because of the profusion of the flower on his property. In his landscape paintings, Breckenridge sought to represent every season and mood of nature, as well as a variety of light effects.

Estimate: $100,000-$150,000

The reserve for this lot is available at HA.com/FineArt.

23097

CHARLES ALLAN GILBERT (American 1873-1929)
Untitled (Portrait Of A Woman)
Graphite on paper
17 x 11 inches (43.2 x 27.9 cm)
Signed lower margin: *C. Allen Gilbert*

Estimate: $500-$1,000

This lot is being sold without reserve. Unreserved lots generally open at 50% of the low estimate.

23098

Attributed to FRANK WESTON BENSON (American 1862-1951)
Portrait Of A Young Woman, 1912
Watercolor on paper
51-1/2 x 29-1/2 inches (130.8 x 74.9 cm)
Signed and dated lower right

Exhibited:
Wichita Art Museum, 1978 (Wichita, Kansas);
Union League Club of New York, 1980

Estimate: $15,000-$25,000

The reserve for this lot is available at HA.com/FineArt.

23099

HARRY HERMAN ROSELAND
(American 1866-1950)
The Light of the Home
Oil on illustration board
8 x 11 inches (17.1 x 23.5 cm)
Signed upper left: *Harry Roseland*

Estimate: $1,500-$2,500

The reserve for this lot is available at HA.com/FineArt.

23100

MARIE STOBBE (American b.1912)
In The Park
Oil on panel
8-1/4 x 11-1/4 inches (21 x 28.6 cm)
Signed lower left

Provenance:
Meredith L. Long & Co. (Houston, Texas);
Mr. and Mrs. Edgar E. Townes, 1966 (Houston, Texas)

Estimate: $1,000-$2,000

The reserve for this lot is available at HA.com/FineArt.

23101

EDMUND WILLIAM GREACEN (American 1877-1949)
The Grey Bonnet
Oil on canvas
16 x 12 inches (40.6 x 30.5 cm)
Signed lower right: *Edmund Greacen*

Provenance:
Meredith L. Long & Co., (Houston, Texas);
Mr. and Mrs. Edgar E. Townes, 1981 (Houston, Texas)

Estimate: $4,000-$6,000

The reserve for this lot is available at HA.com/FineArt.

23102

RUTHERFORD BOYD
(American 1884-1951)
Harriet Boyd Knitting Before Fireplace
Pastel on paper
12-1/2 x 19 inches (31.7 x 48.2 cm)
Signed lower left: *Rutherford Boyd*

Provenance:
Meredith L. Long & Co.
(Houston, Texas);
Mr. and Mrs. Edgar E. Townes,
1983 (Houston, Texas)

Estimate: $800-$1,200

The reserve for this lot is available at HA.com/FineArt.

23103

GEORGE DE FOREST BRUSH (American 1855-1941)
Woman And Child With Dog
Oil on panel
9 x 12 inches (22.9 x 30.5 cm)
Signed lower right: *Geo De Forest Brush*

Provenance:
Collection of Albert P. Jones;
Meredith L. Long & Co. (Houston, Texas);
Mr. and Mrs. Edgar E. Townes, 1961 (Houston, Texas)

Estimate: $3,000-$5,000

The reserve for this lot is available at HA.com/FineArt.

23104

ROBERT HENRI
(American 1865-1929)
The Green Coat,
circa 1916
Oil on canvas
24 x 20 inches (60.9 x 50.8 cm)
Signed lower right: *Robert Henri*

Provenance:
Private collection, circa 1960 (New York);
Sale, Christie's New York, American Paintings Sale, Dec. 1, 2005, Lot 2;
Private Collection, (New York)

During the twentieth century, the rugged beauty of the Ogunquit coast of Maine drew burgeoning artists such as Edward Hopper, Marsden Hartley, George Bellows and Walt Khun. Robert Henri also spent the summer of 1915 in Ogunquit, where this particular work was completed. The subject, Lucie Bayard, was a former student of Henri's who visited that summer as confirmed by Valerie Ann Leeds, Ph.D.

Estimate: $60,000-$80,000

This lot is being sold without reserve. Unreserved lots generally open at 50% of the low estimate.

23105

BROR JULIUS OLSSON NORDFELDT
(American 1878-1955)
Woman with Orange Hair, circa 1916
Oil on canvas
27-3/8 x 24-3/8 inches (69 x 61 cm)

Nordfeldt was born in Tullstrop, Sweden. In 1891 his family left the country to settle in Chicago. In 1899, Nordfeldt attended the Art Institute of Chicago and assisted Albert Herter on a mural commission for the McCormick Harvester Company. The following year the company sent Nordfeldt to Paris to view the mural upon its showing at the Paris Exposition of 1900. For the next three years, Nordfeldt lived primarily in Paris. At first he enrolled at the Académie Julian, but left after only two weeks because he was dissatisfied with the academic training. Instead he found a job teaching painting to young German art students and spent time in Reading, England, where he studied woodblock cutting and printing. For most of 1903, Nordfeldt lived in Sweden. During the next seven years he lived for periods in Chicago, France, Germany, Sweden, England, Morocco, Spain and Italy. During these years he worked extensively as an illustrator, completing numerous assignments for *Harper's Magazin* and *The Outlook.*

*Woman with Orange Hai*r dates from the period 1912-1916. By this time Nordfeldt had cast aside the low-toned Whistlerian tonalism of his early paintings and began to adopt the brilliant color and daring formal simplification of French Post-Impressionism. This was prompted by a growing awareness of Matisse and the Fauves, whose work he would have seen at the Salon d'Automne in 1908. In addition to Matisse, Nordfeldt was greatly enamored with the art of Cézanne and Gauguin, and appears to have taken an interest in the figurative paintings of Alexei von Jawlensky. *Woman with Orange Hair* belongs to a series of portraits dating from the 1910s in which Nordfeldt applied paint with quick strokes of pure, bold color, often used a palette knife, traced black outlines, around forms, and treated space in a compressed manner. In these portraits Nordfeldt usually emphasized vibrant tones of green, yellow and orange. The series includes artist friends, people involved with the cultural scene in Chicago, and professional models.

Estimate: $25,000-$35,000

This lot is being sold without reserve. Unreserved lots generally open at 50% of the low estimate.

23106

JOHN SLOAN (American 1870-1951)
Mosaic, 1917
Etching and aquatint
8-1/4 x 10-1/8 inches (21 x 25.7 cm)
Signed in pencil lower right
Numbered lower left in pencil: 100 proofs
Signed and dated in the plate

Estimate: $1,500-$2,500

The reserve for this lot is available at HA.com/FineArt.

23107

CHARLES EPHRAIM BURCHFIELD (American 1893-1967)
Old Barn, May 2, 1919
Watercolor on paper
14-3/4 x 21-3/4 inches (37.4 x 55.2 cm)
Signed and dated lower right: *C. Burchfield / 1919*
Inscribed verso: *21 / Old Barn / 75.00 / May 2, 1919*

Provenance:
Nancy S. Street;
Rehn Gallery (New York);
Private collection (Boca Raton, Florida)

Estimate: $30,000-$50,000

The reserve for this lot is available at HA.com/FineArt.

23108

CHARLES EPHRAIM BURCHFIELD
(American 1893-1967)
Untitled, Eighteen Sketches
Pencil, colored pencil or charcoal on paper
5-1/2 x 8-1/4 inches
(13.9 x 20.9 cm) (largest)
Unsigned

Provenance:
From the home of Charles Burchfield;
Acquired by the present owner from the above

Estimate: $3,000-$5,000

This lot is being sold without reserve. Unreserved lots generally open at 50% of the low estimate.

23109

GEORGE BENJAMIN LUKS (American 1867-1933)
Chair Warmer, 1924
Soft graphite on paper
9-3/4 x 7-1/4 inches, (sight) (24.8 x 18.4 cm)
Inscribed verso: *"There's babe Ruth being struck out again. Why, when I was on the college team, I never let any bloke do such a thing to me." / Chair Warmer*
Stamped verso: *"Vanity Fair* with handwritten No. 282B and used in issue of December 1924

Estimate: $800-$1,200

The reserve for this lot is available at HA.com/FineArt.

23110

HARRIET WHITNEY FRISHMUTH
(American 1880-1980)
The Vine, 1921
Bronze with green patina
11-1/5 inches high (29.2 cm)
Inscribed: *1921 / HARRIET W. FRISHMUTH / ©*
Foundary mark: *GORHAM CO. FOUNDERS / QBWS*

Estimate: $10,000-$15,000

The reserve for this lot is available at HA.com/FineArt.

23111

CHARLES DEMUTH
(American 1883-1935)
Tulips, circa 1920-1925
Watercolor and pencil on paper
18 x12 inches (45.7 x 30.5 cm)
Signed verso: *C. Demuth*

Provenance:
Collection of George A. Gay;
Kraushaar Gallery, label (New York);
Sale, Sotheby's, New York, May 24, 2001, Lot 50

Exhibition:
Wadsworth Atheneum Exhibition, Modern American Water Colors, Morgan Memorial, May 1928, Hartford, CT (label and copy of the catalog entry included)

Estimate: $40,000-$60,000

The reserve for this lot is available at HA.com/FineArt.

23112

EMIL CARLSEN (American 1853-1932)
Still Life With Garlic On A Ledge, circa 1920s
Oil on panel
33 x 24-1/2 inches (83.8 x 62.2 cm)
Signed in full at lower left: *Emil Carlsen*

This enigmatic and sophisticated late work by the Danish-born painter Emil Carlsen combines his lifelong interest in the evocation of mood and the emotional tension that can be evoked through the powerful presence of a still-life object. In this sizable easel painting, Carlsen obscures the boundaries between landscape (albeit an interior environment) and still life-his two specialties as a painter: most of the image is suffused with a ruddy darkness reminiscent of Rembrandt's work. The very spare interior space he has portrayed is activated by a shaft of light which comes from outside the scene in the manner of Caravaggio. It strikes two round objects on a plain wooden ledge, giving them a solemn plasticity and importance beyond anything they might actually represent. Are these onions or heads of garlic-two herbs Carlsen frequently included in his kitchen still lifes from the 1880s on-or are they apples blanched by the light, or possibly two hard rolls of bread? Regardless, they suggest the presence of someone who set them there, and who might still be present beside them in the fringed, red woolen shawl to the right. The shaft of light then moves past the bench to strike the stone floor below, illuminating the groove between the two pieces of pavement, calling sharp attention to the gash. The scene is intentionally mysterious, a suggestion. The viewer is at liberty to fill in the details.

Both shadowy and radiant in its palette and attention to the fall of light on form, this meditative still life is the work of a mature painter who, during the course of his career, made a very careful study of the Old Masters as well as the Impressionists. During the 1870s, following a brief return trip to his native Denmark, Carlsen went to Paris where he stayed for six months and discovered the work of the eighteenth-century French still-life master, Chardin. When he returned to New York, Carlsen began to develop a reputation as a still-life painter, and began producing a wide variety of subjects from Chardin-like fish pieces to kitchen still-lifes with glinting copper pots to arrangements incorporating oriental objects. Commissioned by a dealer to paint saleable flower pieces, he returned to Paris in 1884, where he remained for two years, painting numerous brightly-colored pictures and adopting an impressionistic palette. Eventually, he grew tired of this repetitious work and broke the contract he had made with the dealer. Carlsen went back to New York and opened a studio on West 57th Street. He worked there until 1887, when he began a two-year tenure as director of the San Francisco Art Association's school. He resigned this post in 1889 but remained in San Francisco until 1891.

Carlsen settled again in New York in 1891 when he began teaching at the National Academy of Design. For the 19 years of his tenure there, he was a well-liked and influential instructor. At this phase of his career, Carlsen became friendly with William Merritt Chase, J. Alden Weir, and Childe Hassam-all of whom worked in an impressionist mode which he, too, adopted at various points in his development.

During his lifetime, Carlsen's still-life paintings were noted for their beauty and elegance, and as one contemporary writer remarked, Carlsen was "unquestionably the most accomplished master of still-life painting in America today." During the 1920s when the present work was painted, Carlsen often painted his still-life subjects on panel rather than canvas.

Estimate: $7,000-$9,000

The reserve for this lot is available at HA.com/FineArt.

23113

DAVID HOWARD HITCHCOCK
(American 1861-1943)
Forest Scene, June 21, 1910
Oil on canvas
20 x 16 inches (50.8 x 40.6 cm)
Signed lower left: *D HOWARD HITCHCOCK*
Dated lower right: *June 21, 1910*

Provenance:
Acquired by descent from step-father, 1984

Estimate: $17,000-$20,000

The reserve for this lot is available at HA.com/FineArt.

23114

PAUL CORNOYER
(American 1864-1923)
The Old Inn
Oil on panel
12 x 16 inches (30.5 x 40.6 cm)
Signed lower left

Provenance:
Sale, Salmagundi Club Auction, label verso

Estimate: $3,000-$5,000

The reserve for this lot is available at HA.com/FineArt.

23115

T. HUDSON SMITH
(American Twentieth Century)
The Orchard
Oil on canvas
11-/1/2 x 7-1/2 inches (29.2 x 44.5 cm)
Signed lower right: *T. Hudson Smith*
Signed and titled verso: *The Orchard / T. Hudson Smith*

Estimate: $1,000-$2,000

This lot is being sold without reserve. Unreserved lots generally open at 50% of the low estimate.

23116

AMERICAN TONALIST SCHOOL
Landscape, circa 1900-1920
Oil on panel
18-1/2 x 24-1/4 inches
(46.9 x 61.5 cm)
Unsigned

The subtle nuances of color gradation within a relatively narrow range of hues signals this work as an example of American tonalist painting from the early years of the twentieth century. While a particular name cannot be attached to it, the work reflects the techniques favored by tonalists—specifically the practice of glazing portions of the image with translucent layers of pigment to soften the contours of objects and suggest rather than define a mood. There are affinities with the work of George Inness as well as the brilliant luminosity favored by William Keith.

Estimate: $2,000-$4,000

The reserve for this lot is available at HA.com/FineArt.

23117

WILLIAM HENRY DRAKE (American 1856-1926)
Masters Of The Jungle, 1919
Oil on canvas
30 x 40 inches (76.2 x 101.6 cm)
Signed and dated lower right

William Drake, born in New York in 1856, studied painting in Paris at the Académie Julian with Benjamin Constant and Doucet, both of whom were Orientalist painters. His style and subject matter were greatly influenced by the trends in European painting at the time.

Upon returning from Europe, he studied at the Cincinnati School of Design, and would often go to the zoo in that city, where he could draw animals first hand. He was briefly employed at the Museum of Natural History, where he did some illustrational work. He also studied at the Art Student's League in New York City. Drake's work was widely reproduced in the *Century* and *Harpers* magazines. In 1902, Drake was made an associate member of the National Academy of Desing.

Drake illustrated The Jungle Book by Rudyard Kipling when it was first published in 1894. His specialty of subject matter became wild animals, particularly wild cats, which he portrayed with tenderness and endowed with almost "human" characteristics. This painting, *Masters of the Jungle,* was exhibited at the National Academy in 1919. Drake was the only American artist of the time to specialize in the portrayal of wild animals in the great gradation of Gérome and Delacroix.

Estimate: $12,000-$15,000

The reserve for this lot is available at HA.com/FineArt.

23118

JOHN WHORF
(American 1903-1959)
Stream Fisherman
Watercolor on paper
20-1/2 x 24-5/8 inches (52.1 x 62.5 cm)
Signed lower left: *John Whorf*

Provenance:
Gordan Dunthorne (Washington D.C.);
Walter Klinkhott Gallery (Montreal, Quebec);
Acquired as gift from Mrs. Joseph B. Ryan (Mont Tremblant, Quebec) to brother, 1985 (Dallas, Texas)

Estimate: $9,000-$11,000

The reserve for this lot is available at HA.com/FineArt.

23119

PAUL BERNARD KING (American 1867-1947)
Harbor Scene
Oil on masonite
30 x 25 inches (76.2 x 63.5 cm)
Signed lower right: *PAUL KING*

Estimate: $4,000-$6,000

The reserve for this lot is available at HA.com/FineArt.

23120

FREDERICK LEO HUNTER (American 1858-1943)
Old East India Docks, 1919
Oil on canvas
18 x 24 inches (45.7 x 61 cm)
Signed and dated lower right: *F. Leo Hunter/ 1919*

Estimate: $2,500-$5,000

The reserve for this lot is available at HA.com/FineArt.

23121

FREDERICK LEO HUNTER (American 1858-1943)
Old East India Docks, 1919
Oil on canvas
18 x 24 inches (45.7 x 61 cm)
Signed and dated lower right: *F. Leo Hunter/ 1919*

Estimate: $2,500-$5,000

The reserve for this lot is available at HA.com/FineArt.

23122

CHEE CHIN S. CHEUNG LEE (Chinese-American 1896-1966)
Landscape, circa 1947
Watercolor on paper
22 x 30 inches (55.9 x 76.2 cm)
Signed lower left: *Chee Chin S. Cheung Lee*

Provenance:
Sale, Butterfield & Butterfield, October 1989;
Private collection (Washington)

Estimate: $2,500-$3,500

The reserve for this lot is available at HA.com/FineArt.

23123

CHEE CHIN S. CHEUNG LEE (Chinese-American 1896-1966)
The Railroad
Oil on canvas
20 x 18 inches (50.8 x 45.7 cm)
Signed lower left: *Chee Chin S. Cheung Lee*

Provenance:
Kerwin Galleries (Burlingame, California)
Private collection (Washington)

Estimate: $2,500-$3,500

The reserve for this lot is available at HA.com/FineArt.

23124

HENRY MCCARTER (American 1866-1942)
Men's Gods, circa 1923
Oil on canvas
42 x 50 inches (106.7 x 127 cm)
Signed at lower left: *Henry McCarter*
Carved verso into frame: *HARER*

Provenance:
Harold Adams, (Philadelphia), in 1926

Exhibition:
February 4-March 25, 1923, The 188th Pennsylvania Academy of the Fine Arts Annual Exhibition, Philadelphia, Pennsylvania, no. 247 (label verso, artist's address given as The Hamilton, Philadelphia);
1923, Corcoran Biennial Exhibition, The Corcoran Museum of Art, Washington, D.C., no. 290 (label verso, artist's address given as 219 S. 17th St. Philadelphia);
1926, The Sesqui-Centennial International Exhibition, Department of Fine Arts, Pennsylvania Academy of the Fine Arts, Philadelphia, Pennsylvania (label verso indicates "invited work");
January 16-March 13, 1955, The One-Hundred and Fiftieth Anniversary Exhibition, Pennsylvania Academy of the Fine Arts, Philadelphia, Pennsylvania (label verso, owner given as Harold Adams, Chestnut St.)

Literature:
The Pennsylvania Academy of the Fine Arts, *Catalogue of the 188th Annual Exhibition,* February 4 to March 25, 1923, Philadelphia, 1928, n.p., ill.
The Pennsylvania Academy of the Fine Arts Annual Exhibition Record, ed. Peter Hastings Falk, Sound View Press, 1989, vol. III, p. 318.
The Biennial Exhibition Record of the Corcoran Gallery of Art 1907-1967, ed. Peter Hastings Falk, Sound View Press, 1991, p. 193.

For forty years (1900-1940), Henry McCarter taught on the faculty of the Pennsylvania Academy of the Fine Arts in Philadelphia, initially as the school's first Instructor in Illustration in 1900, and eventually as its primary advocate of modern painting. McCarter's dominant presence at the Academy influenced many artists, including Arthur B. Carles and Charles Demuth (both represented in the present auction), as well as Charles Sheeler, all of whom became important American modernists. Born in Norristown, Pennsylvania, McCarter himself was a product of the Pennsylvania Academy, and had trained under Thomas Eakins before making an extended trip to Paris in the later 1880s where he came into contact with the art of the Post-Impressionists. On a second trip to Europe he met many celebrated French artists, including Puvis de Chavannes and Léon Bonnat, with whom he studied as well as van Gogh, Pissarro, Degas and Toulouse-Lautrec whose work profoundly influenced the future direction of his painting.

McCarter's estimable reputation as a successful illustrator in New York following his return from Paris preceded his tenure at the academy. He produced many illustrations for *Collier's, Scribner's* and *Harper's.* From this conservative beginning, McCarter grew to become a champion of the moderns, and by the 1920s his mythic, dreamlike subjects (such as the present work) as well as his landscapes of the Lancaster countryside changed radically from the realism that had won him medals at the Buffalo and St, Louis expositions in 1901 and 1904. Although like that of his colleagues at the academy, Hugh Breckenridge and Thomas Anschutz, McCarter's teaching was considered progressive, and invoked an expressive use of color evident in the present work, the painter consistently placed primary emphasis upon draftsmanship. One of the students who most completely absorbed McCarter's flair for stylized draftsmanship married to prismatic color, and a knack for grand design was James Daugherty, who went on to a versatile career as illustrator, easel painter, and muralist.

Men's Gods of circa 1923, a work McCarter exhibited widely, possesses the hallmarks of his particular interpretation of modern painting. As many contemporaries noted, McCarter's work doesn't have the plasticityof a Leger and Picasso. Rather, his modernity relies heavily upon (and succeeds almost effortless as the result of) its forceful insistence upon the primacy of color and design. In *Men's Gods,* McCarter presents an Art Deco-style frieze of deities drawn from Christian, Buddhist, African, Egyptian, Chinese, and Norse religions and mythologies, all rendered in a vigorous manner that easily calls to mind the work of the Post-Impressionists in its daubs, dabs, and sinuous outlines. McCarter was essentially painting *alla prima*-drawing with the brush. Moreover, there seems to be a subtext to the work of art, painted shortly after the Second World War, which moves beyond pleasing decoration. In this commanding canvas, McCarter parades the world religions across a painted stage bearing the loaded title "Men's Gods." Unfortunately, no artist's statement survives to explicate his specific painterly intentions.

As a writer for the *Arts Digest* noted in his December 1, 1942 obituary of McCarter, who died of a heart attack at age 76: "Perhaps the most pleasant duty for McCarter during his last years was his work as sole surviving administrator of the famous Lambert Fund-through which the Academy acquires exhibits from its annuals. More and more toward the end McCarter's choices were promising unknowns. It seemed as if the old man were renewing his own youth by helping some young artist up the ladder, which he himself had first attempted a half century ago."

In an even more personal tribute to the artist, published in the brochure to the McCarter Memorial Exhibition held at the Pennsylvania Academy from December 12, 1943 to January 9, 1944, Weeks Hall wrote: "How difficult it is to write about such a man. No one who really knew him remained unaffected by him, and yet this curious and pervasive influence, however strong, is so subtle that printed words seem uselessly to fracture an emotion which might best remain inviolate. There was something magical about him as there is about his painting. That, I repeat, is a quality beyond words to convey."

Estimate: $6,000-$8,000

The reserve for this lot is available at HA.com/FineArt.

23125

ARTHUR BEECHER CARLES (American 1882-1952)
Untitled Abstraction, circa 1921-27
Oil on canvasboard
16 x 20-1/2 inches (40.6 x 52.1 cm)

Provenance:
Private collection;
Sale, Bonham's, New York, November 29, 2005, Lot 95

Arthur B. Carles was one of the finest colorists among the early American modernists as well as one of the most original American interpreters of the Fauvist and Cubist styles. A native of Philadelphia, Carles trained from 1900 to 1907 at the local Pennsylvania Academy of Fine Arts where he quickly mastered the rigorous academic curriculum under an exceptional group of artists with very different styles and philosophies: William Merritt Chase, Thomas Anschutz, Hugh Breckenridge, Cecilia Beaux, and Henry McCarter. Perhaps owing to this early exposure to wide artistic diversity, Carles was extremely open-minded as a painter as well as enthusiastically experimental. For Carles, Chase proved a particularly influential figure: he taught his students to paint quickly, with loose, dynamic brushwork and the idea that the abstract composition of a painting was more important than its story or subject matter. Under Henry McCarter, who was universally regarded as the academic bastion's recognized modernist, Carles adopted a preference for a radically colorful palette which doubtless predisposed him to the work of the Fauves a little later on.

Carles enjoyed early artistic recognition at the Academy, winning numerous prizes and awards for his work, including the prestigious Cresson Traveling Scholarship which he won not once but twice. In 1905 the first Cresson took him abroad for the summer, while the second (1907) with its cash award of $2,000 enabled him to spend the next three years abroad (1907-1910). Like many of his contemporaries, Carles selected Paris as his place for European art training, but unlike so many other young Americans, Carles gravitated to the radical avant-garde rather than ateliers of academic figure painters and impressionists. He renewed his association with the American modernist John Marin, whom he had known as the Academy, and visited the home of Leo and Gertrude Stein-probably through contact with the another talented American, Alfred Maurer-where he was exposed to the work of Cézanne, Picasso and Matisse. These figures had a profound impact upon the future direction of his art, specifically in the use of color both for its expressive and structural properties. Also in Paris, Carles formed a fast friendship with the American photographer Edward Steichen, whom photographer/gallery owner Alfred Stieglitz had enlisted to help identify artistic innovations and innovators in the French capital. In the company of Steichen and Marin, Carles began to paint landscapes of the French countryside using electric colors and thick impasto. The contact with Steichen drew Carles into the Stieglitz circle of the American avant-garde. Carles became a founding member of the New Society of American Artists in Paris in 1908-a group which provided the basis for an exhibition at Stieglitz's "291" Gallery in New York two years later. Entitled "Younger American Painters," Stieglitz's show was the first exhibition of American modernism, predating by three years the landmark Armory Show which brought a large concentration of European (and American) modern art to the attention of the American public for the first time. Between Stieglitz's exhibition and the Armory Show, Carles returned to France where he galvanized his modernist style, cropping, conflating and flattening space. Never a timid painter, Carles-even in his earliest efforts in the new idiom-pushed his new style as far as he could. His boldness was recognized and two of his confident French landscapes were chosen for inclusion in the Armory Show.

As the present work from the following decade amply demonstrates, Arthur Carles was far less literal in his approach to the Fauvist and Cubist styles than many American abstractionists who had a very hard time letting go of the subject altogether. This work is a prime example of how radical Carles' work could be, and how close he came to non-representational painting some twenty-five years *before* the advent of Abstract Expressionism. Indeed, while this painting probably has as its objective inspiration a still life arranged on a tabletop (a related work from circa 1921-27 showing a similar blue vase with a multicolored handle is reproduced in *Arthur Beecher Carles 1882-1952,* exh. cat., essay by Meredith E. Ward, Richard York Gallery, New York, 1997, no. 8, p. 12), there are few real "markers" identifying the subject. The subject is quite obviously the paint. Not surprisingly, because such abstractions were extremely precocious, often rendered with a painterly abandon and a gloppy, overloaded brush in the manner of a later artist like Hans Hoffmann (who vastly admired Carles' work), Carles' paintings were difficult for the public to accept and understand. Interestingly, his daughter, Mercedes, who herself became an artist and married the noted Swiss-born graphic designer, Herman Matter, became close friends with the maverick Abstract Expressionist painter, Jackson Pollock, around the time he was developing his breakthrough "drip" paintings. Clearly her father's brand of creative freedom led her to seek out like-minded artists.

Artistically, Arthur Carles pushed the envelope very far. While his persistence in painting abstractly did win him the support of a tight group of discerning Philadelphia collectors such as R. Sturgis Ingersoll and Earl Horter and the admiration of Leopold Stokowski, it also made him art world adversaries. On the other hand, his energetic support of modern art intensely endeared him to his students at the Pennsylvania Academy, where he taught from 1917 to 1925 (roughly the same timeframe as the present painting). During his tenure at his *alma mater,* Carles worked to bring an awareness of his modernism not only to his students, but to Philadelphia at large, organizing many exhibitions of contemporary art. Sadly, his efforts were not only unappreciated but discouraged by the staid faculty. He was reprimanded for his outspoken advocacy of modernism in 1920, and then eventually dismissed from his post in 1925. Undaunted, Carles continued painting in his chosen style, teaching privately, and exhibiting widely. By 1928, Carles had developed a new interest in Cubism. In his paintings of still-lifes, nudes and landscapes-his three primary subjects-the artist began fracturing forms into planes that intersect and collide with one another.

By the 1930s, Carles' health began to deteriorate largely from a lifelong practice of drinking, which he felt enhanced his perceptions. In 1941, just a year after his first one-man show at the Pennsylvania Academy, he experienced a tragic fall while he was intoxicated which left him paralyzed and unable to paint. He spent the final decade of his life confined to a nursing home, where he died in 1952.

The most important holdings of Arthur Carles' work are the permanent collections of the Philadelphia Museum of Art and the Pennsylvania Academy of Fine Arts.

Estimate: $10,000-$15,000

The reserve for this lot is available at HA.com/FineArt.

23126

WILLIAM LUMPKINS (American 1909-2000)
Lineal, 1976
Watercolor
18 x 9-1/2 inches (46.9 x 24.1 cm)
Signed and dated lower left: *Lumpkins 76*
Signed, dated and titled verso

Provenance:
Private collection (New Mexico)

Estimate: $2,000-$4,000

The reserve for this lot is available at HA.com/FineArt.

23127

CARL R. KRAFFT (American 1880-1938)
Homeward Bound, 1925
Oil on board
17 x 18-1/2 inches (43.2 x 47 cm)
Signed lower left, with thumbprint: *CARL R. KRAFFT*

Provenance:
Mr. and Mrs. Emil F. Smrz (Chicago, Illinois);
Private collection (Dallas, Texas)

Exhibition:
Summer Exhibition, The Art Institute Of Chicago, July 20-October 29, 1939 (cat. 8)

The catalog for The Art Institute's Summer Exhibition accompanies this lot, as well as a letter from the Director of Fine Arts, Daniel Catton Rich, July 24, 1939, thanking Mr. and Mrs. Smrz for their loan.

Estimate: $3,000-$5,000

This lot is being sold without reserve. Unreserved lots generally open at 50% of the low estimate.

23128

CARL R. KRAFFT
(American 1884-1938)
At Forest Spring
Oil on canvas laid on board
6 x 8 inches (15.2 x 20.3 cm)
Signed lower right: *KRAFFT*

Provenance:
Mr. and Mrs. Emil F. Smrz
(Chicago, Illinois);
Private collection (Dallas, Texas)

Estimate: $2,000-$4,000

This lot is being sold without reserve. Unreserved lots generally open at 50% of the low estimate.

23129

CARL R. KRAFFT
(American 1880-1938)
Still Life
Oil on board
20 x 18 inches (50.8 x 45.7 cm)
Signed lower left: *CARL R. KRAFFT*

Provenance:
Mr. and Mrs. Emil F. Smrz (Chicago, Illinois);
Private collection (Dallas, Texas)

Estimate: $2,000-$4,000

This lot is being sold without reserve. Unreserved lots generally open at 50% of the low estimate.

23130

EDMUND WILLIAM GREACEN
(American 1877-1949)
Winter Stream
Oil on canvas
7-1/4 x 10-1/4 inches (18.4 x 26 cm)

Provenance:
Meredith L. Long & Co. (Houston, Texas);
Mr. and Mrs. Edgar E. Townes, 1973 (Houston, Texas)

Estimate: $3,000-$5,000

The reserve for this lot is available at HA.com/FineArt.

23131

MARIUS DE JONGERE
(Dutch 1912-1978)
Windmill By The River
Oil on canvas
16 x 23 inches (40.6 x 58.4 cm)
Signed lower right

Provenance:
Mr. and Mrs. Edgar E. Townes (Houston, Texas)

Estimate: $1,500-$3,000

The reserve for this lot is available at HA.com/FineArt.

23132

ALFRED HEBER HUTTY
(American 1877-1954)
Charleston, circa 1920
Watercolor on Whatman paper on board
17-1/2 x 23-3/8 inches
(44.4 x 59.3cm)
Signed lower right: *Alfred Hutty*

Provenance:
From the Estate of Linda S. Firestone

Alfred Hutty first moved to Charleston in 1920 to teach at the school at the Gibbes Museum and returned every summer thereafter. He worked primarily in drypoint but also painted non-romantized scenes similar to the present lot depicting figures in doorways and dilapidated buildings.

Estimate: $4,000-$6,000

The reserve for this lot is available at HA.com/FineArt.

23133

ALFRED HERBER HUTTY (American 1877-1954)
Portrait of a man, circa 1952
Charcoal on paper
15 x 11-1/2 inches (38.1 x 29.2 cm)
Signed lower right: *Alfred Hutty;*
Inscribed in the corner in pencil: *P-85;* and inscribed verso: *Bought from Alfred Hutty / Charleston, SC / Mar. 1952 / pencil sketch*

Provenance:
Acquired from the artist, March 1952;
Bessie Heard (McKinney, Texas);
Bessie Heard Trust

Estimate: $3,000-$5,000

This lot is being sold without reserve. Unreserved lots generally open at 50% of the low estimate.

23134

LUIGI LUCIONI
(American 1900-1988)
Crystal Fountain And Loggia At Laurelton Hall, 1925
Oil on canvas
25 x 20 inches
(63.5 x 50.8 cm)
Signed and dated lower left:
L Lucioni 1925

Provenance:
Mrs. H.H. Wehrhane (Manchester, Vermont);
Acquired by descent to her nephew

Luigi Lucioni has long been considered one the leading figures of American twentieth century realism. He is best-known today for the crisply-drawn and modeled still lifes and landscapes, which he painted in his New York City and Vermont studios. In 1925, however, while a Fellow of the Tiffany Foundation, Lucioni adopted a bright impressionistic style of soft brushwork, rich tonalities, and careful attention to the play of light. While living at Laurelton Hall, the home on Long Island which Louis Comfort Tiffany had designed for himself, Lucioni painted what is probably the only extant view of Tiffany's crystal fountain and loggia. The fountain, and the house have long since been destroyed, although a few of the ornate mosaic columns from the loggia have been preserved at the Metropolitan Museum of Art, New York.

Estimate: $40,000-$60,000

This lot is being sold without reserve. Unreserved lots generally open at 50% of the low estimate.

23135

AARON SHIKLER, A.N.A. (American b.1922)
Figure On Beach (Portrait Of Artist's Wife In His Mother's Dress), 1972
Oil on canvas
12 x 8 inches (30.5 x 20.3 cm)
Signed and dated lower left:

Provenance:
Mr. Roy Davis (New York);
Meredith L. Long & Co. (Houston, Texas);
Mr. and Mrs. Edgar E. Townes, 1972 (Houston, Texas)

Estimate: $5,000-$7,000

The reserve for this lot is available at HA.com/FineArt.

23136

ANTHONY HENDERSON EUWER
(American 1877-1955)
The Water Of Elysium, 1927
Oil on canvas
30 x 50 inches (76.2 x 127cm)

Signed and dated lower right:
Anthony Euwer 1927

Estimate: $2,000-$3,000

The reserve for this lot is available at HA.com/FineArt.

23137

ELIE ANATOLE PAVIS (French 1873-1948)
Interior Brenton A Carenton
Watercolor on paper
11-1/4 x 17 inches (28.6 x 43.2 cm)
Signed and inscribed at lower right: *E. Pavis*

Estimate: $1,500-$2,500

The reserve for this lot is available at HA.com/FineArt.

23138

STUART DAVIS (American 1894-1964)
Composers of Musical Comedies, circa 1922
India ink and brush with red ink wash on paper
23 x 17-1/4 inches (58.4 x 43.8 cm)
Signed upper left: *STUART DAVIS*
Titled lower right: *Composers of Musical Comedies*

Provenance:
The Downtown Gallery (New York);
Sale, Sotheby Parke-Bernet (No. 3520), May 16, 1973, Lot 21;
The Edith Gregor Halpert Collection;
Property from a Private New York Estate

Exhibition:
New York, The Downtown Gallery, American Drawings, 1964

Literature:
Ani Boyajian and Mark Rutkoski, *Stuart Davis: A Catalogue raisonné,* October 2007 (illustrated)

Estimate: $6,000-$8,000

The reserve for this lot is available at HA.com/FineArt.

23139

EVERETT SHINN (American 1876-1953)
Curtain Call, 1925
Oil on canvas
9-1/4 x 11-1/4 inches (23 x 29 cm)
Signed and dated lower left: *E. Shinn/1925*

Provenance:
Tullah and Thomas Edward Hanley (Bradford, Pennsylvania);
William Benton (Connecticut);
Private collection

Exhibitions:
Gallery of Modern Art, New York, *Selections from the Collection of Dr. and Mrs. T. Edward Hanley,* January 3 - March 12, 1967;
Berry-Hill Galleries, New York, *The Spectacle of Life,* November 29, 2000 - January 13, 2001

Literature:
Janay Wong, *Everett Shinn: The Spectacle of Life* (New York: Berry-Hill Galleries, 2000), pp. 86-87, 167 (reproduced);
Janay Wong, *"Curtain Call"*, entry in *American Paintings IX,* (New York: Berry-Hill Galleries, 2001), pp. 98-99 (reproduced)

Shinn's portrayals of the theater provide some of his most visually spectacular pictures and reveal a life-long fascination with the stage that went beyond the role of mere observer. An active participant in his own productions, he was also on friendly terms with several actors and actresses. Around 1910, after receiving a commission to paint 22 x 45 foot murals for Trenton City Hall, Shinn built a large studio behind his Waverly Place residence. The studio also doubled as a theater which included crimson curtains, a proscenium, and a perfectly equipped miniature stage. Home to "The Waverly Street Players", an amateur theater group, which included the Shinns, the Glackenses, Jimmy Preston, and David Belasco's assistant, Wilfred Buckland, the theater had the character of a private club for friends. For the performances, Shinn wrote three four-act melodramas: *The Prune Hater's Daughter, More Sinned Against than Usual,* and *Wronged from the Start.* Shinn first exhibited representations of the theater in 1899 when he showed *Scene - Julia Marlowe, Fourteenth Street Theater,* and *Interior Keith's* at the home of his friend Elsie de Wolfe. Following his trip to Europe in 1900, theater pictures appear with increasing frequency culminating in the eight paintings of performers on stage shown in the landmark exhibition of The Eight at William Macbeth's Gallery in February 1908.

Curtain Call most likely a represents a Vaudeville performance, which by 1900, was America's unrivaled leader in the world of entertainment. Shinn was particularly attracted to the Vaudeville stage and portrayed it numerous times in well-known paintings such as *Keith's Union Square* (c. 1906, The Brooklyn Museum of Art) and *The Orchestra Pit, Old Proctor's Fifth Avenue Theater* (c. 1906-07, Collection of Mr. and Mrs. Arthur G. Altschul). In *Curtain Call* a slender female performer holds a parasol in one hand and extends her arms gracefully to crisscross the arm of her male partner forming an undulating line. The pairing of a male and female dancer is unusual for Shinn, who typically depicted only female dancers. Here he seems to appreciate the juxtaposition of opposites - male beside female and dark against light. Unlike his earlier, more rounded figures, the dancers featured here are slender with long limbs. Contemporary fashion favored tall, thin figures, a trend that is reflected in the artist's paintings and illustrations for this period. In the background, the scenery is painted with a verdant wooded landscape recalling the style of Jean-Antoine Watteau or Jean-Honoré Fragonard. The palette is jewel-like, consisting of crimson red, emerald green, gleaming white.

The origin of *Curtain Call* can be traced to *The Vaudeville Act* (1902-03, The Palmer Museum), which itself is a version (perhaps earlier) of a painting illustrated in the original exhibition catalogue of The Eight. *The Vaudeville Act,* with its well-rendered performers and their placement on stage before a green, painted backdrop, looks forward to *Curtain Call.* The same red trousers and white dress appear, but in the later picture the dress has been transformed into a delicate tutu revealing the dancer's long tapering legs. In *Curtain Call,* the dance is livelier, evoking the spirit of the roaring twenties. Another significant difference is the absence of the orchestra pit. Beginning around 1910, Shinn started occasionally to crop the compositions of his theater pictures, eliminating the audience and orchestra pit in favor of a close-up view of the performers on stage.

Estimate: $120,000-$180,000

This lot is being sold without reserve. Unreserved lots generally open at 50% of the low estimate.

23140

WILLIAM GLACKENS (American 1870-1938)
Standing Gentleman
Charcoal on brown paper
9 x 6 inches, approximately (22.9 x 15.2 cm)
Unsigned

Provenance:
Kraushaar Galleries (New York)

Estimate: $500-$700

The reserve for this lot is available at HA.com/FineArt.

23141

WILLIAM GLACKENS (American 1870-1938)
Nude Pulling On Stocking (Nude With Red Hair),
circa 1925
Oil on canvas
32 x 26 inches (81 x 66 cm)

Provenance::
Estate of the artist, 1938 to present

Literature:
Touchstone 7 (June 1920): 193 (reproduced);
List made in 1943 of works in estate of William J. Glackens left to Mrs. William J. Glackens, William Glackens File, Whitney Museum of American Art Papers, Archives of American Art, microfilm reel no. N658, frame 601, no. 47;

William Glackens File, Whitney Museum of American Art Papers, Archives of American Art, micofilm reel no. 658, frame 273;

Card file of works by William J. Glackens, William and Ira Glackens Papers, Archives of American Art, microfilm roll 4710, frame 376, no. 30;

Richard Joel Wattenmaker, 'The Art of William Glackens,' Ph.D. Dissertation, New York University Institute of Fine Arts, 1973, pp. 247-248m 454, 457 (reproduced)

William Glackens was born in Philadelphia, Pennsylvania. In 1891, following his graduation from Philadelphia's Central High School where John Sloan was a fellow student, he joined the Philadelphia Record as an artist-reporter, and worked in a similar capacity from 1892 to 1895 for the Philadelphia Press. Also working for the Press at this time were Sloan, George Luks, and Everett Shinn—all of whom became associated with a group of progressive painters known as "The Eight." In 1893 Glackens studied briefly with Thomas Anschutz at the Pennsylvania Academy of the Fine Arts. Glackens and the artist Robert Henri shared a studio in 1894, and traveled to Europe together the following year. Upon his return to America in 1896 Glackens settled in New York and worked as an illustrator for the *New York Herald* and later for the *New York World*. In 1908 he became a member of the Eight(Henri, Sloan, Shinn, Luks, Maurice Prendergast, Arthur B. Davies, and Ernest Lawson) who held a landmark exhibition at the Macbeth Galleries. This exhibition marked the ascendancy of a realist style of American painting, later dubbed the "Ashcan school."

Glackens went to France in 1912 as an agent for the important Philadelphia collector of European modernist art, Dr. Albert C. Barnes, returning with works by Degas, Manet, Renoir, and Matisse, among others. In 1913 Glackens was chairman of the committee selecting American entries in the Armory Show, and in 1917 was elected the first president of the Society of Independent Artists. The growing recognition of his paintings enabled him to accept only occasional illustrating assignments from then on. Upon his death in 1938, a memorial exhibition of his work was organized by the Whitney Museum of American Art.

Nude Pulling On Stocking is one of a radiant group of female nudes by Glackens from the 1920s. The present work is an outstanding example of this aspect of Glackens' production which was inspired a close study of nudes by Renoir in the collection of Dr. Barnes. –A painting closely related to the present work was awarded the Temple Gold Medal from the Pennsylvania Academy of the Fine Arts in 1924. Glackens' nudes usually feature young models posed in interior settings, and feature some of the artist's most harmonious and complex arrangements of color and marvelous expressions of volume. Richard Joel Wattenmaker has noted that in many of his nudes, Glackens studied the 'figure in its entirety. Often [they] were portrayed in pictorial settings which included . . . draperies . . . and a background . . . of striking wallpaper floral or vegetative pattern. The nude itself was almost always . . . represented in some casual informal attitude, and frequently was partially attired in [an] undergarment' ('The Art of William Glackens' Ph.D. dissertation, New York University Institute of Fine Arts, 1973, p. 247). A small oil study for this work is recorded in the artist's inventories although its present whereabouts are unknown.

Estimate: $200,000-$300,000

This lot is being sold without reserve. Unreserved lots generally open at 50% of the low estimate.

23142

CHARLES ROSWELL BACON (American 1868-1913)
Female Nude In An Interior
Oil on canvas
54 x 54 inches (137.2 x 137.2 cm)
Signed lower right: *C. R. Bacon*

Relevant Literature:
"Interview with Peggy Bacon Conducted by Paul Cummings," the artist's home in Cape Porpoise, Maine, May 8, 1973, Artists' Oral Histories, Archives of American Art, Smithsonian Institution, Washington, D.C.

The landscape and figure painter Charles Roswell Bacon was the talented and colorful father of Peggy Bacon (1895-1987), the well-known 20th-century painter, poet, printmaker, author and illustrator. A native of New York, he met his wife Elizabeth Chase at the newly-formed Art Students' League in New York where they took classes under Kenyon Cox before heading off to Paris to study for year under Lefebvre and Collin. Upon their return, they married and settled for awhile in Ridgefield, Connecticut where they started a family. Their first child, Peggy, was followed by two boys who died in infancy. This left Peggy as an only child. The three of them thus became a very tight-knit family-something Peggy Bacon described with tremendous enthusiasm when she was interviewed by Paul Cummings for the Archives of American Art artist interview project in 1973. She told Cummings that her parents "were professionals" and provided an important sketch of her father's artistic interests and personality: "Father...had exhibitions in New York at the Fulton Gallery and at the Milch Gallery. We spent certain winters in New York when I was a child. He took me around to galleries. Then we lived in France for a couple of years, at Montreaux-sur-Mer in Picardy. It was absolutely delightful. I had the most charming and amusing parents. We led a very close life together. There was a great deal of reading aloud. They were both very well read. They were passionate readers of Henry James as fast as his novels came out. Every evening there was reading aloud. Well, it was a lovely life, really. Well, Father was very gregarious."

Because he and his wife traveled so much in connection with their artistic interests and careers, Charles Bacon hired private tutors for their daughter. Peggy Bacon recalls never having set foot in a school, speculating that back then, private tutors could not have been very expensive since "Mother and Father were never affluent. That's putting it mildly. As I recall, all my life we had an extraordinary amount of amenities and delicacies even and delights considering that they were poverty-stricken. The food was marvelous, very gourmet food. And there were quantities of books, endless books arriving. And a great deal of charm. They were people of taste. Father was very well-read in French. He spoke French so well that French people mistook him for a Frenchman. And yet he had no schooling from the age of ten."

The present figure painting by Charles Bacon is characteristic of the lyrical, impressionistic palette the artist adopted after his exposure to the work of Whistler and even more directly to the work of the American painter, Theodore Robinson. On one of his early trips to France, Bacon lived and painted for an extended period in Giverny, the home of Claude Monet, alongside Robinson who became an intimate friend and mentor.

Despite his successes as an artist, Charles Bacon suffered from severe depression-the same illness which led his father, Otto Bacon, an importer of marble, to drink himself to death after the failure of his business. Several months after the Armory Show, Charles Bacon took his own life in his studio, which was crammed with many unfinished canvases. Among his close friends was the successful illustrator, Ernest Peixotto, who wrote a beautiful celebration of Charles Bacon-the man and the artist-in the catalogue accompanying the memorial exhibition and public sale of Bacon's work at the Metropolitan Art Association's Anderson Galleries on January 19 and 20, 1914: "The Art of Charles Roswell Bacon was, pre-eminently, the art of a colorist-of a lover of gamuts of pearly grays and the blonde harmonies of sunlight and sky. In this love of color lay the delightful breeziness and out-door feeling of his landscapes and the subtle grays and Whistlerian reticence of his interiors. . . In their sketchiness, [Bacon's canvases] much resemble the work of John Twachtman, whose splendid achievement has only come into its own since his death. There was much in common in the personality of these two men-in their great personal charm that made warm friends and held them-the quality that the Latins call simpatico; and that it was, that gave to their work its emotional, delicate feeling."

Estimate: $3,000-$5,000

The reserve for this lot is available at HA.com/FineArt.

23143

ALFRED S. MIRA
(American 1900-1980)
La Magdalene
Oil on canvas
6-1/4 x 8 inches (15.9 x 20.3 cm)
Signed lower right: *Mira*

Estimate: $3,000-$5,000

This lot is being sold without reserve. Unreserved lots generally open at 50% of the low estimate.

23144

JOHANNES SCHIEFER
(Dutch/American 1896-1978)
Paris Street Scene
Oil on canvas
25 x 30 inches (63.5 x 76.2 cm)
Signed lower right:
Johannes Schiefer

Provenance:
Stephen Silagy
(Los Angeles, California);
Private collection (Dallas, Texas)

Estimate: $1,000-$2,000

This lot is being sold without reserve. Unreserved lots generally open at 50% of the low estimate.

23145

RALSTON CRAWFORD (American 1906-1978)
Nantucket, 1932
Oil on canvas
26 x 22 inches (66 x 55.9 cm)
Signed lower right: *CRAWFORD*
Inscribed on stretcher: *NANTUCKET, 26" X 22" / 1932*
Stamped on stretcher: *Ralston Crawford Estate 32.24*

Provenance:
Lee Nordess Galleries, label verso (New York)

Art historically Ralston Crawford has been grouped with the American Precisionists-Charles Sheeler, Charles Demuth and Morton Livingston Schamberg—whose slices of the American landscape and vernacular architecture have characteristic sharp-edged forms, and clearly distilled planes and volumes. Their iconic presentations of grain elevators, docks, shipyards, barns, even common garden flowers in inexpensive vases were, in the 1930s, a new brand of realism—streamlined realism—and were prized as archetypal American imagery. Indeed, within seven years of painting this silvery-blue arrangement of boats and houses at Nantucket, Ralston Crawford produced *Overseas Highway* (1939), the work which catapulted him to national fame. In *Overseas Highway,* an empty causeway rushes confidently and aggressively into deep perspective. As Carter Ratcliff noted, "After nearly a decade of economic depression, it [Crawford's painting] was a welcome message" of hope, and relief, and was reproduced in Life magazine.

Crawford produced the present work, *Nantucket,* in 1932, at the moment in his career when his pictorial style began the shift from a more painterly, European-inspired brand of modernism, to one that was more severe and reductive (Precisionist). Notably, in this and a handful of related works which Crawford produced during the summer of 1932, the artist chose the subject of the sea as the vehicle for exploring a tighter flattening of form, and a greater clarification of planes. For Crawford, the sea was the environment in which he felt most at home, and the motifs associated with it were those with enormous personal resonance for him.

Ralston Crawford was born in Ontario, Canada, to a Canadian mother and American father who worked as a captain on cargo ships. His father's work took the family to Buffalo where he grew up and where he discovered his aptitude for art. By the time he was fourteen, he had traveled all the Great Lakes with his father, and later worked on ships as an able-bodied seaman. In 1926-1927, he sailed on tramp steamers to Santiago, Honduras, Havana, Jamaica, and through the Panama Canal to San Francisco. The sea was in his blood—along with art.

In 1927, Crawford studied at the Otis Art Institute and worked in Walt Disney's garage studio before moving back east where he trained from 1927 to 1930 at the Pennsylvania Academy of Fine Arts. There he became especially close to Hugh Breckenridge, whose summer school in Gloucester Crawford attended during the summer he painted the present work, and Henry McCarter, the most progressive artist on the faculty. During his period of study at the Pennsylvania Academy, Crawford worked for two years at the Barnes Foundation in the Philadelphia suburb of Merion, where he got to know Dr. Barnes personally, and became enormously inspired by the work of Cezanne. In particular, Crawford learned to appreciate the underlying structure of Cezanne's imagery, which eventually resulted in a more individual pictorial architecture expressed in the present work.

At some level, Crawford's experiences of making a painting and making a life on the sea were intricately related. As he once revealed to Edward H. Dwight, probably in preparation for his exhibition at the Milwaukee Art Center in 1958: "To go back to the sea, I remember lines in one of O'Neill's plays, *Long Day's Journey Into Night,* where he talked about the 'Dawn Watch'; I never heard it called that before but I know the watch that he is referring to. He refers to the four to eight watch in the morning which is also in effect in the evening. He talked about the beauty he found standing that watch. It was there I suppose that a particular kind of solitude related to color and movement were perhaps my deepest and most meaningful early experiences in relation to painting. . . . There was the color, and the intensely human character of many of the situations, involving my ship. Sometimes for a very young man, scarcely more than a boy, the action was a little bit frightening. . . . There was the courageous speculative character of the men living this life. . . . They were very high rollers and high rolling is essential to picture-making." (William Agee, *Ralston Crawford,* Twelve Trees Press, 1983, p. 8)

Estimate: $30,000-$50,000

The reserve for this lot is available at HA.com/FineArt.

23146

EMILE ALBERT GRUPPE
(American 1896-1978)
Bass Rocks
Oil on canvasboard
12 x 16 inches (30.5 x 40.6 cm)
Signed lower left: *Emile A. Gruppe*

Provenance:
Richard Carta (Boca Raton, Florida);
Private collection (Houston, Texas)

Estimate: $3,000-$5,000

The reserve for this lot is available at HA.com/FineArt.

23147

PHILLIP HERSCHEL PARADISE (American 1905-1997)
Haitian Schooner
Watercolor and ink on paper
29-3/8 x 20-3/8 inches, sight (74.6 x 51.8 cm)
Signed lower right

Phil Paradise worked in California and taught at the Chouinard Art Institute and Scripps college. From the mid-1940's onward his style evolved from Regionalism into a more stylized approach, reflecting his time spent in the Caribbean, South America and Mexico.

Estimate: $4,000-$6,000

The reserve for this lot is available at HA.com/FineArt.

23148

GROUP OF SIX PRINTS
LUIGI KASIMIR (Austrian 1881-1962); **TANNA KASIMIR-HOERNES** (Austrian/American 1887-1972); **OTTO WACKERNAGEL** (American)
Nassau Hall; Chartres Cathedral; Yosemite Falls; London, Tower Bridge; N.Y. Stock Exchange; George Washington Bridge
Etchings and aquatints
17-1/2 x 10-7/8 inches, largest (44.45 x 27.62 cm)
All signed lower right or center in pencil and inscribed in the lower margin

Provenance:
Kennedy & Co. (New York) (Kasimir and Kasimir-Hoernes)
Bessie Heard (McKinney, Texas);
Bessie Heard Trust

Estimate: $2,000-$3,000

This lot is being sold without reserve. Unreserved lots generally open at 50% of the low estimate.

23149

GEORGE FORD MORRIS (American 1873-1960)
Man O' War, 1921 -
Lithograph
12-1/2 x 9-1/4 inches (31.8 x 23.5 cm)
AAA, pub.
Signed lower right: in pencil: *Geo. Ford Morris,* and inscribed in the lower margin

Provenance:
Bessie Heard (McKinney, Texas);
Bessie Heard Trust

Estimate: $1,500-$2,500

This lot is being sold without reserve. Unreserved lots generally open at 50% of the low estimate.

23150

MORGAN DENNIS (American 1892-1960)
"Scot's Home Surprise" Best of Breed Westminster, 1930
Etching
8-7/8 x 6-7/8 inches (22.5 x 17.4 cm)
Signed lower right: in pencil: *Morgan Dennis / T.P.,* titled and inscribed in the lower margin

Provenance:
Bessie Heard (McKinney, Texas);
Bessie Heard Trust

Estimate: $300-$500

This lot is being sold without reserve. Unreserved lots generally open at 50% of the low estimate.

23151

JOHN STOCKTON DE MARTELLY (American 1903-1980)
Chore Boy
Lithograph
9 x 12-1/8 inches (22.8 x 30.8 cm)
AAA, pub.
Signed lower right: in pencil: *John S. de Martelly,* and inscribed in the lower margin

Provenance:
Bessie Heard (McKinney, Texas);
Bessie Heard Trust

Estimate: $300-$500

This lot is being sold without reserve. Unreserved lots generally open at 50% of the low estimate.

23152

GRANT WOOD (American 1891-1942)
Fertility, 1939 -
Lithograph
9 x 11-7/8 inches (22.9 x 30.2 cm)
ed. 250
AAA, pub.
Signed lower right: in pencil: *Grant Wood*; inscribed lower right *P-53*; and with Bess Heard stamp on the reverse
Cat. Rais.: Cole, 15

Provenance:
Bessie Heard (McKinney, Texas);
Bessie Heard Trust

Estimate: $3,000-$5,000

This lot is being sold without reserve. Unreserved lots generally open at 50% of the low estimate.

23153

LUIGI LUCIONI
(Italian-American 1900-1988)
Classic Pastures; Tree Tapestry; Two Silos; Birch Group; Pattern of Trees; Vermont Splendor; Beyond the Elm; The Big Willows; Peaceful Pastures; The Spreading Maple (+ 2 additional works), circa 1940s -
Etchings
10-1/2 x 15-5/8 inches, largest (26.7 x 39.7 cm)
AAA, pub.
Most signed in the plate, and inscribed in the lower margin; all signed in pencil

Provenance:
Bessie Heard (McKinney, Texas);
Bessie Heard Trust

Estimate: $1,000-$1,500

This lot is being sold without reserve.
Unreserved lots generally open at 50% of the low estimate.

23154

GROUP OF FOURTEEN PRINTS
Including works by **SAM THAL** (American 1903-1964); **ASA CHEFFETZ** (American 1897-1965); **MELVILLE T. WIRE** (American b.1877); **PHILIP CHENEY** (American b.1897); **SAMUEL CHAMBERLAIN** (American 1895-1875); **ALICE EDITH RUMPH** (American b.1877); **WILLIAM MACLEAN** (American 1897-1977); **CHAUNCEY F. RYDER** (American 1868-1949)
Jerome's House, Buzzards Bay; Belmont Farm; In Deep Vermont; Along the Winooski; Border Country; Covered Bridge; Cabin by the River; April Thaw; The Church Yard, Williamsburg; The Semple house, Williamsburg; Spanish Oak, Charleston S.C.; Bruton Parish Church, Williamsburg, VA; The Sentinel; Farmyard in Winter
Etchings, wood engravings and lithograph
9-3/4 x 12 inches, largest (24.8 x 30.5 cm)
Signed; some titled and numbered; inscribed in the lower margin

Provenance:
Bessie Heard (McKinney, Texas);
Bessie Heard Trust

Estimate: $400-$600

This lot is being sold without reserve. Unreserved lots generally open at 50% of the low estimate.

23155

GROUP OF EIGHT PRINTS
Including works by **GEORGE ELMER BROWNE** (American 1871-1946); **GORDON GRANT** (American 1875-1962); **WALTER RONALD LOCKE** (American b.1883); **DOUGLAS GORSLINE** (American 1913-1985); **FRANCISCO DOSAMANTES** (Mexican b.1911)
The Bailers; Fore And Aft; Beaching The Dory; The Sand Fence; Anclote Light; Live Oak; Dog Days; Mexican Marketplace
Etchings, lithographs and engraving
13-1/4 x 9-7/8 inches, largest (33.7 x 25.1 cm)
Signed; some titled and inscribed in the lower margin

Provenance:
Bessie Heard (McKinney, Texas);
Bessie Heard Trust

Estimate: $500-$700

This lot is being sold without reserve. Unreserved lots generally open at 50% of the low estimate.

23156

ERIC SLOANE
(American 1905-1985)
Parting Clouds, circa 1930
Oil on masonite
19-1/4 x 25-1/2 inches
(48.9 x 64.8 cm)
Signed lower right: *Sloane*

Provenance:
A Retirement gift from Westchester County (New York);
Acquired by descent by the present owner

Estimate: $8,000-$10,000

The reserve for this lot is available at HA.com/FineArt.

23157

MAXFIELD PARRISH (American 1870-1966)
Sugar Hill, Late Afternoon, 1930
Oil on prepared board
25 x 30-1/2 inches (63 x 76 cm)
Signed and dated lower right: *Maxfield Parrish 1930*
Titled, inscribed, dated and signed verso: *Sugar Hill:Late Afternoon/Plainfield, New Hampshire/1930/Maxfield Parrish*

Provenance:
The Artist;
Estate of the Artist;
Eli Lily Collection (Indianapolis, Indiana);
Private collection (Tennessee)

Literature:
Letter of authentication from Maxfield Parrish, Jr., dated July 19, 1975;

Letter from the same to Rosalind Mikesell, discussing a photograph of his father's studio dating from about 1932 in which the painting appears, dated July 19, 1975;
Bruce Weber, *American Paintings IX* (New York: Berry-Hill Galleries, 2001), pp, 110-111 (reproduced)

Sugar Hill, Late Afternoon was painted in 1930 and records a view of the hill located behind Parrish's property in the central New Hampshire town of Plainfield. Where he lived from 1898 until his death in 1966. Parrish, an enormously successful illustrator developed a serious interest in landscape painting during the course of the 1930s, which intensified as a result of a particular commision: in 1934 the firm of Brown and Bigelow engaged him to paint summer and winter scenes of his own choosing for a series of calendars. As Alma Gilbert has noted, during the last thirty years of his life Parrish "sought to capture the "tranquil, idyllic settings of the spectrally picturesque New England area where he lived (Alma Gilbert, *Maxfield Parrish: The Masterbooks* [Berkeley, California: Ten Speed Press, 1995], p. 168).

Parrish purposfully sought to make his images direct and eye-catching. He consistently gave equal attention to all details in his compositions in order to achieve "a quality of reality and consequently a beauty of truth" (quoted in Coy Ludwig, *Maxfield Parrish* [New York: Watson-Guptill Publications, 1973], p. 145). Parrish felt that "pure air and light the magic of distance, and the saturated beauty of color, must be convincingly stated and take the beholder to the very spot." In 1952, Parrish summed up his philosophy on realism as it applied to landscape painting: "Realism should never be the end in view. My theory is that you should use all the objects in nature, trees, hills, skies, rivers, and all, just as stage properties on which to hang your idea, the end in view, the elusive quality of a day, in fact all the qualities that give a body the delights of out of doors. You cannot sit down and paint such things: they are not there, or do not last but for a moment. 'Realism' of impression, the MOOD of the moment, yes. But not the realism of THINGS. The colored photograph can do that better (Letter to Jerome Conally, May 5, 1952, Parrish Family Papers, cited in Alma Gilbert, *Maxfield Parrish: The Masterworks* [Berkeley, California: Ten Speed Press, 1995], p. 170).

Estimate: $300,000-$400,000

This lot is being sold without reserve. Unreserved lots generally open at 50% of the low estimate.

23158

GUY CARLETON WIGGINS (American 1883-1962)
Snow Storm On The Avenue, 1918
Oil on canvasboard
12 x 16 inches (30.4 x 40.6 cm)
Signed lower right: *Guy Wiggins*
Inscribed verso: *Snow Storm On The Avenue / Guy Wiggins A.N.A.,* with a paper label for *Russell's Artist's Canvas Boards* and *Lagakos-Turak Gallery*
Accompanied by a letter of authenticity from Guy A. Wiggins

Provenance:
Lagakos-Turak Gallery (Philadelphia, Pennsylvania)

Estimate: $60,000-$80,000

This lot is being sold without reserve. Unreserved lots generally open at 50% of the low estimate.

23159

GUY CARLETON WIGGINS (American 1883-1962)
The Avenue On A Winter's Day
Oil on canvas
12-1/8 x 16-1/8 inches (30.8 x 41 cm)
Signed lower left: *Guy C. Wiggins*
Inscribed verso: *"The Avenue On A Winter's Day" / Guy C. Wiggins*
Accompanied by a letter of authenticity from Guy A. Wiggins

Provenance:
Private collection (Boca Raton, Florida)

Estimate: $50,000-$70,000

The reserve for this lot is available at HA.com/FineArt.

23160

GUY CARELTON WIGGINS
(American 1883-1962)
Untitled, depicting the Woolworth Building, circa 1930s
Oil on canvasboard
10 x 8 inches (25.4 x 20.3 cm)
Signed lower left: *Guy Wiggins*
Accompanied by a letter of authenticity from Guy A. Wiggins

Provenance:
Private collection (Washington)

Estimate: $10,000-$15,000

The reserve for this lot is available at HA.com/FineArt.

23161

GUY CARLETON WIGGINS
(American 1883-1962)
A Winter's Snow / Plaza
Oil on canvasboard
12 x 16 inches
(30.5 x 40.6 cm)
Signed lower left: *Guy Wiggins N.A.*
Inscribed verso: *A Winter's Snow / Guy Wiggins N.A. / Plaza*
Accompanied by a letter of authenticity from Guy A. Wiggins

Estimate: $25,000-$35,000

The reserve for this lot is available at HA.com/FineArt.

23162

JOHANN BERTHELSEN
(American 1883-1969)
The Plaza Hotel In Winter
Oil on canvas
20-1/8 x 24 (51.1 x 61 cm)
Signed lower right: *Johann Berthelsen*

Provenance:
Estate of Ava Gardner;
Acquired by present owner from the above

Estimate: $12,000-$16,000

The reserve for this lot is available at HA.com/FineArt.

23163

JOHANN BERTHELSEN (American 1883-1969)
St. Patrick's Cathedral In The Snow, circa 1945
Oil on canvas
20 x 14 inches (50.8 x 35.5 cm)
Signed lower right: *Johann Berthelsen,* with illegible writing in red paint beneath

Provenance:
Adamson-Duvannes Galleries (Los Angeles, California)

Estimate: $15,000-$18,000

This lot is being sold without reserve. Unreserved lots generally open at 50% of the low estimate.

23164

JOHN KOCH
(American 1909-1978)
Back Scratcher
Oil on masonite
12-1/8 x 16 inches
(30.8 x 40.6 cm)
Signed lower right

Provenance:
Kraushaar Galleries
(New York);
Passed by descent
through family

Estimate:
$8,000-$12,000

The reserve for this lot is available at HA.com/FineArt.

23165

JOHN KOCH (American 1909-1978)
Study for "The Father"
Oil on masonite
13-1/2 x 9-1/2 inches (34.3 x 24.1 cm)
Signed lower right

Provenance:
Kraushaar Galleries (New York);
Passed by descent through family

This work is accompanied by a black and white photograph of the finished work: *The Father,* and the original letter from Antoinette Kraushaar to the buyer in which Mr. Kraushaar describes taking the painting to John Koch to sign.

Estimate: $3,000-$5,000

The reserve for this lot is available at HA.com/FineArt.

23166

RAPHAEL SOYER (American 1899-1987)
Woman in Blue Blouse (White Collar)
Oil on canvas
18-1/8 x 14-1/8 inches (46 x 35.9 cm)
Signed lower right

Provenance:
Forum Gallery (New York);
Passed by descent through family

Estimate: $5,000-$7,000

The reserve for this lot is available at HA.com/FineArt.

23167

CHARLES DANA GIBSON (American 1867-1944)
Girl in Red and Blue, 1942
Oil on canvas
37 x 28 inches (94 x 71.1 cm)
Signed lower left: *C.D Gibson*
Dated lower right: *1942*

Estimate: $15,000-$20,000

This lot is being sold without reserve. Unreserved lots generally open at 50% of the low estimate.

23168

LOUIS KRONBERG (American 1872-1965)
The Blue Fan
Pastel on paper
20 x 12 inches (50.8 x 30.5 cm)
Signed lower right

Provenance:
Salmagundi Club Exhibition, 1927 (New York);
Private collection (Connecticut)

Estimate: $3,000-$5,000

This lot is being sold without reserve. Unreserved lots generally open at 50% of the low estimate.

23169

ROBERT PHILIPP
(American 1895-1981)
Music Hall
Oil on canvas
16 x 24 inches (40.6 x 61 cm)
Signed upper right
Inscribed verso: *To Berger by Robert Philipp*

Provenance:
Private collection (Connecticut)

Estimate: $3,000-$5,000

This lot is being sold without reserve. Unreserved lots generally open at 50% of the low estimate.

23170

ROBERT PHILIPP
(American 1895-1981)
Girl On A Couch
Oil on board
6-1/8 x 8 inches (15.6 x 20.3 cm)
Signed lower right

Provenance:
Sale, Du Mouchelles, Detroit, January 2000, Lot 2178;
Private collection (Connecticut)

Estimate: $2,000-$3,000

This lot is being sold without reserve. Unreserved lots generally open at 50% of the low estimate.

23171

ROBERT PHILIPP (American 1895-1981)
Two Women In A Cafe
Oil on canvas
16 x 12 inches (40.6 x 30.5 cm)
Signed upper right

Provenance:
Private collection (Connecticut)

Estimate: $4,000-$6,000

This lot is being sold without reserve. Unreserved lots generally open at 50% of the low estimate.

23172

PHILIP REISMAN
(American 1904-1992)
The Bar Maid
Watercolor on paper
17-1/2 x 22 inches
(44.5 x 55.9 cm)
Signed lower left: *Philip Reisman*
Inscribed verso: *#604 / The Bar-Maid / Watercolor /*
17-1/2 x 22 / Philip Reisman

Provenance:
Private collection
(Boca Raton, Florida)

Estimate: $2,000-$3,000

The reserve for this lot is available at HA.com/FineArt.

23173

GEORGE GUSTAV ADOMEIT (American 1879-1967)
Untitled, Japanese Woman In An Interior
Oil on canvas
23-3/4 x 39-3/4 inches
(60.3 x 101 cm)
Signed lower right: *Adomeit*

Provenance:
Private collection (Washington)

Estimate: $1,500-$2,500

The reserve for this lot is available at HA.com/FineArt.

23174

JEAN LIBERTE (American 1896-1965)
View Of Toledo, Spain
Casein on paper
9-1/2 x 12 inches, sight (24.1 x 30.5 cm)
Unsigned

Provenance:
The Collection of the Artist;
A Madison Avenue Gallery (New York)

Estimate: $400-$600

The reserve for this lot is available at HA.com/FineArt.

23175

EMIL BISTTRAM (American 1895-1976)
Untitled
Pastel on paper
14 x 11 inches (35.6 x 27.9 cm)
Signed lower right: *Bisttram 37*

Estimate: $1,500-$2,500

This lot is being sold without reserve. Unreserved lots generally open at 50% of the low estimate.

23176

EMIL BISTTRAM (American 1895-1976)
Untitled
Pastel on paper
14 x 11 inches (35.6 x 27.9 cm)
Signed lower right: *Bisttram 39*

Estimate: $1,500-$2,500

This lot is being sold without reserve. Unreserved lots generally open at 50% of the low estimate.

23177

EMIL BISTTRAM (American 1895-1976)
Untitled
Pastel on paper
14 x 11 inches (35.6 x 27.9 cm)
Signed lower right: *Bisttram 41*

Estimate: $1,500-$2,500

This lot is being sold without reserve. Unreserved lots generally open at 50% of the low estimate.

23178

EMIL BISTTRAM (American 1895-1976)
Untitled
Pastel on paper
14 x 11 inches (35.6 x 27.9 cm)
Signed lower right: *Bisttram 41*

Estimate: $1,500-$2,500

This lot is being sold without reserve. Unreserved lots generally open at 50% of the low estimate.

23179

EMIL BISTTRAM (American 1895-1976)
Untitled
Pastel on paper
14 x 11 inches (35.6 x 27.9 cm)
Signed lower right: *Bisttram 43*

Estimate: $1,500-$2,500

This lot is being sold without reserve. Unreserved lots generally open at 50% of the low estimate.

23180

EMIL BISTTRAM (American 1895-1976)
Untitled
Pastel on paper
14 x 11 inches (35.6 x 27.9 cm)
Signed lower right: *Bisttram 44*

Estimate: $1,500-$2,500

This lot is being sold without reserve. Unreserved lots generally open at 50% of the low estimate.

23181

EMIL BISTTRAM (American 1895-1976)
Untitled
Pastel on paper
14 x 11 inches (35.6 x 27.9 cm)
Signed lower right: *Bisttram 44*

Estimate: $1,500-$2,500

This lot is being sold without reserve. Unreserved lots generally open at 50% of the low estimate.

23182

EMIL BISTTRAM (American 1895-1976)
Untitled
Pastel on paper
14 x 11 inches (35.6 x 27.9 cm)
Signed lower right: *Bisttram 48*

Estimate: $1,500-$2,500

This lot is being sold without reserve. Unreserved lots generally open at 50% of the low estimate.

23183

S. KAPLAN
Female Portrait
Charcoal on paper
29-1/2 x 21 inches, sight (74.9 x 53.3 cm)
Signed lower left: *S. KAPLAN*

Estimate: $1,500-$2,500

The reserve for this lot is available at HA.com/FineArt.

23184

ALBERT W. WEIN (American 1915-1991)
Portrait Of A Gentleman
Ink and gouache on paper
17-3/4 x 15-1/8 inches, sight (45.1 x 38.4 cm)
Signed lower right: *Albert Wein*

Estimate: $1,200-$2,400

The reserve for this lot is available at HA.com/FineArt.

23185

MILTON AVERY (American 1893-1965)
Portrait Study Of A Man And Woman, 1958
Ink on paper
8-1/4 x 4 inches (21 x 10.2 cm)
Signed and dated at lower right: *Milton Avery / 1958*

The directness of Milton Avery's approach to painting is present in his drawings as well. Throughout his career, Avery dashed off lively, spontaneous impressions of faces, figures and landscapes. The quick sketch of the man on the top of this sheet has some affinities with Avery's own likeness.

Estimate: $3,000-$5,000

The reserve for this lot is available at HA.com/FineArt.

23186

MILTON AVERY
(American 1893-1965)
Abstract Study, 1960
Lithograph
3-7/8 x 8-3/4 inches (9.8 x 22.2 cm)
Signed and dated at lower left in the image: *Milton Avery 1960*

Estimate: $1,000-$1,500

The reserve for this lot is available at HA.com/FineArt.

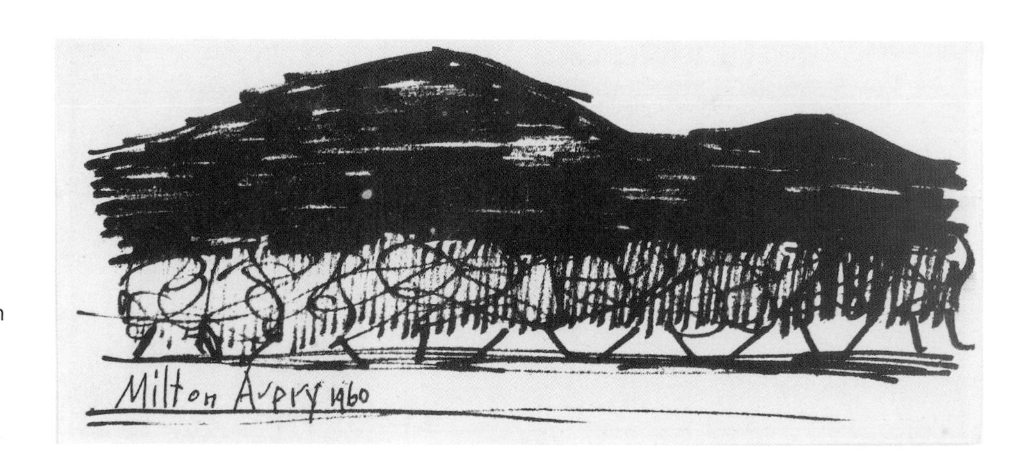

23187

MILTON AVERY (American 1893-1965)
Laguna Beach, 1943
Oil on canvas
16 x 20 inches (40.6 x 50.8 cm)
Signed and dated lower left: Milton/Avery/1943
Inscribed, signed and dated verso: 'Laguna Beach'/by Milton Avery/16 x 20/1943

Milton Avery's generalized treatment of form and flattened color masses linked him artistically with the development of Abstract Expressionism during the 1940s. Indeed, his friendships with Mark Rothko and Adolph Gottlieb proved to be mutually inspirational, even though Avery never entirely relinquished a desire for representation in his painting.

Avery began to achieve critical success in 1944, when he had his first museum exhibition at the Phillips Memorial Gallery in Washington, D.C. Major opportunities soon followed, including this first retrospective at the Baltimore Museum of Art in 1952. The Whitney Museum organized retrospectives of Avery's work in 1960 and 1982. Following Avery's death in 1965, Rothko remarked: 'Avery is first a great poet. His is the poetry of sheer loveliness of sheer beauty. Thanks to him this kind of poetry has been able to survive in our time...There have been several others in our generation who have celebrated the world around them, but none with inevitability where the poetry penetrated every pore of the canvas to the last touch of the brush' ('Commemorative Essay,' in Milton Avery (New York: Whitney Museum of American Art. 1982), p. 181).

Avery typically spent his summers in New England, but in 1941 he drove cross-country from New York to California, and visited Yellowstone and Glacier National Parks along the way. While on the west coast he spent a month in Laguna Beach in Southern California where he painted the present canvas.

Estimate: $140,000-$180,000

This lot is being sold without reserve. Unreserved lots generally open at 50% of the low estimate.

23188

JULIUS MOESSEL (American 1872-1960)
Tropical Landscape, 1942
Oil on canvas
30 x 26 inches (76.2 x 66 cm)
Signed and dated lower left: *MOESSEL / 1942*

Estimate: $3,000-$5,000

The reserve for this lot is available at HA.com/FineArt.

23189

FERNANDO DE SYSZLO (Peruvian b.1925)
Abstract
Mixed media embossed print
29-1/2 x 21-3/4 inches (74.9 x 55.2 cm)
Signed lower right: *Syszlo*
Signed lower left: *H. C.*

Estimate: $2,000-$4,000

The reserve for this lot is available at HA.com/FineArt.

23190

KARL KNATHS (American 1891-1971)
Number Seven — Saul, 1948
Oil on canvas
60 x 40 inches (152.4 x 101.6 cm)
Signed lower right: *Karl Knaths*

Provenance:
Paul Rosenberg & Company (New York);
Private collection (Dallas, Texas)

Exhibition:
Four American Expressionists, at five venues from 1959-1960: Whitney Museum of American Art, NY, January 14 - March 1; Currier Gallery of Art, NH, April 8 - May 10; Colorado Springs Fine Arts Center, CO, May 24 - June 30; Columbus Gallery of Art, OH, July 15 - August 30; and the Dallas Museum of Fine Arts, TX, November 22 - January 3

Literature:
Whitney Museum of American Art, *Four American Expressionists,* New York, 1959, p.11

An American modernist, Karl Knaths worked primarily in a cubist aesthetic, closely to that of Cezanne. Knaths was one of the most theoretical painters of his time and his compositions, like the above, were harnessed to a complex set of mathematical and geometrical relations. Knaths moved to Provincetown, Massachusetts, where he exhibited regularly with the Provincetown Art Association. There Knaths drew repeatedly from his surroundings often depicting fishermen, boats in the harbor, and deer in landscape. He also found inspiration, however, in American folklore and religion. The above example, *Number Seven — Saul,* is from a series inspired by Old Testament, including *Number Zero — Adam,* which is currently in the Albright-Knox Collection.

Estimate: $12,000-$18,000

The reserve for this lot is available at HA.com/FineArt.

23191

WILLIAM THOMAS LUMPKINS
(American 1909-2000)
La Jolla
Oil on canvas
60 x 47-1/2 inches (152.4 x 120.7 cm)

Estimate: $12,000-$16,000

The reserve for this lot is available at HA.com/FineArt.

23192

DAVID ALFARO SIQUEIROS (Mexican 1896-1974)
Dance (Torment)
Lithograph in color
22 x 15 inches (sheet size) (55.9 x 38.1 cm)
18 x 14 inches (plate size) (45.7 x 35.6 cm)
Signed in pencil lower right: *D. A. Siqueiros*
Numbered lower left: *68/70*

Exhibited:
Arkansas Art Center, 1977

Estimate: $700-$900

The reserve for this lot is available at HA.com/FineArt.

23193

CARL ROBERT HOLTY (American 1900-1973)
Composition
Oil on fiberboard
13-5/8 x 10-7/8 inches, framed (34.6 x 27.6 cm)
Signed upper right

Estimate: $1,500-$3,500

The reserve for this lot is available at HA.com/FineArt.

23194

BYRON BROWNE (American 1907-1961)
Nude With An Easel, 1958
Mixed media on paper
26 x 20 inches (66 x 50.8 cm)
Signed and dated lower right: *1958 / Byron Browne*

Estimate: $2,000-$4,000

The reserve for this lot is available at HA.com/FineArt.

23195

LOUIS BOSA
(Italian-American 1905-1981)
Night Edition, 1952
Oil on canvas
15 x 25 inches (38.1 x 63.5 cm)
Signed and dated lower right

Provenance:
Kleeman Galleries (New York)

Estimate: $3,000-$5,000

The reserve for this lot is available at HA.com/FineArt.

23196

EMILIO BAZ VIAUD (Mexican circa 1918-circa 1991)
His Majesty
Oil on canvas
27-1/2 x 20 inches (69.9 x 50.8 cm)
Signed lower left: *EMILIO BAZ VIAUD*

Estimate: $5,000-$8,000

The reserve for this lot is available at HA.com/FineArt.

23197

ALFREDO ZALCE
(Mexican 1908-2003)
Naturaleza Muerta, 1943
Oil on canvas
16-1/2 x 26 inches (41.9 x 66 cm)
Signed and dated at lower left:
Alfredo/ Zalce .43.

Provenance: Christie's East (New York), Latin American Paintings..., November 21, 1995, Lot 2;
Private collection (Dallas, Texas)

Zalce, a premier Mexican Modernist, was influenced Cezanne's early works. An influence which is reminiscent in this particular still life, which depicts an assortment exotic fruits that plays upon spatial relationships.

Estimate: $6,000-$8,000

This lot is being sold without reserve. Unreserved lots generally open at 50% of the low estimate.

23198

RAUL ANGUIANO (Mexican-American b.1915)
Juchiteca, 1955
Oil on masonite
29 x 23 inches (73.7 x 58.4 cm)
Signed and dated upper left: *R. Anguiano 1955*
Signed, dated and titled verso: *R. Anguiano/ "Juchiteca" / 1955*

Provenace:
Instituto Nacional de Bellas Artes, Museo Nacional de Artes Plasticos (Mexico City, Mexico)

Estimate: $10,000-$20,000

The reserve for this lot is available at HA.com/FineArt.

23199

GRISSON (Twentieth Century)
Trompe L'Oeil, January 1952
Oil on canvas
37 x 48 inches (94 x 121.9 cm)
Signed and dated lower right:
Grisson/ Jan 1952

Estimate: $1,500-$2,500

The reserve for this lot is available at HA.com/FineArt.

23200

HELEN FARR SLOAN (American 1911-2005)
Cityscape
Oil on canvasboard
24 x 17-3/4 inches (61 x 45.1 cm)
Signed lower right: *Farr*

Estimate: $6,000-$8,000

The reserve for this lot is available at HA.com/FineArt.

23201

STEPHEN MORGAN ETNIER
(American 1903-1984)
Autumn Sun, 1959
Oil on canvas
23 x 38-1/4 inches
(58.4 x 97.2 cm)
Signed and dated lower left

Estimate: $10,000-$15,000

The reserve for this lot is available at HA.com/FineArt.

23202

EDWARD JOHN STEVENS JR.
(American 1923-1988)
Desert Stallion, 1961
Gouache on paper
18 x 22 inches, sight (45.7 x 55.9 cm)
Signed and dated lower right:
© *Edward John StevenS Jr. 1961*

Provenance:
Weyhe Gallery, Inc. Art Books and Prints, 1962 (New York)

Estimate: $800-$1,200

The reserve for this lot is available at HA.com/FineArt.

23203

MARCH AVERY
(American Twentieth Century)
Winter Lake, 1962
Oil on canvas
31-1/2 x 46 inches (80 x 116.8 cm)
Signed and dated lower right

Provenance:
A Madison Avenue Gallery (New York)

Estimate: $800-$1,200

The reserve for this lot is available at HA.com/FineArt.

23204

REUBEN NAKIAN
(American 1897-1986)
Untitled Composition
Ink on paper
14 x 16-3/4 inches, sheet (35.6 x 42.5 cm)
Inscribed lower right in pencil: *EE*

Estimate: $600-$800

This lot is being sold without reserve. Unreserved lots generally open at 50% of the low estimate.

23205

ELAINE MARIE DE KOONING (American 1918-1989)
Head Of Ethel
Pencil on paper
24 x 18 inches (61 x 45.7 cm)
Signed lower right

Estimate: $600-$800

This lot is being sold without reserve. Unreserved lots generally open at 50% of the low estimate.

23206

ELAINE MARIE DE KOONING (American 1918-1989)
Seated Ethel, 1964
Pencil on paper
17 x 14 inches (43.2 x 35.6 cm)
Signed and dated lower right

Estimate: $800-$1,200

This lot is being sold without reserve. Unreserved lots generally open at 50% of the low estimate.

23207

GABRIEL SPAT
(American 1890-1967)
Riva Bella
Oil on canvas
6-1/2 x 10 inches (16.5 x 25.4 cm)
Signed lower left

Provenance:
Acquired directly from the artist;
Meredith L. Long & Co. (Houston, Texas);
Mr. and Mrs. Edgar E. Townes, 1969 (Houston, Texas)

Estimate: $1,000-$2,000

The reserve for this lot is available at HA.com/FineArt.

23208

HARRIETTE BOWDOIN
(American 1880-1947)
On The Boardwalk
Oil on panel
8-1/2 x 11-1/2 inches
(21.6 x 29.2 cm)
Signed lower right

Provenance:
Meredith L. Long & Co. (Houston, Texas);
Mr. and Mrs. Edgar E. Townes, 1966 (Houston, Texas)

Estimate: $2,000-$3,000

The reserve for this lot is available at HA.com/FineArt.

23209

JOHN CLYMER
(American 1907-1989)
French Boat In A Harbor
Oil on canvas
24 x 36 inches (61 x 91.4 cm)
Signed lower left: *John Clymer*

Estimate: $8,000-$12,000

The reserve for this lot is available at HA.com/FineArt.

23210

RICO TOMASO
(American 1907-1989)
Seascape, 1971
Oil on canvas
24-1/4 x 48 inches (61.6 x 121.9 cm)
Signed lower right: *Rico Tomaso*
Inscribed verso: *Rico Tomaso / Rico Tomaso / Feb. '71*

Estimate: $4,000-$6,000

The reserve for this lot is available at HA.com/FineArt.

23211

ANDY WARHOL (American 1928-1987)
Gee, Merrie Shoes, 1956-
Offset lithograph with hand coloring on paper
9 x 8 inches (22.9 x 20.3 cm)
Signed lower right: with facsimile signature *Warhol,* and inscribed *Gee, Merrie Shoes;* and a blue oval with illegible lettering bleeding through in the lower left corner

Estimate: $1,500-$2,500

The reserve for this lot is available at HA.com/FineArt.

23212

PABLO PICASSO
(Spanish 1881-1973)
El Arrastre, avec Ecuyère et Putto,
from *Séries 347,* 1968-
Etching on paper
12-3/4 x 16-1/4 inches
(31.1 x 41.3 cm) (platemark)
Edition 45/50
Cat. Rais.: Bloch, 1509
Published: Galerie L. Leiris
Impression: 1969
Signed in pencil lower right
Picasso, numbered lower left
45/50, and inscribed on the reverse with Bloch catalogue raisonné number in pencil

Estimate: $7,000-$9,000

The reserve for this lot is available at HA.com/FineArt.

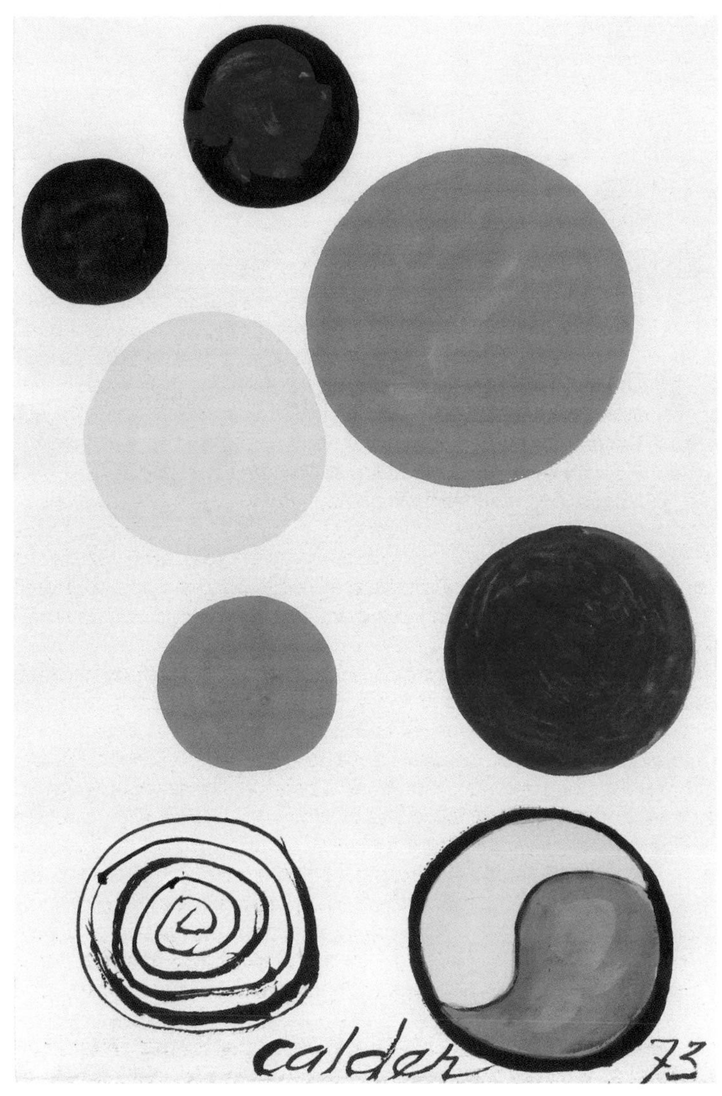

23213

ALEXANDER CALDER (American 1898-1976)
Kakemono, 1973
Gouache and Ink on paper
22-3/4 x 15-1/4 inches (57.8 x 38.7 cm)
Signed and dated lower margin

Estimate: $18,000-$22,000

The reserve for this lot is available at HA.com/FineArt.

23214

RAYMOND JOHNSON (American Late Twentieth Century)
Polymer No. 9, 1973
Polymer on canvas
30 x 40 inches (76.2 x 101.6 cm)
Signed and titled verso

Provenance:
Gerald Peters Gallery (Santa Fe, New Mexico)

Estimate: $8,000-$12,000

The reserve for this lot is available at HA.com/FineArt.

23215

DON KINGMAN (American 1911-2000)
Market Scene, Taxco
Watercolor on paper
22-1/4 x 14-3/4 inches (38.1 x 37.5 cm)
Signed lower right: *D. Kingman*

Provenance:
Wildenstein Gallery, 1961 (New York);
The Hersy Collection (New York)

Estimate: $4,000-$6,000

The reserve for this lot is available at HA.com/FineArt.

23216

ANDREW WYETH
(American b.1917)
Sea Running, 1978
Collotype, reproduced 1981
Edition 101/300
Printed by Triton Press
11 x 14-1/2 inches, image size
(27.9 x 36.8 cm)
Signed and numbered in pencil
lower right: *Andrew Wyeth*
101/300

This image depicts a lighthouse fog bell tower at the water's edge on a Maine island.

Estimate: $2,000-$4,000

This lot is being sold without reserve. Unreserved lots generally open at 50% of the low estimate.

23217

ANDREW WYETH (American b.1917)
Untitled
Collotype
20 x 30 inches, image size (50.8 x 76.2 cm)
Signed in pen lower right: *Andrew Wyeth*

Estimate: $1,500-$2,500

This lot is being sold without reserve. Unreserved lots generally open at 50% of the low estimate.

23218

ANDREW WYETH
(American b.1917)
Night Sleeper, 1979
Collotype, reproduced 1980
Edition 187/300
20 x 30 inches, image size (50.8 x 76.2 cm)
Signed and numbered in pencil lower right: *Andrew Wyeth 187/300*

Estimate: $2,000-$4,000

This lot is being sold without reserve. Unreserved lots generally open at 50% of the low estimate.

23219

KIM DOUGLAS WIGGINS (American b.1960)
Chimayo In Autumn
Oil on canvas
30 x 40 inches (76.2 x 101.6 cm)
Siged lower left: *KD Wiggins*
Alterman Galleries, label verso

Estimate: $6,000-$8,000

The reserve for this lot is available at HA.com/FineArt.

23220

LOUISE NEVELSON, (American 1899-1988)
Night Column II
Bronze with black patina
15 inches high (38.1 cm)
Inscribed on base: *Nevelson 11/11*

Russian-born Louise Nevelson's surrealist compositions deconstruct furniture and rooms transforming them into sculptural collages. Known for her monochromatic creations primarily in gold or black and composed of wood, the present offered work represents one of her rare bronze creations.

Estimate: $8,000-$10,000

The reserve for this lot is available at HA.com/FineArt.

23221

LEONARD BASKIN (American 1922-2000)
The Seer, 1975 -
Bronze
42-1/2 x 15 x 14 inches (107 x 38.1 x 35.6 cm)
Inscribed on base: *Baskin / 1975,* and stamped
Bedi-Makky / Art Foundry N.Y / © Kennedy Gallery / N.Y.

Provenance:
Crow Art Partnership

Son of a Rabbi, Baskin was an artist accomplished in a variety of mediums including sculpture, printmaking, watercolor, book illustration and graphic art. He also notably wrote and taught for many years, however he regarded himself first and foremost as a sculptor. His art tackled political and social issues resulting in a number of awards including the Jewish Cultural Achievement Award and the Gold Medal of the National Academy of Arts and Letters. Baskin is considered one of the universal sculptors of the twentieth century.

Estimate: $10,000-$15,000

23222

JOHN DOYLE
Taos Pueblo, 1975
Acrylic on board
30 x 40 inches (76.2 x 101.6 cm)
Signed and dated lower right: *Doyle 75*

Provenance:
Carlson-Lowe Galleries (Taos, New Mexico)

Estimate: $600-$1,000

This lot is being sold without reserve. Unreserved lots generally open at 50% of the low estimate.

23223

ROBERT WATSON
(American 1923-2004)
Sanctuary, 1979
Oil on canvas
24 x 30 inches (61 x 76.2 cm)
Signed and dated lower right: *R. WATSON 79*

Estimate: $1,000-$1,500

This lot is being sold without reserve. Unreserved lots generally open at 50% of the low estimate.

23224

ROBERT WATSON
(American 1923-2004)
Figures
Oil on canvas
18 x 32 inches (45.7 x 81.3 cm)
Signed lower right: *R. WATSON*

Estimate: $1,000-$1,500

This lot is being sold without reserve. Unreserved lots generally open at 50% of the low estimate.

23225

ANDRE GISSON
(American 1921-2003)
Still Life, circa 1979
30-1/4 x 40 inches
(76.8 x 101.6 cm)
Signed lower right

Provenance:
Acquired from the artist;
Sale, Simpson Gallery (Houston, Texas), April 2, 2006, Lot 167;
Private collection (Dallas, Texas)

Estimate: $5,000-$7,000

The reserve for this lot is available at HA.com/FineArt.

23226

GREG McHURON
(American b. 1945)
Light Snow At Spring Lake, 1980
Oil on canvas
18 x 24 inches (45.7 x 61 cm)
Signed lower right: *Greg I. McHuron ©*
Sketch verso, inscribed: *"Light Snow at Spring Lake"/04-25-80/All reproduction rights reserved by the artist/ Greg I. McHuron*

Estimate: $1,500-$2,500

This lot is being sold without reserve. Unreserved lots generally open at 50% of the low estimate.

23227

LARRY POONS (American, born in Toyko, Japan 1937)
Untitled, 1981
Acrylic on canvas
34-3/8 x 21-3/4 inches (87.3 x 55.2 cm)
Signed and dated verso: *1981 / L. Poons*

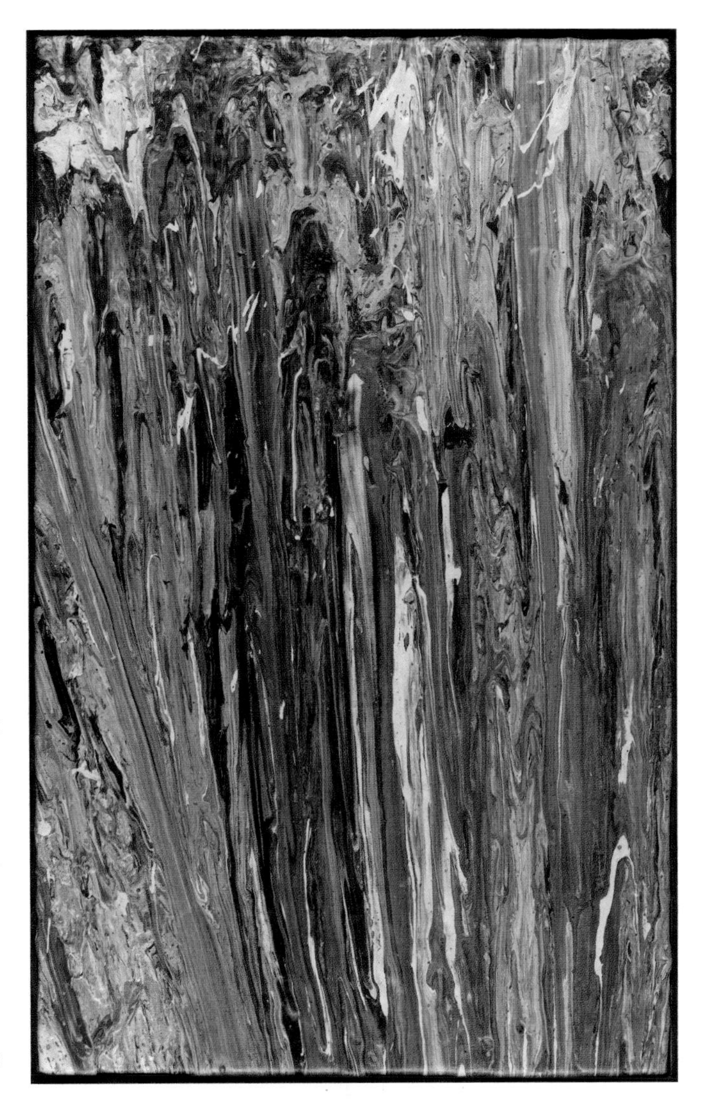

The American abstract painter Larry Poons had, as David Carrier has noted, "a fast breaking career—he became famous when he was very young." After studying at the New England Conservatory of Music (1955-57) he switched schools to pursue his other artistic interest—painting—at the Boston Museum School of Fine Arts in 1958. When he was barely twenty, he attracted critical attention for his elegant paintings in the minimalist/pop vein that had replaced the gestural, emotionally-charged art of the Abstract Expressionists a decade and a half before. The high-grade materiality of paint found in the dripped skeins of enamel by Jackson Pollock, the slashes of pigment made with household brushes in the billboard-sized work of Franz Klein, and the puddling and pouring of thinned out pigment onto a canvas so that it bleeds and drips gave way, in the early sixties, to clarity and flatness. Getting messy with materials had been eclipsed by paint that had to behave according to definite lines, patterns and abstract shapes to achieve optical effects of evenly modulated color. Paintings were preplanned designs. It was into this new art world, where formalism rather than the paint or the gesture reigned supreme, that Larry Poons emerged as a major figure. His work had the grid, the mathematics, the geometry, and the incredible discipline of a Mondrian behind it. But it also had his musical sense, too, of timing and syncopation which gave his early canvases a distinctive, personal timbre.

But Poons didn't want to keep making the paintings which made him an art star-nor could he. The tide had turned, plus Poons had new interests. By the beginning of the 1970s, Poons wanted to begin exploring the raw materiality of paint, even though the current trends continued to move even further away from the type of paint manipulation that most intrigued him. As the 70s wore on, and moved into the 80s, the most popular art trends were conceptual art, performance art, video art, Neo Geo-all "endeavors" which artist Frank Stella aptly noted were a "drive toward indirect expression, the use of any devices which are not the direct expression of the artist's hand and body."

Poons-at the top of his game [i.e., art world notoriety]-went against the grain. During the course of the 1970s, he started throwing paint onto canvas-actually *along* canvases-on the floor. He would apply it exclusively by throwing it layer upon layer, in coats. The coats would build one upon the other, accommodating all intentions and accidents, and sculpt themselves into luscious surfaces. During the course of the 70s, the artist discovered that acrylics worked better than oil because they dried more quickly and were therefore less prone to slip off or crack.

Poons's method of painting in this untrammeled fashion on the floor on a long continuous piece of canvas has an important second stage. After building up the surface, he selects the sections of the image which have the most dynamic properties, masks them, and cuts them out of the larger field. His imagery is aggressively vertical owing to his method, and to accentuate this quality the artist generally crops his works so that they are narrower in width than length.

The present work was created according to this procedure, which depends upon the masking and cropping process to capture the most exciting surges of pigment. On the back of the painting, where Poons signs so that he doesn't interrupt the gesture, the paint runs all the way to the very edges of the canvas, providing evidence of his method. This marvelous work of 1981, with its silvery blue palette, shows Larry Poons giving full rein to the sculptural potential of paint.

Estimate: $6,000-$8,000

The reserve for this lot is available at HA.com/FineArt.

23228

DONALD SULTAN
(American b.1951)
Black Lemons, 1984
Aquatint, artist's proof
48 x 62-1/2 inches, sheet (121.9 x 158.8 cm)
Signed and inscribed upper right: *A.P. Black Lemons Nov 30 1984 D.S.*

Estimate: $6,000-$8,000

This lot is being sold without reserve. Unreserved lots generally open at 50% of the low estimate.

23229

KIM DOUGLAS WIGGINS (American b.1960)
Voice Of Jealousy, 2000
Oil on canvas
44 x 58 inches (111.8 x 147.3 cm)
Signed and dated lower left: *K.D. Wiggins / '00*
Inscribed verso by artist: *Voice of Jealousy / oil / 2000 / 44 x 56 / Kim Douglas Wiggins / Santa Fe, N.M. / (Repaired after damage on 4/22/03 by cutting image down from 48 x 60)*

Estimate: $10,000-$20,000

The reserve for this lot is available at HA.com/FineArt.

23230

DENNIS HARE (American)
Reflections, 2001
Mixed media assemblage
36 x 36 inches (91.4 x 91.4 cm)
Signed, dated and titled on verso:
2001 / Reflections / Dennis Hare

Estimate: $3,000-$4,000

The reserve for this lot is available at HA.com/FineArt.

23231

DENNIS HARE (American)
Violins, 1998-2006
Mixed media assemblage
36 x 36 inches (91.4 x 91.4 cm)
Signed lower left: *D. Hare*
Signed, dated and titled verso: *Violins / 2006 / Dennis Hare / 1998 / Dennis Hare*

Estimate: $3,000-$4,000

The reserve for this lot is available at HA.com/FineArt.

23232

BILL BARRETT (American b.1934)
Template, Study For A Sculpture, 2001
Oil on canvas
48 x 36 inches (121.9 x 91.4 cm)
Signed, titled and dated verso

Estimate: $2,000-$3,000

The reserve for this lot is available at HA.com/FineArt.

ORIENTALIST ART

23233

EDWIN LORD WEEKS (American 1849-1903)
The Hour of Prayer at Muti-Mushid (Pearl Mosque), Agra,
circa 1888-89
Oil on canvas
79 x 118.5 inches (205.7 x 299.7 cm)
Signed at lower left: *E L WEEKS*

Provenance:
Sale, American Art Association, New York, "Very Important Finished Pictures, Studies, Sketches and Original Drawings by the Late Edwin Lord Weeks to be sold at unrestricted public sale by order of his widow," March 15-17, 1905, lot 189, to George D. Pratt;
Mr. George D. Pratt, Brooklyn, New York, purchased for the collection of the Brooklyn Museum of Art in 1905;
Brooklyn Museum, Brooklyn, New York, 1905-1947;
Tobias Fisher and Company, New York in 1947;
Private collection

Exhibition History:
Paris, Salon of 1889 (medalist);
London, Earl's Court, "Empire of India Exhibition," 1895;
"Romance of the Taj Mahal," Los Angeles County Museum of Art, Los Angeles, California (December 17, 1979 through March 11, 1990); Toledo Museum of Art, Toledo, Ohio (April 28 through June 24, 1990); Virginia Museum of Fine Arts, Richmond, Virginia (August 23 through November 25, 1990);
Asia Society, New York

Relevant Literature:
Salon de 1889. Catalogue illustré, Ludovic Baschet, ed., Paris, 1889, no. 2713, p. 44.
A. Hustin, *Salon de 1892,* Paris, Ludovic Baschet, ed., Paris, 1892, p. 55 reproduces "Lord Edwin WEEKS" seated before *The Hour of Prayer at Muti-Mushid (Pearl Mosque), Agra* on the easel in his studio.

Edwin Lord Weeks, *From the Black Sea through Persia and India,* London, Harper and Brothers, Co., 1895.
University Art Galleries, University of New Hampshire, Durham, *The Art of Edwin Lord Weeks (1849-1903),* 1976.
Pratapeditya Pal et al, *Romance of the Taj Mahal,* exh. cat. Los Angeles and New York, Thames and Hudson and the Los Angeles County Museum of Art, 1989, pp. 214-15.
Lois Marie Fink, *American Art at the Nineteenth-Century Paris Salons,* Washington, D.C. and Cambridge, National Museum of American Art Smithsonian Institution and Cambridge University Press, 1990, p. 403.
Ulrich W. Hiesinger, *Edwin Lord Weeks, Visions of India,* New York, Vance Jordan Fine Art, Inc., 2002.

Edwin Lord Weeks' 1888-89 masterpiece, *The Hour of Prayer at Muti-Mushid (Pearl Mosque), Agra,* is one of five monumental scenes of India which secured his reputation as America's most celebrated Orientalist painter of the late nineteenth century. Based upon the artist's second of three extended trips to India, in 1886-1887, *The Hour of Prayer at Muti-Mushid (Pearl Mosque), Agra* won a medal at the 1889 Paris Salon where it was displayed to enviable advantage. Six years later, Weeks chose this expansive sun-drenched view of the inner courtyard of the Pearl Mosque to represent him in the colossal "Empire of India" exhibition in London in 1895, where his achievement as the premier painter of Indian scenes was lavishly acknowledged with a medal of distinction, a monetary prize, and a special display of 78 of his works. From the time it was sold by the artist's widow in 1905, the Salon-scale *Hour of Prayer at Muti-Mushid* has had only two owners-the Brooklyn Museum of Art (1905-1947), which deaccessioned it at a time when academic painting had fallen sharply out of fashion, and a private American collection (1947-present). As such, it is in a fine state of preservation: it is unlined and in its original nineteenth-century frame that includes ornamental motifs complementing those depicted in the painting and reflecting the work of the noted American enthusiast of Indian design and Tiffany partner, Lockwood de Forest II (1850 - 1932), whose studio Weeks visited in Ahmedabad, India. Although not well-acquainted when they first met in India, Weeks and de Forest were distantly related (De Forest's mother was Julia Weeks de Forest).

Of all the Western "Orientalist" painters of his day, Edwin Lord Weeks produced the largest as well as the most compelling pictorial album of India. Unlike many of his contemporaries who explored Northern Africa and the Near East in their paintings, Weeks visited all the places he chose to portray and immersed himself in their cultures, particularly that of India which fascinated him above all others. In addition to the three visits he made to India in 1882-83, 1886-87, and 1892-93 at the height of his career (two accompanied by his wife), Weeks also journeyed to North Africa, Egypt, Syria, Palestine, Turkey, and Persia, where travel was often not only arduous but dangerous owing both to disease and to political upheaval. During his lifetime, Weeks was often described not simply as a "painter" but as a "painter-explorer" because his wanderlust compelled him to publish marvelous accounts of his

travels fairly regularly in the major illustrated magazines (*Scribner's* and *Harper's New Monthly Magazine*). The artist's written descriptions of his travel experiences were as colorful as his paintings in their observation and detail. He also seems to have been something of a thrill-seeker by nature, and routinely went for extended climbs in the most treacherous parts of the Alps.

Even in terms of his outward appearance, the rather slight, bright-eyed and mustachioed New England "puritan" eventually came to resemble his subjects. As a mature artist, Weeks had acquired a sun-darkened complexion from his practice of sketching and painting outdoors in the streets, markets and bazaars beneath the relentless Indian midday sun. In choosing to settle in Paris, where his Salon-style academicism was more enthusiastically received than it had been in the United States, Weeks set himself up as a soft-spoken, but flamboyantly dressed ex-patriot in a studio first at 128 Avenue de Wagram, and later on the rue de Léonard da Vinci. He furnished his ateliers lavishly with carvings, furniture, textiles, metalwork, ceramics and assorted bric-a-brac from his Eastern travels (which doubled as props for his paintings), and often attired himself in a long flowing eastern robe and carpet slippers. A close friend of the painter's, S. G. W. Benjamin, once remarked that "he was so decidedly oriental in looks that habited in Moorish garb, Weeks could easily have passed for an Arab gentleman of Damascus." Weeks also stated, quite matter-of-factly, that living in Paris suited him in part because "it was much more convenient to India" than his native Boston or New York! From a practical standpoint, for an artist who exhibited for more than 20 years at the Paris Salon, was embraced by the Parisian art-buying public, and sold his works lucratively through his longtime dealer Durand-Ruel, the French capital was an ideal base from which to paint, live, exhibit, and travel.

Edwin Weeks painted *The Hour of Prayer at Muti-Mushid (Pearl Mosque), Agra* in his atelier on the rue de Wagram, where he worked from sketches he produced during his second trip to India. Judging from the painter's extant preparatory work, it appears that by the time he was making on-site studies for this painting, Weeks had dispensed with using sketch pads with pencil and ink as he had done earlier in his career. Instead, he sketched from life directly in oil on canvas-a practice also favored by the great Hudson River School landscapist, Frederic Edwin Church, who traveled into remote territory across the globe in search of his own artistic inspiration. As Ulrich Hiesinger noted in his lively and very readable account of Weeks' career, some of the oil studies Weeks "created in the field were relatively large, at twenty by thirty inches." A surviving oilstudy by Weeks for the two central figures near the pool in *The Hour of Prayer at Muti-Mushid (Pearl Mosque), Agra,* which recently sold at auction in London, measured a substantial 26 x 45 3/4 inches (Christie's, London, "Ottomans and Orientalists" sale, June 21, 2000, lot 71). Although they were not tiny, such sketches were still portable enough to be rolled up and transported back to Paris with little difficulty.

Ultimately, Weeks' lifelong fascination with the exoticism of far away places probably reached back into his family experiences as a young boy growing up in Newtonville, Massachusetts, just outside Boston. Weeks' parents were highly successful import merchants whose stock-and-trade was eccentric exotic goods from around the globe. Although undocumented, his parents evidently encouraged his interest in art, supporting his early pilgrimage to Paris to acquire the professional art training he sought. Interestingly, not long after his initial visit to Paris, the young painter was already looking for artistic inspiration much further afield than the French capital. As a young artist he visited Surinam, and after his marriage, he and his new bride quickly headed off to the Near East.

Although Weeks was and remains art historically categorized as an "Orientalist" on account of his subject matter, the artist himself generally shunned the monicker, preferring to call himself a "colorist." Indeed, when he spoke about his paintings over the course of his career, he usually spoke in terms of color, light and atmosphere instead. Indeed, his description of *The Hour of Prayer at Muti-Mushid (Pearl Mosque), Agra* published in the catalogue of *The Empire of India* exhibition stressed that his aim was "to express the effect of white marble in sunlight, with its delicate reflections in the shadow." One Boston critic gave particularly high praise to Weeks' gift for painting light in words that aptly describe the blistering sunshine in *The Hour of Prayer*: "Weeks will take anything-a blank wall, a dusty street, a well, no matter what, if it only have brilliant effects of light and shade to attack and conquer. [He is] a painter and a chiaroscurist. He seems to delight in the projection of an old wall upon the deep Oriental sky, in the play of light and shade on cobble stones, in the innumerable textures of a street scene. . . Give him a hundred different textures to paint: a bewildering play of lights, half-lights, reflected lights, shades, shadows; an imperative demand for such technical powers as would dismay another-he is delighted. As a painter of these qualities he is supreme." (*Daily Evening Transcript,* Boston, January 7, 1885, p. 2)

In most accounts of Edwin Lord Weeks' career, the great French Romantic painter of Orientalist subjects, Jean-Léon Gérôme, is usually credited as Weeks' most important teacher. This, apparently, was not actually the case. While it is true that during his 1874-75 period of study in France, Weeks petitioned to study with Gérôme at the École des Beaux-Arts, he discovered there was a waiting list. While he eventually did gain access to Gérôme's class, the eager-and impatient-young Weeks decided in the meantime to study with Léon Bonnat, the Basque-born painter of portraits and exotic genre subjects whose technique was much lusher than Gérôme's. In fact, Bonnat, who was very popular with American painters, stressed the marvelous physicality of paint in his own work, which has a highly tactile, almost crusty surface that celebrates the pigment in the manner of the masterful Spaniard Mariano Fortuny. This is the facture that Weeks emulates in his *Hour of Prayer* and, in fact, in all his canvases, just as he emulates Bonnat's passion for intense color. In comparison with the porcelain finish of Gérôme's canvases, Weeks' paintings are far closer in spirit and technique to those of Bonnat.

Although he explored Moorish Spain (probably under Bonnat's influence) as well as North Africa shortly after his training in Paris, Weeks eventually turned to the radiant scenes of India as his greatest artistic enthusiasm. It was this passion that ultimately made him an artistic celebrity. Generally recognized as the first American to have painted the Taj on the spot, Weeks was also the first American painter to live and work in India for an extended duration. In the travelogue of his final journey to India, From the Black Sea through Persia and India published in 1895, Weeks described his visit to the Pearl Mosque as eloquently as he had painted it: "The 'Moti Musjid,' or Pearl Mosque, which is seemingly restful from its appearance of extreme simplicity, artfully conceals beneath this exterior a great deal of studied proportion and elaborate detail. The broad court, when one enters it on a bright day, has the blinding dazzle of a snow-field, for nothing meets the eye but marble and the deep blue sky. Nothing could exceed the delicacy of color and subtle gradations of tint when the eye penetrates from the outer glare into the depths of shadow behind the arches. But, as in the Taj, there is no darkness in this shadow, and the details of the innermost wall are clearly visible from across the court." The artist's atelier sale catalogue of 1905 describes this work in very similar terms, stressing that it was "most exquisite in its architectural features and the rich and pearly tones of its white marble. The graceful interior of the central court, all of the purest white, with its shimmering purplish shadow, seems to reveal all the extravagant fancy and lazy Luxuriousness of this land of sunshine. In the foreground is a "moolah," or holy man, reading and explainingto a companion who is drinking in his words."

Weeks' final voyage to India was the last of his tours into uncharted territories. By 1901 the artist bemoaned the fact that India had become spoiled by a massive network of railways and was disinterested in returning. There probably was another reason behind his unwillingness to venture far from home again, however. Although he had been reluctant to reveal it, Weeks had begun suffering with a lingering illness that he had evidently contracted during his final trip to India. For nearly two months prior to his death at the age of fifty-four in Paris, on November 16, 1903, he had largely been confined to his house. Shortly before he died, Weeks told his wife that he wanted to go into his studio, purportedly with the idea that

being there among his paintings would serve as a tonic. There he died, at 10 in the evening, surrounded by the paintings of far away places he had shared with a public who would never know most of those countries firsthand. At his funeral held two days later, his pallbearers Frederick Bridgman (Weeks' greatest competitor among Orientalist painters), Gari Melchers, Julius Stewart and Henry Bisbing were among the most prominent American ex-patriot artists living in Paris, as well as Weeks' close friends.

In addition to his many international awards, medals and honors, in his later years the painter had been made a *chevalier* of the Legion of Honor of France, and in 1898 an officer of the Order of St. Michael of Bavaria. But perhaps one of the most moving tributes to Weeks appeared in his hometown paper: "Of all the Boston-born painters who have made a name for themselves in the European world of art, there is none whose reputation has been greater, whose honors have been more numerous, or whose work has been better known or esteemed. . . . Particularly luminous and spectacular are some of his pictures of the cities of India. . . .Without being theatrical, these scenes are finely dramatic, and they are among the best illustrations of Oriental life that we have in color. The pageantry of Indian life appealed powerfully to the artist, and he rendered it with all its splendor and gorgeousness" (as quoted in Hiesinger, p. 49.)

In 1905 in New York, the artist's widow sold his studio effects as well as his paintings, drawings and studies at auction. The present work was purchased from the sale by a trustee of the Brooklyn Museum of Art, George D. Pratt for that museum's permanent collection. Pratt, a scion of the distinguished Pratt family whose fortune was linked to that of John D. Rockefeller and Standard Oil Company of America, was a discerning collector of contemporary American painting as well as an enthusiast of Persian and Indian art. Among other works, Pratt donated Thomas Eakins' most famous rowing scene, *Max Schmidt in a Single Skull,* to The Metropolitan Museum; George Bellows' magnificent *Anne in Black Velvet* to the Mead Art Museum, and a major Thomas Moran landscape to the National Gallery, Washington. Pratt was also an amateur filmmaker whose 1923 film of a trip down the Nile is preserved in the Field Museum in Chicago. His interest in Orientalism clearly manifested itself in the purchase of this painting by Edwin Weeks.

Paintings by Edwin Lord Weeks are represented in the permanent collections of the Metropolitan Museum of Art, New York; the Smithsonian Institution National Museum of American Art, Washington, D.C.; the Brooklyn Museum of Art, New York; the Joslyn Art Museum, Omaha, Nebraska; the Berkshire Museum, Pittsfield, Massachusetts; Syracuse University Art Collection, Syracuse, New York; Staatliche Museen zu Berlin-Preussischer Kulturbesitz, Nationalgalerie/bpk, Berlin, Germany; The Dallas Museum of Art, Dallas, Texas; and the Portland Museum of Art, Portland, Maine.

Sepia-toned image of Edwin Weeks from the deluxe edition of the "Paris Salon de 1892" catalogue. On the easel is this painting of the Pearl Mosque, nearly completed. By the time the Salon catalogue was actually published, the painting was finished (though it was not included in the 1892 exhibition). Weeks was featured, along with other distinguished painters of the time (both French and Foreign), in an atelier photograph in that year's Salon catalogue.

One of the greatest surviving examples of American Orientalist art still in private hands, *The Hour of Prayer at Muti-Mushid (Pearl Mosque), Agra* is worthy of the greatest public holdings of Western art. Apart from the intrinsic merits of the painting itself, its ornate frame also holds special appeal: the intricate interlace pattern is derived from the long traditions of fine Indian woodcarving much admired by Weeks and his Orientalist contemporaries. Indeed, the pattern of this particular molding relates closely to some of the designs by Lockwood de Forest, which were inspired by the fast-disappearing Indian traditional handicrafts he had discovered in Ahmedabad. Because it is in original condition and in the frame the artist specifically chose for it, the painting appears today exactly as it did one hundred and seven years ago, when it was first exhibited in Paris.

Condition Report:

The overall condition of the painting and structural integrity of the support are very good considering the size. Everything is original with no major alterations to both the painting and frame. However, it is my recommendation that the painting may be strip-lined along the tracking edges and re-stretched to the existing stretcher to eliminate the rippled appearance. It should also be cleaned and re-varnished. The old repairs should be removed and treated properly with restoration materials.

The secondary support is a wood stretcher that is original to this piece. It is made of pine and tenon and mortise joints with one horizontal and two vertical crossbars. Each joint has one key. The wood is oxidized and shows writing (Weeks - Mosque) on both the left and right vertical stretcher bars. There is an old label with the number six written on it tacked near the writing on the right. There is also a new label from the Los Angeles County Museum of Art with the provenance of the painting in typed text.

The primary support is a medium weight linen canvas. The front of the painting looks as if it is covered with superficial dirt giving the surface a grayish appearance. The varnish layer is thin and looks slightly yellowed as well. The canvas has had a loss of tension, causing the canvas fabric to creep on the bottom half. Also, because of over-extending of the stretcher there is a rippled effect along the top and bottom edges. The edges of the canvas extend to the back of the stretcher and are secured to the side and back with tacks. There are three old patches from previous restoration. There are also two new patches which were treatment for small tears, the first below the signature, the second approximately 36" from the left side. Both tears were relaxed with humidity and set into place with textile welding powder and then patched with Beva film and monofilament fabric, and were then covered with a Beva coated linen. All losses in these two areas were filled and inpainted with Maimeri restoration colors.

The frame is a 10" oak frame with a caseta profile and orientalist design created with plaster in the flat center panel and top outside edge. It has been finished with gold paint and toned with a gray wash. The corner joints are open but secured with plywood brackets from the back.

Estimate: $800,000-$1,000,000

This lot is being sold without reserve. Unreserved lots generally open at 50% of the low estimate.

23234

REINHOLD VON MOELLER
(German 1847-1918)
The Desert Cavalcade, 1881
Oil on canvas
18-1/2 x 30-1/2 inches
(47 x 77.5 cm)
Signed lower left: *R. v. Moeller / München 1881*

Estimate: $6,000-$8,000

The reserve for this lot is available at HA.com/FineArt.

23235

WILLIAM KUHNERT (German 1865-1926)
Egyptian Landscape
Oil on canvas
26-3/4 x 15-1/2 inches (67.9 x 39.4 cm)
Signed lower left: *W. Kuhnert*

Provenance:
Gallery G (Heidleberg, Germany)

Estimate: $25,000-$35,000

The reserve for this lot is available at HA.com/FineArt.

23236

EMILE JEAN HORACE VERNET (French 1789-1863)
Judith & Holifer
Oil on canvas
42-1/4 x 35 inches (107.3 x 88.9 cm)

Estimate: $2,000-$3,000

The reserve for this lot is available at HA.com/FineArt.

23237

WALTER CRANE (British 1845-1915)
Europe, Asia, Africa, circa 1870
Panel Triptych
56-1/2 x 16-3/8 inches, each, approximately
(143.5 x 41.6 cm)
Monogrammed, right panel lower right: *CW*

Estimate: $20,000-$30,000

The reserve for this lot is available at HA.com/FineArt.

23238

PAUL FRIEDRICH MEYERHEIM
(German 1842-1915)
The Lion, 1870
Oil on canvas
18 x 33-1/4 inches (45.7 x 84.5 cm)
Signed and dated lower right: *Paul Meyerheim 1870*

Provenance:
Private collection (New York)

Estimate: $5,000-$7,000

The reserve for this lot is available at HA.com/FineArt.

23239

CHARLES JAMES THERIAT (American 1860-1937)
Algerian Men
Oil on canvas
13 x 18-1/8 inches (33 x 46 cm)
Signed lower left

Estimate: $9,000-$12,000

The reserve for this lot is available at HA.com/FineArt.

23240

BENJAMIN CONSTANT (French 1845-1902)
Tangiers, 1873
Oil on panel
15 x 21-1/4 inches (38.1 x 54 cm)
Inscribed lower right: *B. Constant / Tangier, 1873*

Provenance:
Boos Auction Gallery (Famington, Michigan);
Estate of Mr. Robinson, Curator, Detroit Institute of Art (Detroit, Michigan)

Estimate: $6,000-$9,000

The reserve for this lot is available at HA.com/FineArt.

23241

JANE PETERSON (American 1876-1975)
A Market, Biskra
Oil on canvas
24 x 18-1/4 inches (61 x 46.4 cm)
Signed lower right

Estimate: $12,000-$18,000

The reserve for this lot is available at HA.com/FineArt.

23242

ORIENTALIST SCHOOL (Early Twentieth Century)
Village Scene
Oil on Panel
6-7/8 x 11-3/4 inches (17.3 x 29.7 cm)
Signed lower right: (indecipherable)
Signed lower right: (indecipherable)

Estimate: $3,000-$5,000

The reserve for this lot is available at HA.com/FineArt.

23243

GEORGES JULES VICTOR CLAIRIN (French 1843-1919)
A Puppetshow On A Spanish Street, 1869
Oil on canvas
30-1/2 x 47 inches (77.5 x 119.4 cm)
Signed lower left: *Clairin Madrid 1869*

The present painting is an early career work by Clairin. A similar version of the same subject, somewhat smaller in scale, was offered at Tajan, Paris, August 3, 2005, lot 45.

Georges Clairin was one of the last successful practitioners of Orientalist painting. He studied at the Ecole des Beaux-Arts in Paris with Francois Picot and Isidore Pils, and first exhibited at the French Salon in 1866. In 1868, he joined the painter Henry Regnault in Spain, where he was entranced by the Moorish architecture, which quickly figured prominently in his paintings. The present work was painted on that first sojourn to Spain, when he also fell sharply under the sway of the Spanish Orientalist painter, Mariano Fortuny y Marsal. With Regnault, Clairin subsequently traveled to Tangier where he made extensive study of local costume and set up an atelier with Regnault.

During the 1870s, Clairin contributed ceiling paintings to the grand decorative scheme of the Paris Opéra. In contrast to the efforts of his teacher, Pils, Clairin's paintings for the Opéra have a far greater lightness and expressive energy. His sensual, colorful and vibrant way of manipulating paint resulted in wonderful large-scale effects, and the artist soon won other major decorative commissions for public buildings in Cherbourg, Tour and Monte Carlo. In addition to his Orientalist subjects, Clairin produced numerous landscapes and society portraits. Perhaps his most famous sitter was Sarah Bernhardt, whom he portrayed in various roles.

Estimate: $15,000-$20,000

The reserve for this lot is available at HA.com/FineArt.

23244

Manner of WILLIAM MERRITT CHASE (American 1849-1916)
Still Life with Peacock Feathers
Oil on canvas
36 x 22 inches (91.4 x 55.8 cm)
With signature lower right and dated: *Chase 89*

Provenance:
Private collection (Glendora, California)

Estimate: $4,000-$8,000

This lot is being sold without reserve. Unreserved lots generally open at 50% of the low estimate.

23245

JULIUS STEWART (American 1855-1919)
Reclining Nude by an Oriental Screen, circa 1900
Oil on canvas
28-1/2 x 47-3/4 inches (72.4 x 121.3 cm)

Stewart was born in Philadelphia, but he moved permanently to Paris with his family. Through his father William Hood Stewart, a wealthy patron of Spanish and French artists, he became acquainted with leading figures in the art world. His father's collection was extremely strong in contemporary Spanish art, particularly the work of Mariano Fortuny, Eduardo Zamacrois, and Raimundo de Madrazo. Stewart studied at various times with Zamacrois, Madrazo and Jean-Léon Gérôme, and inspired by their example developed a colorful academic realist style. His oeuvre also includes nudes, genre scenes, and views of Venice. Stewart exhibited at the Paris Salon and at major international expositions, where he won many awards and prizes. Stewart received the French Legion of Honor in 1895. After 1900, Stewart rarely exhibited his art.

Reclining Nude By an Oriental Screen dates from about 1900. At roughly the end of the decade he devoted to painting the nude in indoor as well as outdoor settings. He generally prefered creating compositions which focus upon a single woman in an elegant interior. The woman portrayed here appears to be Juliette V., who was one of Stewart's favorite models as well as his mistress (*Julius LeBlanc Stewart: American Painter of the Belle Époque* [New York: Vance Jordan Fine Art Inc., 1998], p. 59).

Stewart's approach to the nude remained formal and academic. Decorously posed before decorative backdrops. They always appear to be in perfect harmony with their surroundings. According to Bailey Van Hook, Stewart "often exhibited [his nudes] as studies and they have the character of academes in their obviously posed positions" ("The Genre Paintings of Julius L. Stewart: A Myriad of Influences," unpublished paper, for Dr. H. Barbara Weinberg, City University Graduate Center, 1981, p. 28).

Estimate: $40,000-$60,000

This lot is being sold without reserve. Unreserved lots generally open at 50% of the low estimate.

SESSION III
EUROPEAN ART

25001

Ascribed to PIER FRANCESCO BISSOLO (Italian 1492-1554)
Madonna And Child
Oil on panel
23-3/4 x 19-3/4 inches (60.3 x 50.2 cm)

Provenance:
Newhouse Galleries (New York);
Mr. and Mrs. F. Howard Walsh (Fort Worth, Texas);
Walsh Family Art Trust

Estimate: $20,000-$30,000

The reserve for this lot is available at HA.com/FineArt.

25002

After AGNOLO BRONZINO (Italian 1503-1572)
Madonna And Child
Oil on panel
31 x 25-1/2 inches (78.7 x 64.8 cm)
Unsigned

Estimate: $2,000-$4,000
The reserve for this lot is available at HA.com/FineArt.

25003

BARTOLOMEO PASSAROTTI (Italian 1529-1592)
Two Grotesque Heads, circa 1575
Oil on canvas
19 x 25 inches (48.3 x 63.5 cm)

The imagery of this extraordinary painting by the Bolognese artist Bartolomeo Passarotti ultimately derives from Leonardo da Vinci's expression studies, which are considered some of the earliest caricatures—or precedents to caricature—in Western art. During the course of the Renaissance, the intention behind the creation of such studies went through a subtle evolution. It began as a device for studying human character, particularly under the auspices of the pseudo-science of physiognomy, i.e., outward appearances revealing traits of personality, intelligence, and other more elusive internal qualities. Through an exaggeration of certain facial features, these heads soon became a powerful device for humorous portraiture, for personality types or characters seen as the counterpart of the Renaissance ideal, and eventually for satire. The term 'caricature' was first applied to the work of the Carracci, also based in Bologna, around 1590.

Bartolomeo Passarotti was a central and fascinating figure within the development of character studies and caricature proper in Italy during the last quarter of the sixteenth century. Although one facet of his work (his altarpieces) can be properly described as Mannerist, and exceedingly decorative, another side displays an intense exploration of the phenomenon of Nature in all its manifestations. These *Two Grotesque Heads* are a prime example of the latter, while still maintaining a quite decorative quality. In Bologna, Passarotti engaged in continuous dialogue with an enlightened circle of intellectuals: educated patrons, professors of the University, and learned doctors and collectors, all of whom had an enormous impact on his art, and his interest in realism (the unvarnished side of Nature). One of his most important friends and influences was Ulisse Aldrovandi (1522-1605), the important Italian naturalist and the moving force behind Bologna's botanical garden, one of the first in Europe. Both Carolus Linnaeus and the Comte de Buffon regarded him as the father of natural history. For Passarotti, Androvandi's passion for observing and documenting Nature in an encyclopedic manner provided a model for his approach to art. Passarotti's openness to a wide range of influences enabled him to contribute to something entirely new and fresh in Italian painting—a focus on low life subjects, scenes of everyday life, and the use of such imagery for moralizing or allegorical painting.

Passarotti is best known for his ground-breaking works in the arena of genre painting, which was virtually unknown in Italy. He painted market stalls and butcher shops depicting peasants selling their wares, often engaging the viewer directly with weather-worn faces and toothless grins not dissimilar from the heads in the present work. Such imagery was painted earlier in Flanders, and was probably introduced to the south by a painter such as Joachim Beuckelaer who was active in Cremona for a period. Passarotti's encyclopedic disposition would have attracted him to this type of painting, which records a subject previously absent from the Italian canon.

The exotic costumes of these figures suggest a possible connection with the Italian Commedia dell'Arte, popular Italian theatre. Within this connection, they also might have allegorical significance as well. The facial types and the disposition of heads in this work have close parallels to a painting by Passarotti in a Parisian private collection showing a pair of intoxicated lovers in which a coarse man presents the viewer with the breast of his companion, a slatternly prostitute (see Carinna Höper,*Bartolomeo Passarotti (1529-1592),* Wernersche Verlagsgesellschaft Worms, II, cat. no. G 96, ill. Plate 21b).

Passarotti exemplified a style typically northern in taste which is evident in the satirical and "genre" qualities of the subjects, and provided a springboard for the achievements of the Carracci. In contrast with Passarotti's tendency to treat low life subjects as material for coarse burlesque representations, the Carracci tended to observe scenes from everyday life without the subtext of allegory.

Estimate: $120,000-$160,000
The reserve for this lot is available at HA.com/FineArt.

25004

FRENCH SCHOOL (Seventeenth Century)
Putti Dancing
Oil on canvas
38 x 36 inches (96.5 x 91.4 cm)
Unsigned

Estimate: $2,000-$4,000

The reserve for this lot is available at HA.com/FineArt.

25005

CONTINENTAL SCHOOL
Christ And The Doctors
Oil on canvas
69-1/2 x 52-3/4 inches
(176.5 x 134 cm)
Unsigned

Estimate: $8,000-$10,000

The reserve for this lot is available at HA.com/FineArt.

25006

School of SIR PETER PAUL RUBENS (Flemish 1577-1640)
Untitled, (Possibly Alexander at the battle of Malli)
Oil on copper
25-3/4 x 32-3/4 inches (65.4 x 83.1 cm)
Unsigned

Estimate: $8,000-$12,000
The reserve for this lot is available at HA.com/FineArt.

25007

BALTHAZAR GERBIER D'OUVILLY (British 1583-1667)
Portrait Of William Fielding, 1st Earl Of Denbigh And *Portrait Of Susan Villiers, 1st Countess Of Denbigh*
Oil on canvas
82 x 50-1/2 inches, each (208.3 x 128 cm)
Signed at lower right: *William 1st Earl of Denbigh/ Balthazar Gerbier, pinx* and *Susan Villiers 1st Countess of Denbigh/ Balthazar Gerbier pinx*

Provenance:
Sale, Sotheby's London, April 3, 1996, Lot 18;
Sale, Sotheby's New York, Old Master Painting, May 1998, Lot 86;
Private collection (New York)

A pair of full-length portraits of William Fielding and his wife, Susan Villiers. He is depicted wearing an ornate red jacket with gold embroidery and tan boots holding a staff. She is wearing a beautiful red gown with a white silk bodice and decadent gold embroidery standing before an open window. William Fielding (circa 1582-1643) was a highly regarded political figure who held positions at court under James I and Charles I. He was created baron and viscount Fielding in 1620 and Earl of Denbigh on September 14, 1622. Susan Villiers, daughter of Sir George Villiers, and brother to the royal favorite George Villiers, 1st Duke of Buckingham. The couple facilitated the introduction of Balthazar Gerbier to Charles I, who he would eventually serve as his art advisor.

Estimate: $150,000-$250,000
The reserve for this lot is available at HA.com/FineArt.

25008

FRANS FRANCKEN II (Flemish 1581-1642) and **JAN BRUEGHEL THE YOUNGER** (Flemish 1601-1678)
The Virgin And Child With Saint Anne And The Infant John The Baptist, Surrounded By A Garland Of Flowers, circa 1630s
Oil on wooden panel
21-1/2 x 16-1/2 inches (54.6 x 41.9 cm)
Signed lower right corner of the medaillion: *FFrancken d [...]*

Provenance:
Galerie Sanct Lucas (Vienna, Austria);
Private collection (Vienna, Austria);
Newhouse Galleries (New York);
Mr. and Mrs. F. Howard Walsh (Fort Worth, Texas);
Walsh Family Art Trust

Beginning around 1616-18 and continuing through the middle decades of the seventeenth century, numerous examples of a new type of painting, a kind of still life-cum-devotional-image began to be produced in quantity, particularly in Catholic Antwerp, where figure painters and still-life specialists were in abundance and routinely collaborated with one another. The artists who were among the earliest practitioners of this genre of devotional painting with its magnificent floral embellishments were in the circle of Peter Paul Rubens, namely Jan Brueghel I and his son Jan Brueghel the Younger, Hendrik van Balen, Frans Snijders, Frans Francken and his son Frans Francken II (the latter painted and signed the central medallion of the present work), Hans Rottenhammer, and Joos de Momper, among others.

The popularity of this type of devotional painting with floral accompaniments coincided with the popularity of the so-called "fifteen mysteries of the Rosary." The cult of the Madonna of the Rosary (Rozenkrans) arose in Antwerp in the late 1610s, where churches began commissioning the city's most prominent painters and sculptors to create large devotional images of the Virgin or episodes from her life framed with wreaths that resemble the shape of a rosary. In the work of some of the artists, namely Frans Francken II who was known to have painted both the figurative and the floral aspects of such paintings (usually on a smaller scale), the flowers in the wreaths around the central medallion resemble rosary beads: they are large and rest on the surface of the arrangement almost in the shape of a string (one such work by Frans Francken II, *Madonna and Child,* sold through Dorotheum, Vienna, Oct 14, 1997, lot 8). In the best-known examples of this genre, the Rubens-Brueghel I collaborations (see for example, their masterful *Madonna in Floral Wreath* of circa 1620 in the Alte Pinakothek, Munich, Germany), the wreaths are more densely packed with flowers of a variety of size, shape, and color, as they are in the present painting. The popularity of this type of devotional image is also recorded in secular works from the same period, notably in the elaborate views of the private picture galleries (the so-called *kunst-und-wunderkammern*) that often double as allegories of the senses (see, for example, the Jan Brueghel the Elder and Peter Paul Rubens collaboration, *Allegory of Sight* of circa 1618, in the Museo del Prado, Madrid, Spain).

The present devotional painting with its brilliant floral wreath was a collaboration between Frans Francken II and the workshop of Jan Brueghel the Younger (Jan II). The younger Brueghel was the son of Rubens' frequent still-life collaborator, Jan Brueghel I. After studying with his father, Jan II traveled in Italy before taking over his father's studio upon the Elder's death in 1625. He became a leading artist in Antwerp, where he was elected to the painters' guild in 1625 and became dean in 1630-31.

Owing to the collaborative nature of artists' workshops in early seventeenth-century Antwerp, it is often difficult to distinguish the hand of the "master" from all the competent members of his studio whom he had personally trained. In the case of Jan Brueghel II, it appears that after his return from Italy and his assumption of his father's studio in 1625, his personal production was rather low. Only somewhat later, by the 1630s, did larger numbers of flower pieces and garlands of this type begin emerging from his workshop. Surviving documents show that by 1646, works from his studio were sold at the rate of about seven a month, suggesting that his entire family was actively involved in production (this includes his wife Anna Janssens, his sons Jan Peeter and Abraham, his nephew Jan (I) van Kessel, and possibly his brother Ambrosius). Because Jan Brueghel II's collaborator on this painting (Frans Francken II) died in 1642, the work cannot be considered one of the workshop's late productions. Its quality, rather, seems consistent with slightly earlier efforts of the 1630s, where there was more participation from the master himself.

Highly finished works such as this, which combine the specialized skills of history and flower painting, were prized cabinet pieces among seventeenth-century collectors.

Estimate: $60,000-$80,000
The reserve for this lot is available at HA.com/FineArt.

25009

Circle of JUSTUS SUSTERMANS (Flemish 1597-1681)
Portrait Of A Man
Oil on canvas
32-3/4 x 26-1/8 inches, oval (83.2 x 66.4 cm)

Provenance (labels verso):
Chase collection;
F.F. Hicks collection

The Flemish painter Justus Sustermans served as court painter to the Medici Grand Dukes in Florence beginning in 1621 and worked for them for nearly the rest of his career. He was responsible for producing the most complete visual record of the likenesses of the later members Medici family including: Grand Duke Ferdinand II de' Medici and his wife Vittoria della Rovere; Grand Duke Cosimo III de' Medici; Grand Duchess Maria Magdalena of Austria; Leopoldo di Cosimo II de' Medici; Giancarlo de' Medici; and Claudia de' Medici. He also painted a distinguished portrait of Galileo (Uffizi). His reputation as a skilled portraitist in the Baroque tradition won him commissions at many other European and Italian courts including Vienna, Parma, Piacenza, Milan, Mantua, Ferrara, and Rome. Many examples of his work are preserved in the collections of the Uffizi Gallery and Pitti Palace, Florence.

Estimate: $6,000-$9,000

The reserve for this lot is available at HA.com/FineArt.

25010

Studio of GERRIT VAN HONTHORST (Dutch 1590-1656)
Portrait Of Elizabeth Stuart, Queen Of Bohemia
Oil on panel, in painted oval
28-1/2 x 22-3/4 inches (72.3 x 57.7 cm)
Inscribed verso on a paper label: *Antique oil painting of "Queen Elizabeth of Bohemia" cir. 1650 (sale no. 5135) / $485.00 / Miss Bessie Heard / Bought from Henry Stern / 329 Royal Street New Orleans, La. / April 25, 1956*

Provenance:
Henry Stern (New Orleans, Louisiana);
Bessie Heard (McKinney, Texas);
Bessie Heard Trust

Estimate: $3,000-$5,000

This lot is being sold without reserve. Unreserved lots generally open at 50% of the low estimate.

25011

SPANISH SCHOOL
(Early Seventeenth Century)
Baskets Of flowers, a pair
Oil on canvas
13-1/2 x 14-1/4 inches (34.3 x 36.2 cm)
Partial inscription, *A Fe* at lower left on the panel showing a white cloth under the basket

Provenance:
Newhouse Galleries, as Jan-Baptiste Bosschaert (New York);
Mr. and Mrs. F. Howard Walsh (Fort Worth, Texas);
Walsh Family Art Trust

These companion paintings by an unidentified hand draw upon still life developments in the Netherlands, Germany, France, Spain and Italy, from the first three decades of the seventeenth century, at a time when still life painting was emerging as a specialty genre, and baskets were commonly depicted as containers for fruit and flowers. The broad handling and the treatment of the cloth with gilt thread suggests a Spanish origin for the pictures. The works probably date no later than about 1630, after which time still life arrangements in this genre generally became more complex.

A remnant of a signature and/or inscription is located on the far left side of the white tablecloth, on the portion which falls over the edge. The inscription seems to read *"A Fe..."* possibly a shortened form of *Anno Fecit,* a common Latin phrase for *"year in which I made this"* used by seventeenth-century painters. The name and the date are not discernible.

Estimate: $8,000-$12,000

The reserve for this lot is available at HA.com/FineArt.

25012

ALBERT ERNEST CARRIER-BELLEUSE (French 1824-1887)
Bust of Albrecht Dürer
Bronze, dark brown patination set on base
15-1/2 inches, high (39.4 cm)
Inscribed to reverse: *A. CARRIER*

Estimate: $3,000-$5,000

The reserve for this lot is available at HA.com/FineArt.

25013

REMBRANDT VAN RIJN (Dutch 1606-1669)
Rembrandt Drawing At A Window, 1648
Etching
6-1/4 x 5-1/8 inches, plate (15.9 x 13 cm)
Signed and dated in the plate
From the: *Recueil de Quatre-Vingt-Cinq Estampes Originales*
Printed by: *H.L. Basan,* 1807-1808

Provenance:
Park West Galleries (Southfield, Michigan);
Private collection (Michigan)

Estimate: $4,000-$6,000

The reserve for this lot is available at HA.com/FineArt.

25014

REMBRANDT VAN RIJN (Dutch 1606-1669)
Head Of Saskia And Others, 1636
Etching
5-7/8 x 4-7/8 inches, plate (14.9 x 12.4 cm)
Signed and dated in the plate
From the: *Recueil de Quatre-Vingt-Cinq Estampes Originales*
Printed by: *Michel Bernard,* after 1846

Provenance:
Park West Galleries (Southfield, Michigan);
Private collection (Michigan)

Estimate: $4,000-$6,000

The reserve for this lot is available at HA.com/FineArt.

25015

FLORENTINE SCHOOL
(Second half of the Seventeenth Century)
Elisabeth And Mary With The Infants Jesus And St. John The Baptist In The Carpentry Shop Of Joseph
Oil on canvas
48 x 57-1/4 inches (121.9 x 145.4 cm)
Unsigned

Estimate: $5,000-$10,000

The reserve for this lot is available at HA.com/FineArt.

25016

Circle of JAN HACKAERT (Dutch 1629-circa 1685)
A Hunting Party In A Wooded Landscape
Oil on canvas
32-7/8 x 47-3/8 inches (83.5 x 120.3 cm)
Unsigned

The seventeenth-century Dutch landscape painter Jan Hackaert specialized in scenes of drovers, or aristocrats hunting deer or fowl on horseback along paths through dense woodlands. Hackaert often collaborated with Nicolaes Berchem who contributed the animals and figures to his compositions. This painting shares stylistic and compositional similarities with a work attributed to the Circle of Hackaert sold at Christie's on April 4, 2007. The coloration and more abbreviated handling suggests a later seventeenth/early eighteenth-century hand.

Estimate: $5,000-$7,000

The reserve for this lot is available at HA.com/FineArt.

25017

ADAMS FRANS VAN DER MEULEN
(Flemish 1632-1690)
Horsemen In A Landscape (said to be near Dinan)
Oil on panel
8-1/2 x 11-3/4 inches (21.6 x 29.8 cm)
Signed lower right:
A. F. V. MEULEN

Provenance:
Newhouse Galleries (New York);
Mr. and Mrs. F. Howard Walsh (Fort Worth, Texas);
Walsh Family Art Trust

Estimate:
$15,000-$20,000

The reserve for this lot is available at HA.com/FineArt.

25018

Circle of William Hogarth (British 1697-1764)
Country Scene Of Low Life In A Village
Oil on canvas
26 x 36 inches (26 x 91.4 cm)
Unsigned

Inspired by William Hogarth's famous series of paintings of a harlot's progress and of a rake's progress, this painting by an unknown follower portrays many contemporary social types in an identifiable location. Such paintings were designed to be a generalized satire on local manners and customs.

Estimate: $3,000-$5,000

The reserve for this lot is available at HA.com/FineArt.

25019

BOGDAN THEODOR LUBIENIECKI (Polish born after 1653)
Portrait Of A Man Of Science
47 x 38 inches (119.4 x 96.5 cm)
Oil on canvas
Unsigned

Exhibition:
Kosciuszko Foundation, January - February, 1978 (New York)

Estimate: $5,000-$7,000

The reserve for this lot is available at HA.com/FineArt.

25020

Circle of JEAN RESTOUT II (French 1692-1768)
The Entombment Of A Cleric By Torchlight
Oil on canvas
64 x 62 inches (162.6 x 157.5 cm)
Unsigned
An alternate attribution to Noel Halle (French 1711-1781) has also been suggested.

Estimate: $10,000-$15,000

The reserve for this lot is available at HA.com/FineArt.

25021

CONTINENTAL SCHOOL (Eighteenth Century)
Oval Portrait Of A Gentleman
Oil on canvas
32-1/4 x 25-1/4 inches (82 x 64 cm)
Unsigned

Estimate: $800-$1,200

The reserve for this lot is available at HA.com/FineArt.

25022

BENJAMIN FERRERS (British d.1732)
Lady Hockley, circa 1710
Oil on canvas
50 x 40-3/8 inches (127 x 102.5 cm)
Signed lower right: *Benj Ferrers Pinx*
Verso, an old paper label: *Arnold Wiggins & Sons, Ltd., London*

Provenance:
Art Market (London) 1980s

Estimate: $5,000-$8,000

The reserve for this lot is available at HA.com/FineArt.

25023

H. BOUAT (French)
Floral Still Life
Oil on canvas
37 x 27-1/4 inches (94 x 69.2 cm)
Signed lower left: *Honufrius Bouat*

Estimate: $12,000-$16,000

The reserve for this lot is available at HA.com/FineArt.

25024

LOUIS-NICOLAS LEMASLE
(French 1788-1870)
Henri IV And His Mistress, 1826
Oil on canvas
61-3/4 x 42-1/4 (157 x 107.3 cm)
Signed, dated and inscribed: *Henri IV avec / Sa Maitresse / Peint par Louis Lemasle / chevalier de la Legion / d'honneur / 1826*
On verso is a canvas maker's stamp from France

Provenance:
Castle Hotel (Velden, Carinthia);
Sale, the Art Trade (Vienna, Austria);
Shepherd Gallery (Robert Kashey) (New York) (by 1993; acquired at the above sale)

Exhibition:
Shepherd Gallery (New York), Fall 1993, *From Isabey to Noguchi; Paintings, Drawings, Sculptures,* Cat. No. 9, color illus.

The offered painting depicts one of six scenes from the life of Herny IV (1533-1610), all executed by Lemasle during a revivalist period known as *style Troubadour.* This particular work depicts an event from 1587 when Henry IV was in need of additional troops, which Countess de Gramont funded. Henry IV's subsequent triumph assisted him in securing the crown and thus after the battle of Coutras he laid the captured flags at the feet of his mistress.

Lemasle studied under David at the *Ecole des Beaux-Arts* before traveling to Rome where he had his portrait drawn by Ingres in 1812. He was fortunate enough to become enlisted in service to the Prince of Salerno in Naples. The prince's patronage would provide Lemasle with security and opportunity for years to come in the form of the prince's sister, the Duchess de Berry.

Relevent Literature:
Catalogue, *From Isabey to Noguchi; Paintings, Drawings, Sculpture*; Shepherd Gallery, New York, NY, Fall 1993 (No. 9, color illus.);
Hans Naef, *Die Bildniszeichnungen von J.-A.-D. Ingres*, Bern 1977, Vol. 1, pp. 268-272

Estimate: $40,000-$60,000

The reserve for this lot is available at HA.com/FineArt.

25025

EUROPEAN SCHOOL (Nineteenth Century)
Portrait Of A Young Lady With Pearls
Oil on canvas
30-1/8 x 25 inches (76.5 x 63.5 cm)
Unsigned

Estimate: $3,000-$5,000

The reserve for this lot is available at HA.com/FineArt.

25026

FRENCH SCHOOL (Nineteenth Century)
Cavalier Caressing A Lady
Oil on canvas
22 x 17 inches (55.9 x 43.2 cm)
Signed lower right (indecipherable): *Michel*

Estimate: $2,000-$4,000

The reserve for this lot is available at HA.com/FineArt.

25027

A. GALEOTTI (Italian)
Portrait Of The Three Eldest Children Of Charles I (after Sir Anthony Van Dyck), circa 1800-1825
Watercolor on paper laid on canvas
26 x 23-3/4 inches (66 x 60.3 cm)
Signed lower left: *Agaleotti*

Provenance:
Private collection (Glendora, California)

Estimate: $4,000-$6,000

This lot is being sold without reserve. Unreserved lots generally open at 50% of the low estimate.

25028

FLEMISH SCHOOL
Landscape
Oil on canvas
29-3/4 x 35-1/2 inches
(75.6 x 90.2 cm)
Unsigned

Estimate: $2,500-$5,000

The reserve for this lot is available at HA.com/FineArt.

25029

FLEMISH SCHOOL (Eighteenth Century)
Landscape With Village,
Oil on canvas
10-1/2 x 16-1/2 inches (22.5 x 35.3 cm)
Unsigned

Estimate: $6,000-$8,000

The reserve for this lot is available at HA.com/FineArt.

25030

FRANCIS WHEATLEY (British 1747-1801)
The Affectionate Daughter
Oil on canvas
12 x 10 inches (30.5 x 25.4 cm)

Estimate: $4,000-$6,000

The reserve for this lot is available at HA.com/FineArt.

25031

Attributed to JEAN BAPTISTE GREUZE (French 1725-1805)
Portrait Of A Young Girl
Oil on canvas
19 x 17 inches (48.3 x 43.2 cm)
Unsigned

Estimate: $3,000-$5,000

The reserve for this lot is available at HA.com/FineArt.

25032

School of JEAN BAPTISTE CHARPENTIER (French 1728-1806)
The Young Farm Girl
Oil on board
18 x 15 inches (45.7 x 38.1 cm)
Unsigned

Estimate: $1,000-$2,000

The reserve for this lot is available at HA.com/FineArt.

25033

Attributed to THOMAS GAINSBOROUGH, R.A. (English 1727-1788)
Portrait Of Elizabeth Honywood And Her Son Philip, 1767
Oil on canvas
30 x 25 inches, oval (76.2 x 63.5 cm)

Provenance:
Newhouse Galleries (New York);
Mr. and Mrs. F. Howard Walsh (Fort Worth, Texas);
Walsh Family Art Trust

Estimate: $30,000-$40,000

The reserve for this lot is available at HA.com/FineArt.

25034

Attributed to THOMAS GAINSBOROUGH (British 1727-1788)
The Waggoner: Landscape Near Bath
Oil on canvas
9-3/4 x 12 inches
(24.8 x 30.5 cm)
Signed with indecipherable inscription verso

Provenance:
Newhouse Galleries (New York);
Mr. and Mrs. F. Howard Walsh (Fort Worth, Texas);
Walsh Family Art Trust

Estimate: $12,000-$18,000
The reserve for this lot is available at HA.com/FineArt.

25035

Attributed JOHANN JOSEPH ZOFFANY (British 1733-1810)
Portrait Of A Gentleman
Oil on canvas
33-1/2 x 25-1/4 inches (85.1 x 64.1 cm)
Unsigned

Estimate: $3,000-$5,000
The reserve for this lot is available at HA.com/FineArt.

25036

Style of THOMAS LAWRENCE (British 1769-1830)
Portrait Of Fanny Kemble
Oil on canvas
40 x 51-1/4 inches (101.6 x 130.2 cm)
Unsigned
Partial label verso from Chicago exhibition
Label verso: *Lincoln Warehouse Corportation, New York*

Provenance:
Collection of Ira N. Morris;
Collection of Mrs. Constance Morris

Estimate: $9,000-$11,000
The reserve for this lot is available at HA.com/FineArt.

25037

Studio of THOMAS LAWRENCE (British 1769-1830)
Portrait Of Lady Hertford
Oil on canvas
29 x 23-1/2 inches, oval (73.6 x 59.6 cm)
Unsigned

Estimate: $4,000-$6,000
This lot is being sold without reserve. Unreserved lots generally open at 50% of the low estimate.

25038

MARIE-PHILIPPE COUPIN DE LA COUPERIE (French 1773-1851)
Woman At The Organ Before A Statue Of The Virgin And Child (Saint Cecilia?)
Oil on canvas
65 x 51 inches (165.1 x 129.5 cm)
Unsigned

French painter and lithographer Marie-Philippe Coupin de la Couperie was born at Versailles and trained under the celebrated French romantic painter, Girodet. He was employed by the Sèvres porcelain manufactory and, in 1815, was named professor of drawing at the military college of La Fleche, and six months later at the Ecole de Saint-Cyr. In 1832, he received the *croix de chevalier* of the Legion of Honor. He exhibited at the Paris Salon from 1812 to 1833. Paintings by Coupin de la Couperie are in the collections of the Louvre, Paris; the Napoleon Museum, Arenberg; and the Musée national du château, Pau.

This ambitious painting is characteristic of the type of large-scale works with literary or historical themes Coupin de la Couperie produced for his greatest patron, the Duchess de Berry—Marie-*Caroline*-Ferdinande-Louise de Bourbon (1798-1870). She was the eldest daughter of King Francis I of the Two Sicilies and his first wife, Marie-Clementine of Austria, daughter of Emperor Leopold II and the niece of Marie-Antoinette . Thus she was from a generation younger than her husband, Charles Ferdinand, Duke of Berry (1778-1820), the younger son of Charles, Count of Artois, later Charles X of France (1757-1836), whom she married at the age of seventeen in 1816, and with whom she had four children. She was one of the leading collectors and patrons of her day, as well as the owner of important old masters including a Vermeer now in The Frick Collection, New York. Following the collapse of Charles X's government and his cousin Louis-Philippe 's betrayal of a solemn undertaking to sustain the Duchess's son Henri as King, she became the standard bearer for legitimist resistance. Leading the uprising in the Vendée she was captured by Louis-Philippe 's troops and imprisoned. There she was found to be pregnant and this scandalous discovery, although she had actually secretly married the father of the child, Count don Ettore Lucchesi-Palli, in Rome in December 1831, quickly led to the end of royalist resistance. The Duchess of Berry went on to have a number of children by Lucchesi-Palli, whose descendants ultimately inherited much of her splendid collection.

The large-scale dimensions of this work, as well as its arched top, suggest it may have been commissioned as an altarpiece. Indeed, the figure of the well-attired woman seated at the organ is probably intended to represent Saint Cecilia, who is a patron saint of church music, musicians, and singers and is generally portrayed at the organ.

Estimate: $25,000-$35,000
The reserve for this lot is available at HA.com/FineArt.

25039

ROMAN SCHOOL
Saint Catherine Of Alexandria, circa 1800
Oil on canvas
53 x 41 inches (134.6 x 104.1 cm)

Provenance:
Private collection (New York)

Saint Catherine of Alexandria is the patron of education and learning. Depicted above crowned and dressed in a gorgeous silk gown holding a sword and palm, both symbols of martyrdom.

Estimate: $12,000-$15,000

The reserve for this lot is available at HA.com/FineArt.

25040

EUROPEAN SCHOOL
(Eighteenth Century)
View Of Rome, circa 1773
Oil on canvas
37-1/2 x 53 inches (95.3 x 134.6 cm)
Signed with monogram and dated lower left: *17CB73*
Auction stencil verso: *S09PG*

Estimate: $6,000-$9,000

The reserve for this lot is available at HA.com/FineArt.

25041

ALEXANDRE-HYACINTHE DUNOUY (French 1757-1841)
View Toward A Fortress And Mountain Lake, circa 1830
Oil on beveled mahogany panel partially reinforced with glued fabric (verso)
13-3/8 x 8-1/4 inches (34 x 21 cm)
Initialed at lower right: *AD*
Old auction stencil (verso): *SE311*

Provenance:
Private collection;
Sale, Lauren, Guilloux, Buffetaud, December 1, 2001, Lot 13

One of the most interesting and least known periods of French landscape painting, from the 1780s through the 1830s, coincides with the career of the exceptionally gifted landscapist, Alexandre-Hyacinthe Dunouy-the author of the present painting of the Italian *campagna.* Dunouy's work forms a significant artistic bridge between Claude Lorraine's classical landscapes which are based upon specific pictorial conventions for organizing space, and the more casually composed *plein-air* paintings of Corot, which prize the transitory, emotionally-charged effects of light and atmosphere achieved only by working directly from nature. This meticulously-rendered vertical landscape possesses characteristics of Dunouy's later manner, when atmosphere and a tangle of vegetation (closer to what is observable in nature) assume greater importance than clear spatial recession.

A native of Paris, Dunouy began his career under the tutelage of the painter Briand, depicting views of the city and the surrounding region. During the 1780s, the young artist traveled to Italy where the landscape in and around Rome and Naples (where he resided from 1783 to 1789) profoundly affected the direction of his art, inspiring numerous small-scale landscape compositions which he exhibited regularly at the Paris Salons throughout the 1790s. It is very likely Dunouy met the influential French landscapist Pierre-Henri de Valenciennes (1750-1819) during his travels as his work suggests some ofhis influence. Valenciennes holds a position of considerable importance in the history of landscape painting of the late eighteenth and the nineteenth centuries. In 1800 he published the influential treatise on landscape painting *Eléments de perspective pratique, à l'usage des artistes, suivis de Réflexions et conseils à un élève sur la peinture, et particulièrement sur le genre du paysage* (which was still read by Camille Pissarro in the 1860s). In this book, Valenciennes recommended an almost systematic program of study by painting oil sketches outdoors, to train the hand and eye of the young painter to capture nature's many changing faces. This theory was based on Valenciennes' own practice: since the early 1780s he had been painting a variety of oil studies in the open air, including a notable series executed during a period of study in Rome, between 1782 and 1785, most of which are now in the Louvre, Paris. Although he advocated a systematic approach to landscape, Valenciennes also stressed, "Work in haste, so as to seize nature as she is."

Like Valenciennes, Dunouy produced numerous oil sketches outdoors, paying particular attention to the sky. Valenciennes placed great importance on the study of the sky because it is the main source of light in landscape painting. He recommended that the artist should paint such studies of the sky and its cloud formations in order to learn the different ways light modifies the appearance of nature. In the present pair of paintings, Dunouy's skies, like Valenciennes', are both accurately and poetically detailed.

Upon his return to France, Dunouy was engaged by Louis XVIII to oversee an important scheme of decorative works for a number of palaces including Fontainebleau. Dunouy exhibited regularly from 1791 until 1833 at the Paris Salon and received Medals of Honor in 1819 and again in 1827. He is known to have traveled to Italy again in 1810 under the patronage of the King of Naples, Joachim Murat, and from 1810 until 1815 he received numerous commissions from Murat's wife and Napoleon's youngest sister, Caroline Bonaparte. Dunouy is also associated with the Auvergne, Savoy, and the area around Lyon.

Dunouy was also an accomplished engraver, executing over thirty engravings after his paintings and drawings. His works are found in numerous museums including Chateau-Thierry, Cherbourg, Compiegne, Epinal, Lyon, Orléans, the Marmottan and Carnavalet in Paris, Stockholm, Versailles (a scene showing his patron's brother-in-law, Napoleon, and Pius VII meeting in the forest of Fontainebleau), and The Metropolitan Museum of Art in New York (*Le Palais Royal et le port à Naples,* an early work of circa 1780).

Estimate: $2,000-$3,000
The reserve for this lot is available at HA.com/FineArt.

25042

CONTINENTAL SCHOOL (Late Eighteenth Century)
Landscape
Oil on panel
32-1/4 x 47-1/2 inches (82 x 121 cm)
Unsigned

A large scale extensive landscape depicting two boys at the river's edge, cows at left and center wading in the river which flows right around an island with an abandoned building, curving back to the left with sandy banks and sloping mountains in the background.

Estimate: $2,000-$4,000

The reserve for this lot is available at HA.com/FineArt.

25043

Attributed to JOHN CONSTABLE, R.A. (British 1776-1837)
A View Near Dedham
Oil on canvas on panel
10 x 8-3/4 inches (25.4 x 22.2 cm)

Provenance:
Newhouse Galleries (New York);
Mr. and Mrs. F. Howard Walsh (Fort Worth, Texas);
Walsh Family Art Trust

The village of Dedham in Suffolk is located along the River Stour, where Constable's father owned a profitable mill; the Dedham Vale straddles Suffolk and Essex counties and is less than two miles from East Bergholt, where Constable had his first studio. The artist consistently made drawings and oil sketches of various sites in and around Dedham and East Bergholt. In fact this region is today known as "Constable Country". The present painting depicts the stone walls and grand stairway of what appears to be a sizeable country residence set among dense trees and other vegetation.

Estimate: $15,000-$20,000
The reserve for this lot is available at HA.com/FineArt.

25044

Attributed to JOHN CONSTABLE, R.A. (English 1776-1837)
View Of Langham, Suffolk
Oil on canvas
7-3/4 x 10 inches (19.7 x 25.4 cm)

Provenance:
Newhouse Galleries (New York);
Mr. and Mrs. F. Howard Walsh (Fort Worth, Texas);
Walsh Family Art Trust

Along with J.M.W. Turner, John Constable is renowned as the greatest English landscape artist of the nineteenth century. Constable executed many large, fully finished studio paintings that earned critical acclaim throughout his career; but his smaller oil studies sketched directly from nature are also highly prized for their spontaneous sensibility. These more intimate sketches reveal the artist's interest in capturing the interplay of light and shadow across land and sky.

Golden tones dominate the lower section of the present picture, as sunlight falls across the trees, stone wall, thatched roof, and open field. Passages of sky and vegetation are loosely described, yet the composition is carefully organized. The scene is set against the diagonal lines of distant hills and beneath the horizontal band of clouds; the tallest tree in the center neatly divides the picture, while surrounding trees provide accents of verticality.

Estimate: $15,000-$20,000

The reserve for this lot is available at HA.com/FineArt.

25045

Attributed to JOHN CONSTABLE, R.A. (English 1776-1837)
West Lynn, Lynmouth
Oil on panel
10-5/8 x 14-1/4 inches (27 x 36.2 cm)
Inscribed lower right: *West Lynn Lynmouth*

Provenance:
Newhouse Galleries (New York);
Mr. and Mrs. F. Howard Walsh (Fort Worth, Texas);
Walsh Family Art Trust

Located on the north coast of Devonshire (southwest England), where the East and West Lynn rivers meet, the small village of Lynmouth has attracted artists in search of the picturesque since the early nineteenth century. John Murray's *A Handbook for Travellers in Devon and Cornwall* (1856) describes the scenery around Lynmouth as "far finer than any other of the southern counties can boast; characterized by sub-alpine valleys, impetuous streams, wild gloomy ridges, and precipices and crags which would elicit admiration even in mountainous Wales" (p. 116).

Celebrated for his fresh approach to landscape painting, John Constable executed numerous *plein air* oil sketches of various English topographies, often using them to produce finished studio paintings. The present work is dominated by the broadly painted sky, while details of land, vegetation, and water are loosely and summarily suggested through quickly applied brushstrokes. With such spontaneity and freedom of handling, and attention to the effects of light, this picture anticipates the work of the Impressionists.

Estimate: $45,000-$55,000
The reserve for this lot is available at HA.com/FineArt.

25046

Follower of ELISABETH LOUISE VIGÉE-LEBRUN (French 1755-1842)
M.L.E. Vigée-LeBrun And Her Daughter
Oil on canvas
14 x 10-1/2 inches (35.6 x 26.7 cm)
Unsigned

Provenance:
Newhouse Galleries (New York);
Mr. and Mrs. F. Howard Walsh (Fort Worth, Texas);
Walsh Family Art Trust

Estimate: $3,000-$5,000
The reserve for this lot is available at HA.com/FineArt.

25047

Attributed to LOUIS-LÉOPOLD BOILLY (French 1761-1845)
Portrait Of A Woman, 1801
Oil on panel
11-1/2 x 8-3/4 inches (29.2 x 22.2 cm)
Signed and dated at lower right: *Boilly An. 9*

Boilly was a successful painter both of moralizing, amorous and sentimental genre subjects and of portraits. He devoted himself to the former earlier in his career when he fell under the spell of Jean Honoré Fragonard and Jean-Baptiste Greuze, whose works combine a love of anecdote with delight in rendering the marvelous tactile qualities of textiles and other sensual textures. Since Boilly began his artistic career under the tutelage of Dominique Doncre in Arras-a specialist in trompe l'oeil painting-it seems he was somewhat predisposed to a predilection for careful rendering of texture, which held him in good stead as a portraitist later on. Boilly's focus on amorous genre scenes shifted after an artistic scandal erupted when he exhibited his *Lovers and the Escaped Bird* (now in the Louvre, Paris). Its erotic emphasis was deemed far too flagrant by the *Comité du Salut Public* in 1794 at the height of the Terror, and Boilly was condemned for painting subjects *"d'une obscénité révoltante pour les moeurs républicaines."* He appeased the "decency police" by quickly painting an intensely patriotic *Triumph of Marat,* even though he was, in truth, apolitical.

After 1800, Boilly turned his artistic attention to smaller but more complex scenes of quickly observed urban views as well as portraits of the middle class, which is where he lavished his love of careful description. The present work is characteristic of Boilly's highly refined skills of observation. While this sitter is not ravishingly beautiful by most standards, she radiates a fascinating sense of personality and intelligence. Boilly's portraits of this type strongly betray the artist's deep admiration for Dutch 17th-century painting, of which he had a considerable personal collection. Taking cues from Dutch models, Boilly produced portraits with an understated sobriety which subtly focuses attention on the personality of the face. His use of color is also delicate and harmonious, and quite distinctive.

Boilly signed and dated this work according to Napoleon's Republican calendar. The date "An. 9" he inscribed at lower right corresponds to the year 1801. The calendar ran for 13 years from 1892 to September 9, 1805 when it was abolished by decree.

Estimate: $2,000-$3,000
The reserve for this lot is available at HA.com/FineArt.

25048

Circle of GIUSEPPE TOMINZ (Italian 1790-1866)
Family Portrait, circa 1820
Oil on canvas
29-1/2 x 40 inches (74.9 x 101.6 cm)

Provenance:
Private collection (Dallas, Texas)

Tominz lived and painted bourgeois portraits in Naples, Gorizia, Vienna, Ljubljana and Trieste. He was greatly influenced by the Roman painting of the early nineteenth century and Biedermeier style. This particular painting depicts a dapper man, fashionable woman and young boy, with a distant view of a village atop a mountain. The child presents his father with a tarot card with an allegorical representation of America, which is particularly relevant because some 47 million people entered the United States between 1820 and 1947.

Estimate: $8,000-$12,000

The reserve for this lot is available at HA.com/FineArt.

25049

FRANCOIS BARTHÉLÉMY AUGUSTIN DESMOULINS (French 1788-1856)
Ancestral Grounds, 1829
Oil on canvas
36 x 28-1/2 inches (91.4 x 72.4 cm)
Signed and dated lower left

Parisian-born Francois Barthélémy Augustin Desmoulins was a specialist in history painting and portraiture. The artist debuted at the Salon of 1819, and remained a regular exhibitor through 1845. In 1822 he received a silver medal at the Salon for the genre of history painting typified in the present work-a scene dominated by carefully observed architecture. Desmoulins is represented in the permanent collections of the Musée du Puy and Versailles.

Estimate: $1,500-$2,500

The reserve for this lot is available at HA.com/FineArt.

25050

V. VARILLAZ (French)
Portrait Of Napoleon, 1839
Oil on canvas
23-7/8 x 19-3/4 inches (60.6 x 50.1 cm)
Signed and dated upper right: *V...(illegible) Varillaz / L. 1839*

This portrait depicts Napoleon wearing the *Legion d'Honneur Grande Croix*, the *Order de la Couronne en Fer,* and probably the *Grande Croix du Triomphe*. A religious scene by Varillaz can be found in the main church of Roscoff, France.

Estimate: $2,000-$4,000

This lot is being sold without reserve. Unreserved lots generally open at 50% of the low estimate.

25051

EUGENE-LOUIS LAMI
(French 1800-1890)
Avenue de Champs Elysees
Oil on canvas
13-3/4 x 20-1/8 inches (34.9 x 51.1 cm)
Signed lower left

Estimate: $10,000-$15,000

The reserve for this lot is available at HA.com/FineArt.

25052

EUGENE LUCAS Y VILLAMIL (Spanish 1858-1918)
The Audience Before The King Ferdinand Of Spain And His Queen (ruled 1814-1833)
Oil on canvas
21 x 43-1/4 inches (53.3 x 109.9 cm)
Signed at lower left: *E Lucas Villamil*

Provenance:
Private collection (New Orleans, Louisiana)

Eugene Lucas y Villamil the son of the famous Spanish painter Eugenio Lucas y Padilla (1824-1870), like his father, painted in the style of Francesco Goya (1746-1828). This colorful painting depicts a command concert at the Spanish court for King Ferdinand VII (1784-1833). Ferdinand was placed on the throne by a military coup in March of 1808, but he was promptly deposed by Napoleon in 1814 and returned to Spain and assumed his throne. He and his queen sit on thrones upon a velvet covered dais with the arms of Spain above their heads. To the right on the dais hangings is the lion of Aragon and on the left the tower of Castille. This location is the throne room of the Royal Palace in Madrid, traditionally decorated in red.

Estimate: $30,000-$40,000
The reserve for this lot is available at HA.com/FineArt.

25053

GUSTAVE JEAN JACQUET (French 1846-1909)
Portrait Of A Lady
Oil on panel
12 x 9-3/4 inches (30.5 x 24.8 cm)
Signed at lower right: *G. Jacquet*

Estimate: $4,000-$6,000

The reserve for this lot is available at HA.com/FineArt.

25054

Attributed to
LUDOVICO MARCHETTI
(Italian 1853-1909)
Peasant Dance
Oil on canvas
20-1/2 x 42-1/4 inches (52.1 x 107.3 cm)
Unsigned

Estimate: $4,000-$8,000

The reserve for this lot is available at HA.com/FineArt.

25055

A. SPULAK (Czech circa 1830-1890)
A Family Portrait
Oil on canvas
32 x 25-1/2 inches (81.3 x 64.8 cm)
Signed at lower right: *Spulak pinx 84*

Provenance:
Private collection (New Orleans, Louisiana)

The portrait traditionally served as a symbol for cosmopolitan patrons who commissioned artists to create a testimony to their social standing. This particular *Family Portrait* features a husband and wife of refined character, accompanied by their two children. The fair attributes of the group as well as the accoutrements and setting endow the painting with a decidedly Czech air.

Estimate: $8,000-$10,000
The reserve for this lot is available at HA.com/FineArt.

25056

EUROPEAN SCHOOL
Man In Repose By Candlelight
Oil on canvas
31-1/2 x 27 inches (80 x 68.6 cm)
Unsigned

Estimate: $800-$1,200
The reserve for this lot is available at HA.com/FineArt.

25057

WILLIAM REDMORE BIGG (British 1755-1828)
New Tricks
Oil on canvas
30 x 25 inches, oval (76.2 x 63.5 cm)

Provenance:
Newhouse Galleries (New York);
Sale, Phillips London, June 3, 1997, Lot 26;
Sale, Sotheby's New York, June 9, 1995, Lot 88

Estimate: $2,000-$4,000
The reserve for this lot is available at HA.com/FineArt.

25058

CONTINENTAL SCHOOL (Early Nineteenth Century)
An Amorous Couple
Oil on canvas
21-1/4 x 15 inches (54 x 38.1 cm)
Unsigned

Estimate: $3,000-$5,000
The reserve for this lot is available at HA.com/FineArt.

25059

ANTOINE BERANGER (French 1785-1867)
Les Musiciens Ambulants (The Strolling Musicians)
Oil on canvas
25-3/4 x 32 inches (65.4 x 81.3 cm)

Provenance:
Newhouse Galleries (New York);
Mr. and Mrs. F. Howard Walsh (Fort Worth, Texas);
Walsh Family Art Trust

Estimate:
$20,000-$30,000
The reserve for this lot is available at HA.com/FineArt.

25060

PIERRIE THEODORE COLSON (French 1805-1877)
Dimanche, Dans Le Parc and *Dimanche Au Bord De La Mer*, pair
Oil on canvas
14 x 25-1/2 inches, each (35.6 x 64.8 cm)
Signed lower right: *Colson*

Provenance:
Newhouse Galleries (New York);
Mr. and Mrs. F. Howard Walsh (Fort Worth, Texas);
Walsh Family Art Trust

Estimate: $10,000-$15,000

The reserve for this lot is available at HA.com/FineArt.

25061

LUIGI SCAFFAI (Italian 1837-1899)
The Flirt, Interior Scene
17-3/8 x 12-3/5 inches (44 x 32 cm)
Oil on panel
Signed lower right: *Scaffai / (indecipherable)*

Provenance:
Sale, Ketterer Kunst Hamburg: Wednesday, May 27, 1998, Lot 443

Estimate: $800-$1,200

The reserve for this lot is available at HA.com/FineArt.

25062

ALFRED HOLST TOURIER (British 1836-1892)
Merry Company (The Rivals)
Oil on canvas
16 x 12 inches (40.6 x 30.5 cm)
Signed lower right: *A.H. TOURRIER*

Estimate: $1,000-$2,000

The reserve for this lot is available at HA.com/FineArt.

25063

FRENCH SCHOOL (Eighteenth Century)
Still Life With Fish, Cherries, Walnuts And Grapes
Oil on canvas
13 x 16 inches (33 x 40.6 cm)
Unsigned

Estimate: $2,000-$4,000

The reserve for this lot is available at HA.com/FineArt.

25064

FRANCESCO MALACREA (Italian 1812-1886)
Still Life With Peaches, Currents, Strawberries And Rose, a pair
Oil on canvas
7-3/4 x 10-1/2 inches, each (19.7 x 26.7 cm)
Signed and dated lower right:
F Malacrea 1185

Estimate: $1,500-$2,500

The reserve for this lot is available at HA.com/FineArt.

25065

ALESSANDRO SANI (Italian)
The Baritone Horn Player In Four Stages, group of four
Oil on canvas
12-3/4 x 9-3/4 inches, each (32.4 x 24.8 cm)
Signed upper right: *A. Sani*

Estimate: $6,000-$9,000

The reserve for this lot is available at HA.com/FineArt.

25066

EUGÈNE DELACROIX
(French 1798-1863)
Musicians
(after a detail from Veronese's The Marriage At Cana), circa 1820
Oil on canvas
9 x 12 inches (23.5 x 31 cm)
Initialed to stretcher in graphite: *E.D.*

Provenance:
Delacroix's posthumous sale, February 1864, probably part of lot 176 (*"Six toiles contenant des fragments d'études d'après Rubens, Véronèse, Murillo, etc."* without dimensions), to Gaultron, 18 francs;
Purchased (?) by Bernheim-Jeune from Cher fils, 10 June 1924;
Sold by Bernheim-Jeune to Dru, 25 May 1925 (Archives Bernheim-Jeune: *"Copie des musiciens d'après le Tintoret,"* 26 x 27 cm.);
Private collection, circa 1946-86 (Geneva, Switzerland);
Acquired by the present owners in 1987

Literature:
Inv. Delacroix, no. 78 (*"1 tableau représentant un fragment des 'Noces de Cana,' d'après Véronèse, par [M. Delacroix], 15F."*) or no. 198 (same description and valuation);
Lee Johnson, *The paintings of Eugène Delacroix. A Critical Catalogue,* vol. VI (The Public Decorations and their Sketches, supplement and plates), Clarendon Press, Oxford, 1989, ill. plate 70; cat. no. 13a, p. 199.

An important facet of Delacroix's personal artistic education and inspiration involved making oil sketches after the Old Masters. The artist whose works he studied and emulated most passionately through this process of copying was Rubens. After Rubens, Delacroix was particularly drawn to the work of the Venetians: Titian, Veronese, and Cariani (whose work was given to Bellini at the time). As this sketch after Veronese's sumptuous *Marriage at Cana* in the Louvre [inv. no. RF119] demonstrates, Delacroix frequently studied fragments of large, ambitious multi-figural compositions in relatively small formats. In this intimate canvas Delacroix devoted his attention to a dense group of seated figures, a variety of musical instruments displayed at a rangeof jaunty angles, and even a pair of dogs-all of which the great Venetian painter had managed to compress convincingly into a very shallow space. Delacroix seems to have been particularly fascinated with the Veronese's magical handling of the play of light on form. This is especially apparent in his attention to the marvelous curves of the bass displayed so that it is perpendicular to the picture plane. Working rapidly but with keen concentration to tonal shifts and slight differences in hue, Delacroix masterfully conveyed the essence of Veronese's painterly manner.

Although the catalogue of Delacroix's posthumous sale of February 1864 lists only two paintings after Veronese's *The Marriage at Cana* [the present work and one other], there were three, all attributed to Delacroix, listed in Delacroix's inventory. Another of his artist's oil studies after Veronese's painting records *Two Bearded Heads* (private collection, Paris; see Lee Johnson, vol. I, 1981, cat. no, 14, p. 12; ill. vol. II, plate 11), at the same scale as the original. According to a firsthand account of Delacroix's artist friend, Charles Soulier, the former copied the motif of the bearded men by standing on the top of a tall ladder in the Grand Salon of the Louvre on June 10, 1820. The heads of the two men which captured Delacroix's interest derive from the foreground of *The Marriage at Cana,* just left of the instrumentalists depicted in the present study. Soulier's account is useful is providing an approximate date for this sketch as well.

Estimate: $60,000-$80,000

The reserve for this lot is available at HA.com/FineArt.

25067

Circle of EUGENIO LUCAS VELÁSQUEZ (Spanish 1817-1870)
Rebellion In The Monastery
Oil on canvas
34 x 24-1/2 inches (86.4 x 62.2 cm)
Unsigned

Provenance:
R. Schw…zer Gallery, partial label (New York)

Estimate: $3,000-$5,000

The reserve for this lot is available at HA.com/FineArt.

25068

EDOUARD JACQUES DUFEU
(French 1840-1900)
Venice
Oil on canvas
13 x 20-7/8 inches (33 x 53 cm)
Signed lower right: *E. Dufeu*
Label verso: *Moderne Galerie Thannhauser*

Estimate: $1,500-$2,500

The reserve for this lot is available at HA.com/FineArt.

25069

PAUL DÉSIRÉ TROUILLEBERT
(French 1829-1900)
Landscape With Man In A Boat
Oil on canvas
10 x 15-3/4 inches
(25.4 x 40 cm)
Signed lower right:
Trouillebert

Estimate:
$9,000-$15,000

The reserve for this lot is available at HA.com/FineArt.

25070

DELCOURT (European Nineteenth Century)
The Campfire, 1892
Oil on canvas
29-1/2 x 22-1/4 inches (74.9 x 56.5 cm)
Signed and dated lower right:
(indecipherable) / Delcourt / 1892

Estimate: $1,000-$2,000

The reserve for this lot is available at HA.com/FineArt.

25071

FRANCOIS VANDEVERDONK
(Belgian 1848-1875)
Sheep And Cow
Oil on panel
7 x 9-1/2 inches (17.8 x 24.1 cm)
Signed with inscription verson:
...(inscription indecipherable) / F. Vandeverdonk

Estimate: $4,000-$8,000

The reserve for this lot is available at HA.com/FineArt.

25072

DUTCH or CONTINENTAL SCHOOL (Nineteenth Century)
Possibly Verboeckhoven
Cattle In A Meadow
Oil on canvas
18 x 24 inches (45.7 x 61 cm)
Unsigned

Estimate: $1,500-$2,500

The reserve for this lot is available at HA.com/FineArt.

25073

EUGÉNE RÉMY MAES (Belgium 1849-1931)
Sheep And Chickens In A Barn
Oil on canvas
24 x 31-3/4 inches (61 x 80.6 cm)
Signed lower right: *E.R. MAES*

Estimate: $10,000-$15,000

The reserve for this lot is available at HA.com/FineArt.

25074

ALFRED DE DREUX (French 1810-1860)
Mare And Colt, 1847
Oil on canvas
32 x 40-1/2 inches (81.3 x 102.9 cm)
Signed and dated lower left: *A. de Dreux 1847*

Alfred de Dreux was a celebrated animal painter specializing in romantic, glamorous horse portraits and scenes of the hunt for over thirty years. His marvelous understanding of animal anatomy and behavior won him many fashionable commissions, and his works form part of museum collections worldwide including the Louvre, Paris, the Hermitage, St. Petersburg, the Musee Camondo, Paris and museums in Bordeaux, Dijon and Chantilly. The attitude of the mother to her colt in this painting is characteristic of the painter's sensitivity to and mastery of his subject.

The son of an architect, de Dreux enjoyed a colorful and privileged life. He first studied under Leon Cogniet and then entered the atelier of the distinguished and versatile painter, Eugene Isabey. Throughout his career, however, de Dreux's work was greatly influenced by Theodore Gericault, who was a close friend of his uncle. In 1831, de Dreux exhibited *Interieur d'Ecurie* at the Paris Salon, which won him immediate fame. From 1840, de Dreux began his celebrated series of portraits of horses from the famous stables of the duc d'Orleans.

Following the Revolution in 1848, the French royal family emigrated to England where de Dreux frequently visited them, painting many equestrian portraits of the exiled King Louis-Philippe and his sons. He returned to France and was commissioned to paint a portrait of Napoleon III in 1859 (Musee de l'Armée, Paris). A dispute arose over this equestrian portrait and in March 1860 de Dreux was killed in a duel by Comte Fleury, Napoleon's principal aide-de-camp.

Estimate: $10,000-$14,000

The reserve for this lot is available at HA.com/FineArt.

25075

ALEX DE ANDREIS
(British 1880-1929)
The Message
Oil on canvas
31 x 25 inches (78.7 x 63.5 cm)
Signed lower right

Estimate: $2,500-$5,300

The reserve for this lot is available at HA.com/FineArt.

25076

FRIEDRICH DURCK
(German 1809-1884)
Young Girl With Flower, 1873
Oil on canvas
39-1/2 x 50 inches (100.3 x 127 cm)
Signed and dated lower right: *F. Durck / 1873*

Estimate: $8,000-$12,000

The reserve for this lot is available at HA.com/FineArt.

25077

Manner of RICHARD COSWAY (British 1742-1821)
Portrait Of A Young Woman
Pastel on paper mounted on canvas
30 x 25 inches (76.2 x 63.5 cm)
Unsigned

Estimate: $3,000-$5,000

The reserve for this lot is available at HA.com/FineArt.

25078

EMILE VERNON (British 1872-1919)
Tennis Anyone
Oil on canvas
36 x 26-3/8 inches (91.4 x 66.7 cm)
Signed lower left: *Vernon*

Provenance:
Sale, Christie's New York, April 19, 2005, Lot 213

Estimate: $20,000-$25,000

The reserve for this lot is available at HA.com/FineArt.

25079

IRISH SCHOOL (Nineteenth Century)
Portrait Of A Woman With Harp And Flowers
Oil on canvas
30 x 25 inches (76.2 x 63.5 cm)
Unsigned

Estimate: $3,000-$5,000

This lot is being sold without reserve. Unreserved lots generally open at 50% of the low estimate.

25080

ALBERT NEUHUYS or NEUHUIJS
(Dutch 1844-1914)
Baby's Naptime
Oil on canvas
26-1/4 x 34-3/4 inches (66.7 x 88.3 cm)
Signed lower right

Estimate: $5,000-$7,000

The reserve for this lot is available at HA.com/FineArt.

25081

JOHANN ALBERT NEUHUYS or NEUHUIJS
(Dutch 1844-1914)
Peeling Turnips
Watercolor on paper
24-3/4 x 22-1/2 inches (62.9 x 57.2 cm)
Signed lower right: *Alb. Neuhu... (indecipherable)*

Provenance:
A Madison Avenue Gallery (New York);
Norton Gallery and School of Art (Palm Beach, Florida);
J.J. Gillespie (Pittsburgh, Pennsylvania)

Estimate: $5,000-$7,000

The reserve for this lot is available at HA.com/FineArt.

25082

JACOB SIMON HENDRIK KEVER
(Dutch 1854-1922)
Dutch Family In An Interior
Oil on canvas
31 x 35-1/4 inches (78.7 x 89.5 cm)
Signed lower left: *Kever*

Provenance:
H.W. van Del[...] (Amsterdam, Holland);
Philbrook Art Center (Tulsa, Oklahoma);
Gift of Laura A. Clubb, March 1947, label verso

Exhibition:
Carnegie Institute, Pittsburgh, Pennsylvania (possibly Carnegie International Exhibition, n.d.), label verso gives current owner as H.W. van Del[...], Rokin 126, Amsterdam, Holland, and gives title as "Baby's Au[...illegible]"

Jacob Simon Hendrik Kever was a successful painter of genre scenes of peasant life in humble interiors. Born in Amsterdam, Kever knew as a young men that he wanted to become an artist in the manner of Josef Israels, whose family was friendly with his mother's. As a young artist he worked initially as a lithographer and subsequently pursued his artistic studies with Peter Franciscus Greive in Amsterdam. A number of his classmates became noted artists in their own right as well: Jan van Essen, M.I. de Haan, C. Metselaar and Jan ten Kate. In 1878, he pursued further training at the Academy in Antwerp. After he returned to Holland he befriended Anton Mauve and settled in Laren where his greatest artistic rival was Albert Neuhuys (1844-1914), who is represented in the present auction by two works featuring peasant figures in rustic interiors. Kever participated in numerous international exhibitions including the Brussels exhibition of 1910, Munich exhibitions in 1901 and 1905 where he won medals, the Paris exhibition of 1889, and the American exhibition of 1900. Numerous examples of his work are preserved in the municipal museum of The Hague.

Estimate: $4,000-$6,000

The reserve for this lot is available at HA.com/FineArt.

25083

EUROPEAN SCHOOL
(Nineteenth Century)
Card Game
Oil on canvas
19 x 36-3/4 inches
(48.3 x 93.3 cm)
Signed lower right: *Kotorevincy*
(indecipherable signature)

Estimate: $2,000-$4,000

The reserve for this lot is available at HA.com/FineArt.

25084

ALFRED AUGUSTUS GLENDENING
(British circa 1840-circa 1910)
Autumn Landscape With Pond And Castle Tower, 1869
Oil on canvas
29-1/2 x 19-1/4 inches (74.9 x 48.9 cm)
Signed and dated lower left: *A.A. Glendening / 1869*

Estimate: $5,000-$8,000

This lot is being sold without reserve. Unreserved lots generally open at 50% of the low estimate.

25085

HANS LARWIN
(Austrian 1873-1938)
Camping Gypsies
Oil on canvas
13 x 17 inches (33 x 43.2 cm)
Signed lower left: *Hans Larwin*

Provenance:
The Palette and Chisel Academy of Fine Arts, until March 29, 1923;
The Collection of Mr. and Mrs. Emil F. Smrz (Chicago, Illinois)
Private collection (Dallas, Texas)

Exhibition:
The Palette and Chisel Academy of Fine Art, Exhibtion of the Works of Hans Larwin, March 26-April 14, 1923

This lot includes correspondence, dating February 12, 1963, between the then-owner, Mr. Emil F. Smrz, and the The Palette and Chisel Academy of Fine Art, requesting more information about the history of the painting.

Estimate: $1,500-$2,500

This lot is being sold without reserve. Unreserved lots generally open at 50% of the low estimate.

25086

ANDREAS ACHENBACH
(German 1815-1910)
Fishing Boats Coming Ashore
Oil on canvas
11-1/2 x 16-3/4 inches (29.2 x 42.5 cm)
Signed lower left: *A. Achenbach*

Achenbach was an important and prolific marine and landscape painter. Indeed, he is considered a pioneer of modern German landscape painting. He trained at the academy in St. Petersburg, Russia, worked in Dusseldorf, and traveled extensively in northern Europe and throughout the Netherlands, Sweden, Finland, Norway, Denmark and northern Germany where he found his primary subject-the cold turbulent waters of the North and Baltic Seas. His wanderlust, which provided inspiration for his energetic landscapes never diminished. Well into the later years of his career then artist explored the Tyrolean mountains as well as Southern Italy. His works are represented in numerous museum collections worldwide.

Estimate: $5,000-$7,000

This lot is being sold without reserve. Unreserved lots generally open at 50% of the low estimate.

25087

THOMAS H. HAIR
(British 1810-1882)
Untitled (Seascape With Single-Mast Fishing Vessel), 1870
Oil on canvas
16-5/8 x 11-3/4 inches (42.2 x 29.8 cm)
Signed and dated lower right: *T.H. Hair / 1870*

Estimate: $6,000-$8,000
The reserve for this lot is available at HA.com/FineArt.

25088

School of THOMAS LUNY
(British 1759-1837)
A British Ship Of The Line Of The Red Fleet
Oil on canvas
20 x 28 inches (50.8 x 71.1 cm)
Unsigned

Provenance:
Art Investments (London, England);
Roger King Gallery of Fine Art (Newport, Rhode Island)
Private collection (Houston, Texas)

Estimate: $4,000-$6,000
The reserve for this lot is available at HA.com/FineArt.

25089

Attributed to GEORGE CHAMBERS, JR. (British active 1848-1862)
A View Of London
Oil on canvas
18 x 24 inches (45.7 x 60.9 cm)
Signed lower left: *Chambers*

Provenance:
Private collection (North Yorkshire, England);
Private collection (Houston, Texas)

Estimate: $2,000-$3,000

The reserve for this lot is available at HA.com/FineArt.

25090

CONTINENTAL SCHOOL (Nineteenth Century)
The Shipwreck
Oil on canvas
22-1/2 x 31 inches
(57.1 x 78.7 cm)
Initialed lower right: *M*

Provenance:
Bessie Heard (McKinney, Texas);
Bessie Heard Trust

Estimate: $1,000-$2,000

This lot is being sold without reserve. Unreserved lots generally open at 50% of the low estimate.

25091

After JACOB SIMON HENDRICK KEVER (Dutch 1854-1922)
Child With Pipe, circa Nineteenth Century
Oil on canvas
22-1/4 x 16-1/4 inches (57.2 x 41.3 cm)
Signed at lower right

Estimate: $1,000-$2,000

The reserve for this lot is available at HA.com/FineArt.

25092

GUSTAVE COURBET (French 1819-1877)
Portrait Of Urbain Cuenot, circa 1847
Oil on canvas
37-1/4 x 29-1/2 inches (94.6 x 74.9 cm)
Signed at lower left: *Courbet*

Provenance:
Sale, Paris, December 9,1881, no. 14 to the painter, Alfred Roll;
Mary Cassatt, Paris and Philadelphia until 1912;
Given to the Pennsylvania Academy of the Fine Arts, Philadelphia;
Sotheby's, New York, 19th Century Paintings, 24 April, 2003, Lot 32;
Private collection (Dallas, Texas)

Exhibited:
Paris, Salon of 1848, no. 1016
Paris, Rond-Point de l'Alma, Champs-Elysees, *Exposition des oeuvres de M.G. Courbet,* 1867, no.71
Paris, Ecole des Beaux-Arts, *Exposition des Oeuvres de G. Courbet,* 1882, no.156
Paris, Ecole Nationale des Beaux-Arts, *Le Portrait du siecle* (Second exhibition), Paris, no. 32 (with the title *Portrait of M. Quenot, Maire d'Orleans*)
New York, The Metropolitan Museum of Art, *Loan Exhibition of the works of Gustave Courbet,* 1919, no.2;
Philadelphia, Commercial Museum, *Festival of France,* January 1960;
Tokyo, Keio Department Store, *Millet and his Barbizon Contemporaries,* April 5-24, 1985, no.8 This exhibition later traveled to: The Hanshin Department Store, Ltd., May 2-14, 1985 and Yamanashi Prefectural Museum of Art, August 4- September 8, 1985

Literature:
Le Hir, *Journal des Amateurs,* 1881, p. 183
G. Riat, *Gustave Courbet, peintre,* Paris, 1906, p.98
Franche-Comte-Monts-Jura, Number dedicated to Courbet, Besancon, December, 1927, p. 248 (illustrated)
Bulletin des Amis de Gustave Courbet, 1972, no.48 (illustrated p. 7)
R. Fernier, *La Vie ed l'Oeuvre de Gustave Courbet, catalogue raisonne,* Lausanne-Paris, 1977, vol. 1, p.50-51, no. 85 (illustrated)
P. ten-Doesschate Chu, ed., *Letters of Gustave Courbet,* Chicago, 1992, pp.69-71, (illustrated fig. 20)

An intimate childhood friend and lifelong supporter of the artist, Urbain Cuenot (1820-1867), is depicted here in a larger-than-life-size portrait. Cuenot is presented in muted dress, wearing a brown jacket with velvet trim, a dash of a white shirt visible just below his full beard, and a large wide-brimmed hat. Courbet challenged the current academic styles of painting through the use of monumental unidealized portraiture. In this likeness of his close friend, for example, Courbet showed Cuenot's massive form to suggest class and authority, but contradicts this narrative by including the working-class, provincial wide-brimmed hat, which Courbet himself often wore. Cuenot is thus portrayed by Courbet in the manner the artist liked to portray himself: as a proud, distinguished individual who was fully invested in his provincial heritage and its connections with working the land. Courbet and Cuenot were both from rural Ornans, in the Franche-Comté near the Swiss border, where they grew up together hunting in the forests and exploring the rugged natural terrain along the River Loue which figured prominently in Courbet's paintings. Interestingly, however, neither Courbet nor Cuenot, who were both fiercely Republican in their political sympathies, was from a working-class background. Courbet's parents were well-to-do large-scale farmers, and Cuenot was a man of independent means who spent most of his life as a dilettante and, for a period, served in a mayoral capacity in Ornans. Nonetheless, their deep-rooted connection with the Franche-Comté, and their families' livelihood there, separated both of them from the urban elite of Paris. The large-brimmed hat was a symbol of their independence, socialist sympathies, and to a certain degree, their celebration of being free-thinking "outsiders."

In 1846, Courbet produced another portrait of Cuenot on a smaller-scale, which is now in the Musée Courbet, Ornans. Interestingly, the study depicts Cuenot with analogous features but, notably, without the hat. When Courbet submitted the present portrait to the Paris Salon in 1847, it was rejected. In a letter he wrote to his family shortly afterwards, dated January 1, 1847, Courbet opined, "That particular painting is entirely beyond the jurors' ideas" (quoted in P. ten-Doesschate Chu, p. 69, letter 47-1). Which "ideas" Courbet was referring to are not entirely clear, since we have no surviving record of the original appearance of the painting. However, it seems that Courbet may have been alluding to the presence of the large hat. Although we do not know for certain whether the hat was the reason behind the rejection, we do know that by the time Courbet had resubmitted the work to the Salon of 1848, when it was accepted and exhibited, he had entirely overpainted the hat. Only when the portrait was cleaned in 1943 by the Pennsylvania Academy of Fine Arts was the large hat revealed-a cleaning which ninety-seven years later doubtless uncovered quite literally the subversive subtext of the offending passage in Courbet's original portrait.

Within Courbet's oeuvre this portrait occupies an important place. It embodies the enormous regard Courbet had for the great 17th-century Dutch portraitists Rembrandt and Frans Hals, whose work Courbet discovered on an 1846 trip to Amsterdam. In this work and other portraits he produced directly after his trip to the Netherlands, Courbet's technique reflects the chiaroscuro he admired in Rembrandt, and the free brushwork he discovered in Frans Hals. The American painter Mary Cassatt (1844-1926) was tremendously inspired by Gustave Courbet's realist aesthetic. She traveled frequently to France during the 1880's, where she was introduced to Courbet's oeuvre and eventually acquired this portrait for her personal collection. In 1912, she donated it to the Pennsylvania Academy of the Fine Arts.

Estimate: $250,000-$350,000

The reserve for this lot is available at HA.com/FineArt.

25093

GUSTAVE COURBET (French 1819-1877)
Stream In The Forest, circa 1863
Oil on canvas
26-1/2 x 18-1/2 inches (66 x 41 cm)
Signed lower left: *G. Courbet*

Exhibition:
New York, Salander-O'Reilly Galleries and Roslyn, New York, Nassau County Museum of Art, *Courbet: Later Paintings,* February-May 1998, no. 5, ill;
New York, Salander-O'Reilly Galleries, *Nineteenth-Century European Paintings,* February 4-March 1, 2003, no. 9, ill.;
New York, Salander-O'Reilly Galleries, *Gustave Courbet,* October 28-November 29, 2003, p. 23, ill.

Relevant Literature:
Robert Fernier, *La Vie et l'oeuvre de Gustave Courbet, Catalogue Raisonné,* Lausanne and Paris: 1977-78, vol. I, no. 344, ill.

"Courbet's essential pictorial legacy came to fruition in the late 1860's," Jean-Jacques Fernier wrote in 1998 of the great, irascible, anti-establishment, and deeply poetic French realist. "His work from this period embraced nature in its entirety to the exclusion of all other components, in a mélange of profound and mysterious darkness, green pastures, shadows and water. . . Courbet was deeply tied to the poetic landscape of the Loue valley. Nestled within the Jura mountains, it was the cradle of his youth and the epicenter of his mythology. Courbet's eventual return to his origins as subject matter confirms this, rendering his last period of work far more important than one generally believes."

This rich, verdant landscape of circa 1863 marks the transition in Courbet's oeuvre to his intensive, late-career focus upon the landscape around his native village of Ornans, in the Jura region near the Swiss border. Central to this landscape is the river Loue, seen flowing through the foreground of this vertical slice of dense forest, and brilliant sky. Stretching over 126 kilometers, the Loue, a resurgence of the Doubs River, carved its bed in the deeply wooded plateaus of the Jura before merging into the Doubs River downstream from the city of Dole. The Loue valley is most dramatic between the source of the Loue and Courbet's hometown of Ornans, the capital of the Loue high valley. The river drops 229 meters in altitude over a distance of 20 kilometers, so that there are frequent picturesque waterfalls and rapids marking its descent, such as the gentle one depicted in the present work.

The most obsessive subject of Courbet's work as a landscape painter is the grotto, or the river's source. In the years immediately following his production of the present landscape, Courbet painted again and again the deep rocky cave from which the water of the Loue River emerges, as well as the towering stony outcroppings which flank its course and stand witness to all the water spilling forth. During the 1860s, when Courbet had turned his attention to his region's geologic structures, scientists had begun to explore the territory as well. It provided a prime opportunity to the newly developing field of geology, which opened up the vast perspective of geological time. In fact, Courbet's native landscape of Jura gave the Jurassic period its name. For Courbet as well as for the geologists, the life-giving force emanating from the dark cavern of the Loue had primordial significance. For Courbet, it had a profoundly personal, sexual significance as well: in was in this landscape that he literally came into the world. It is within this context of grotto paintings that Courbet painted his celebrated *Origin of the World* (Musee d'Orsay, Paris), a close-up view between the legs of a sturdy nude woman, in 1866: the nude is the source of the Loue, of Courbet himself, and of his artistic genius.

The specific landscape depicted in the present work is related to a more extensive painting of the same location entitled *Rocks at Chauveroche* (1864), private collection (reproduced in Mary Morton and Charlotte Eyerman, *Courbet and the Modern Landscape,* J. Paul Getty Museum, Los Angeles, California, 2006, plate 4.) The same configuration of rapids, trees and shrubbery appears in the central foreground of the 1864 landscape, but is viewed from a vantage point parallel to the river.

Estimate: $50,000-$70,000
The reserve for this lot is available at HA.com/FineArt.

25094

NARCISSE VIRGILE DIAZ DE LA PENA (French 1808-1876)
Forest Trail
Oil on panel
11-3/4 x 8-1/2 inches (30 x 22 cm)
Signed at lower right: *DIAZ*

Provenance:
Wiggins Fine Arts & Antiques (Rosewell, New Mexico);
Private collection (Dallas, Texas)

Estimate: $7,000-$9,000

The reserve for this lot is available at HA.com/FineArt.

25095

FRANS KEELHOFF
(Belgium 1802-1893)
Landscape With Cattle Grazing, 1866
Oil on canvas
23 x 32-1/4 inches
(49.2 x 69 cm)
Signed at lower right:
F. Keelhoff 1866

Estimate: $8,000-$12,000

The reserve for this lot is available at HA.com/FineArt.

25096

PIERRE OUTIN (French 1840-1899)
The Easter Eggs
Oil on canvas
25-3/4 x 19-1/2 inches (65.4 x 49.5 cm)
Signed lower right: *OUTIN*

Provenance:
Sale, Sotheby's, New York, October 25, 2005, Lot 83

Estimate: $22,000-$24,000
The reserve for this lot is available at HA.com/FineArt.

25097

ENGLISH SCHOOL (Nineteenth Century)
Portrait Of A Gentleman
Oil on canvas
50 x 40 inches (127 x 101.6 cm)
Unsigned

Estimate: $3,000-$5,000
The reserve for this lot is available at HA.com/FineArt.

25098

EUROPEAN SCHOOL (Nineteenth Century)
Portrait Of A Lady With Beautiful Vail
Oil on canvas
40 x 57 inches (101.6 x 144.8 cm)
Unsigned

Estimate: $3,000-$6,000

The reserve for this lot is available at HA.com/FineArt.

25099

ADRIEN ÉTIENNE GAUDEZ (French 1845-1902)
Woman Playing The Lute
Bronze
41-1/2 x 19 x 14 inches (105.4 x 48.3 x 35.6 cm)
Inscribed on base: *Gaudez*

Provenance:
Crow Art Partnership collection (Dallas, Texas)

Estimate: $6,000-$8,000

The reserve for this lot is available at HA.com/FineArt.

25100

FRANCIS GRANT (British 1803-1878)
Portrait Of Lady Digby
Oil on canvas
30 x 25 inches (76.2 x 63.5 cm)

Estimate: $3,000-$5,000

The reserve for this lot is available at HA.com/FineArt.

25101

ENGLISH SCHOOL
Portrait Of The Queen Victoria
Oil on canvas
19 x 27 inches (48.3 x 68.6 cm)
Unsigned

Estimate: $2,000-$3,000

The reserve for this lot is available at HA.com/FineArt.

25102

ARTIST UNKNOWN
Queen Mother
Oil on canvas
40 x 30 inches (101.6 x 76.2 cm)
Unsigned

Estimate: $2,500-$5,000
The reserve for this lot is available at HA.com/FineArt.

25103

EUROPEAN SCHOOL (Nineteenth Century)
Portrait Of A Woman In A Blue Dress
Oil on canvas
36 x 29 inches (91.4 x 73.7 cm)
Unsigned

Estimate: $2,500-$5,000
The reserve for this lot is available at HA.com/FineArt.

25104

JEAN-JACQUES HENNER
(French 1829-1905)
Salome
Oil on canvas
72-1/4 x 36-1/4 inches (183.5 x 92.1 cm)
Signed lower right: *HENNER*

Provenance:
Collection of Harriet W. Judd;
Collection of Jan N. Streep

Estimate: $8,000-$16,000

The reserve for this lot is available at HA.com/FineArt.

25105

FRANZ KNÉBEL the Younger (Swiss 1809-1877)
View Of Tivoli, 1871
Oil on canvas
39-3/4 x 64-3/4 inches (101 x 164.5 cm)
Signed and inscribed by the artist lower right: *F. Knébel fec. / Roma 1871*
Label verso: *Townsend and Valenti*

This luminous view of the dramatic landscape of Tivoli, with its trademark waterfalls, is a late work by the noted Swiss landscapist, Franz Knébel. Born in La Sarrax, Knébel, like his father Franz Knébel the Elder, spent most of his career in Italy. He specialized in the sweeping panoramic views of Italian ruins bathed in a golden light that are strongly indebted to the work of eighteenth-century German Italianate painter Jacob Philippe Hackert, who continued the tradition of Dutch seventeenth-century artists such as Jan Both.

Estimate: $30,000-$50,000
The reserve for this lot is available at HA.com/FineArt.

25106

ALFRED DE BREANSKI, SR., A.R.C.A. (British 1852-1928)
A Perthshire Valley
Oil on canvas
35 x 53 inches (88.9 x 134.6 cm)
Signed lower left: *Alfred de Breanski*
Inscribed verso: *A Perthshire Valley / Alfred de Branski Sr.*

Estimate: $40,000-$60,000
The reserve for this lot is available at HA.com/FineArt.

25107

FANNY GAMBOGI
(French Nineteenth Century)
A Rest On The Journey, 1882
Oil on canvas
19-1/4 x 25-1/2 inches (48.9 x 64.8 cm)
Signed and dated lower left margin: *Fanny Gambogi / 1882*

Provenance:
Sale, Christie's South Kensington, March 20, 2003, Lot 106;
Sale, Christie's South Kensington, April 5, 2001, Lot 151;
Sale, Christie's South Kensington, December 7, 2000, Lot 163

Estimate: $500-$1,000

The reserve for this lot is available at HA.com/FineArt.

25108

A. MALTINO (Italian b.1880s)
Venecia, Early Twentieth Century
Oil on canvas
24 x 36 inches (61 x 91.4 cm)

Estimate: $2,000-$4,000

The reserve for this lot is available at HA.com/FineArt.

25109

GAETANO CAPONE
(Italian 1845-1920)
Caught At Last, circa 1897
Oil on canvas
32 x 22 inches (81.3 x 55.9 cm)
Signed and dated lower right: *G. Capone / Napoli / 97*

Estimate: $2,500-$3,500

The reserve for this lot is available at HA.com/FineArt.

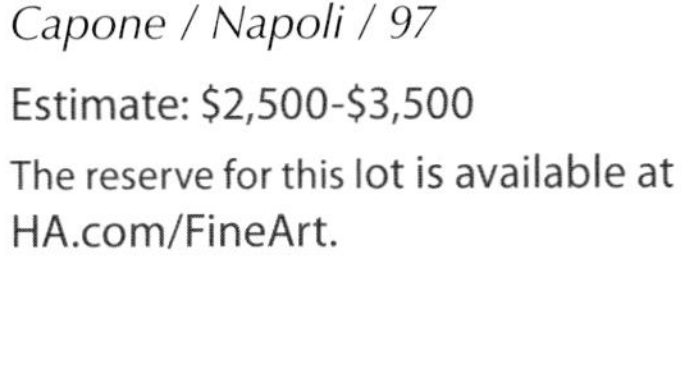

25110

CONTINENTAL SCHOOL
(Late Nineteenth Century)
Swans In A Lake
Oil on canvas
24 x 36 inches (61 x 91.4 cm)
Inscribed lower right: *C.L. 1882*

Estimate: $2,000-$4,000

The reserve for this lot is available at HA.com/FineArt.

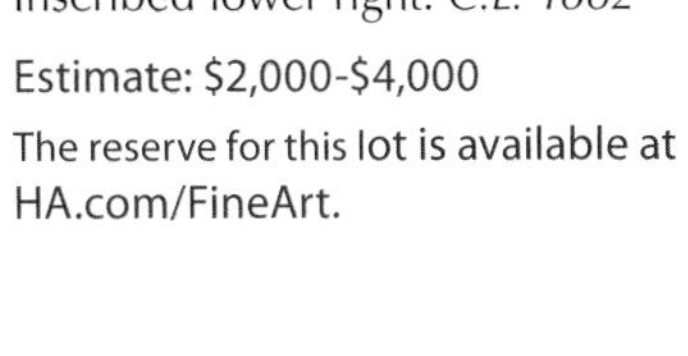

25111

OSWALD GRILL (Austrian 1878-1964)
Two Peasant Girls In A Field (Summertime Idyll), circa 1912
Oil on canvas
41-1/2 x 31-1/2 inches (105.4 x 80 cm)
Signed lower right: *O GRILL*

Provenance:
Collection of Cornelia Rasmussen

Estimate: $4,000-$7,000

The reserve for this lot is available at HA.com/FineArt.

25112

POLLOCK SINCLAIR NISBET
(British 1848-1922)
Kilchurn Castle, Loch Awe, Argyleshire, Scotland, 1902
Oil on canvas
24 x 36 inches (61 x 91.4 cm)
Signed and dated at lower left

Estimate: $1,500-$2,500

The reserve for this lot is available at HA.com/FineArt.

25113

EDGARD FARASYN
(Belgian 1858-1938)
Cows At Pasture
Oil on canvas
53 x 34 inches (134.6 x 86.4 cm)
Signed lower right: *Edg. Farasyn*
Label verso inscribed with artist's name and address

Estimate: $500-$1,500

The reserve for this lot is available at HA.com/FineArt.

25114

ANTON MAUVE
(Dutch 1838-1888)
Cows Watering
Oil on canvas
31-1/2 x 41-1/8 inches
(80 x 104.4 cm)
Signed lower right: *A. Mauve*
Indecipherable stamp verso

In 1854 Anton Mauve apprenticed with Pieter Frederik van Os, a specialist in animal paintings, and during these formative years Mauve became proficient in rendering sheep, cows and horses. In what became typical of his early body of work, he displays a skillfulness in combining peaceful farm animals with a figure in a landscape or rural scene as depicted in the present composition.

In 1858 Mauve traveled to Oosterbeek where he flourished under the influence of his two friends Gerard Bilders and Willem Maris. He was one of the foremost painters of the Hague School, and from 1881 to 1882 he worked closely with his cousin Vincent van Gogh. Mauve's solid reputation as a realist painter is a testament to the many collections and museums in which his works are housed today.

Estimate: $15,000-$25,000

The reserve for this lot is available at HA.com/FineArt.

25115

JOAN BERG (French d.1914)
Ensenada
Oil on canvas
31 x 48 inches (78.7 x 121.9 cm)
Signed and titled lower right: *Joan Berg / Ensenada*

Estimate: $5,000-$7,000

The reserve for this lot is available at HA.com/FineArt.

25116

WILLIAM MELLOR
(British 1851-1931)
Grasmere Lake, Westmoreland
Oil on canvas
20-1/4 x 30-1/4 inches
(51.4 x 76.8 cm)
Signed lower right: *William Mellor*
Inscribed verso: *Grasmere Lake / Westmoreland*

Estimate: $6,000-$8,000

The reserve for this lot is available at HA.com/FineArt.

25117

JACOBUS NICOLAS TJARDA VAN STARKENBORG
(Dutch 1822-1895)
Harvesters In An Alpine Setting
Oil on canvas
56-1/2 x 16-3/8 inches
(143.5 x 41.6 cm)
Signed lower left: *J.N. Tjarda V. Starkenborg*

Estimate: $2,500-$5,000

This lot is being sold without reserve. Unreserved lots generally open at 50% of the low estimate.

25118

CONTINENTAL SCHOOL
Landscape With Hill
Oil on canvas
20 x 24 inches (50.8 x 61 cm)
Signed lower left (indecipherable)

Estimate: $1,500-$2,500

The reserve for this lot is available at HA.com/FineArt.

25119

FREDERICK WILLIAM KOST
(American 1865-1923)
Landscape With Trees
Oil on canvas
24 x 28 inches (61 x 71.1 cm)
Signed lower left: *Kost*

Estimate: $2,000-$4,000

The reserve for this lot is available at HA.com/FineArt.

25120

WALTER STUART LLOYD (British Nineteenth Century)
Landscape With Recumbent Sheep At Twilight, 1875
Oil on canvas
20 x 30 inches (50.8 x 76.2 cm)
Signed and dated lower right: *WALTER S. LLOYD 1875*

Estimate: $2,000-$4,000

The reserve for this lot is available at HA.com/FineArt.

25121

PAUL MICHEL DUPUY (French 1869-1949)
Portrait Of A Young Girl With Toy Horse
Oil on canvas
39-1/2 x 25-1/2 inches (84.5 x 54.6 cm)
Signed at lower right: *P M Dupuy*

Estimate: $4,000-$6,000

The reserve for this lot is available at HA.com/FineArt.

25122

ENGLISH SCHOOL (Nineteenth century)
Portrait Of A Woman
Oil on canvas
16 x 12 inches (40.6 x 30.5 cm)
Unsigned

Estimate: $800-$1,200

The reserve for this lot is available at HA.com/FineArt.

25123

MICHAELANGELO MEUCCI (Italian 1840-1890)
Still Life Of Game Birds On Trompe L'Oeil Ground, a pair
Oil on oval wood panel
18-3/4 x 15 inches, each (47.6 x 38.1 cm)
Signed and inscribed at lower right, each: *M. Meucci Firenze*

Estimate: $3,000-$5,000

The reserve for this lot is available at HA.com/FineArt.

25124

ELISABETH SCHIOTT
Untitled (Landscape)
Oil on canvas
35 x 22-1/2 inches (88.9 x 56.2 cm)
Signed lower right: *Elis Schiott*

Estimate: $600-$1,000

The reserve for this lot is available at HA.com/FineArt.

25125

CHARLES FERNAND DE CONDAMY (French 1855-1913)
The Boar Hunt, 1881
Watercolor on paper
12 x 18-3/4 inches (30.5 x 47.6 cm)
Signed and dated lower right: *de Condamy / 81*

Estimate: $1,800-$2,200

The reserve for this lot is available at HA.com/FineArt.

25126

DONALD GRANT (British 1930-2001)
Black Jackets High, circa 1972
Oil on canvas
28 x 36 inches (71.1 x 91.4 cm)
Signed lower right: *Donald Grant.*

Provenance:
MacConnal-Mason & Sons, Ltd. (London, England);
Alan Barnes Fine Art (Dallas, Texas);
Private collection (Dallas, Texas)

Estimate: $4,000-$5,000

The reserve for this lot is available at HA.com/FineArt.

25127

LIONEL DALHOUISE ROBERTSON EDWARDS
(British 1878-1966)
The Final Turn, 1907
Watercolor and gouache on paper
14 x 20-1/2 inches (35.6 x 52.1 cm)
Signed, titled and dated:
"Eremons" National / The Final Turn / Lionel Edwards 07 –

Provenance:
The Sporting Gallery and Bookshop (New York);
The Estate of Linda S. Firestone

Depicting the infamous Irish-bred chaser, Eremon, in a famous race won despite the fact that his jockey, Alf Newey, broke a stirrup leather on the second fence.

Estimate: $8,000-$12,000

The reserve for this lot is available at HA.com/FineArt.

25128

WILLIAM JOSEPH SHAYER
(British 1811-1892)
The Death, 1857
Oil on canvas
14 x 23 inches (38.1 x 58.4 cm)
Signed and dated lower right

Estimate: $5,000-$8,000

The reserve for this lot is available at HA.com/FineArt.

25129

JOSÉ JIMÉNEZ Y ARANDA
(Spanish 1837-1903)
A Soldier Reading, 1890
Oil on beveled mahogany panel
6 x 4-1/2 inches (15.2 x 11.4 cm)
Signed and dated lower right:
Paris 1890 / JZ (monogram) Aranda
With a paper label verso:
Goupil's

Provenance:
Newhouse Galleries (New York);
Mr. and Mrs. F. Howard Walsh (Fort Worth, Texas);
Walsh Family Art Trust

In 1864 José Jiménez Y Aranda submitted a genre painting for his debut in the Ecole des Beaux-Arts Séville salon. Several years later, in 1871, he traveled to Rome where he met Mariano Fortuny who had a profound impact on his work. He later spent nine years in Paris, influenced by the works of Chardin and Watteau, before returning to his hometown of Séville. Jiménez Y Aranda combined his love of eighteenth century genre painting with his outstanding illustration skills to capture the rich details of everyday life, such as those in the offered work above. He exhibited abroad in London, Munich and Paris salons. Hugely popular in the United States, most of his works reside here such as one of his most ambitious works, *Holy Week in Seville*, 1879, which is located in the Fine Arts Museums of San Francisco.

Estimate: $10,000-$15,000

The reserve for this lot is available at HA.com/FineArt.

25130

FRANZ DVORAK (Austrian 1862-1927)
Bedrich Smetana And His Friends In 1865, 1923
Oil on canvas
49-1/4 x 63-1/2 inches (125.1 x 161.3 cm)
Signed and dated at lower right: *F. Dvorak 1923*

This painting was completed in 1923 in anticipation of the centenary celebration of the birth of Bedrich Smetana (1824-1884). The great Czech composer and founder of the Czech national school of music is depicted here with this friends in 1865. In the painting his second wife Bettina is seated to the right, along with his daughters Zofie, Bozena and Zdenka. Included in the notable audience is poet and writer Josef Wenzig (1807-1876), politician Karel Sladovsky (1823-1880), composer and musician Ferdinand Heller (1824-1912), Czech poet and publicist Jan Neruda (1834-1891), Antonin Dvork (1841-1904) and Leos Janacek (1854-1928).

Estimate: $70,000-$90,000

The reserve for this lot is available at HA.com/FineArt.

25131

HUGO UNGEWITTER
(German 1869-1944)
Frederick The Great Surveying The Field Of Battle, 1922
Oil on canvas
32-1/2 x 43-1/4 inches
(82.6 x 109.9 cm)
Signed and dated at lower left:
UNGEWITTER. BERLIN.1922

Literature:
E. Benezit, *Dictionnaire des Peintres, Sculpteurs, Dessinateurs et Graveurs,* vol.13, cited p.909 as *"Frederic le Grand avec ses generaux"*

Hugo Ungewitter, a well-known German painter of military, hunting, animal and sporting scenes, studied at the Dusseldorf Academy from 1888 to 1897. This particular history painting by Hugo Ungewitter depicts Frederick the Great (1712-1786) of the House of Hohenzollern erect upon his mount, looking into the foggy field of battle. He is accompanied by his brother, Prince Henry, and Prussian Generals, who survey the terrain over which they plan the waging of the next battle.

Estimate: $15,000-$25,000

The reserve for this lot is available at HA.com/FineArt.

25132

THEO VAN RYSSELBERGHE
(Belgian 1862-1926)
Village Roofs, circa 1900
Oil on panel
7-3/4 x 11 inches
(19.7 x 27.9 cm)
Initialed lower right: *V.R.*

Estimate: $10,000-$15,000

The reserve for this lot is available at HA.com/FineArt.

25133

EUGÈNE LAURENT (French 1832-1898)
Pécheur
Bronze
26-1/4 x 10 x 9 inches (66.7 x 25.4 x 22.9 cm)
Signed on base: *Laurent*

Provenance:
Crow Art Partnership collection (Dallas, Texas)

Estimate: $1,500-$2,500

The reserve for this lot is available at HA.com/FineArt.

25134

GUSTAVO BELLUSCI (Italian)
Penatoni
Oil on panel
15 x 11-1/2 inches (38.1 x 29.2 cm)
Signed lower left: *G Bellusci*

Estimate: $600-$1,000

The reserve for this lot is available at HA.com/FineArt.

25135

EUGENIO ZAMPIGHI
(Italian 1859-1944)
Playing With The Baby
Oil on canvas
24 x 18 inches (61 x 45.7 cm)
Signed at lower right: *E. Zampighi*

Provenance:
Sale, Sotheby's New York, 19th Century European Paintings, Oct. 25, 2005, Lot 181;
Private collection (New York)

Estimate: $20,000-$25,000

The reserve for this lot is available at HA.com/FineArt.

25136

FREDERICO NERLY
(Italian 1824-1919)
Rome Landscape With Maiden And Cardinal
Oil on board
16-1/2 x 28-1/4 inches
(41.9 x 71.8 cm)
Signed at lower left:
Nerly

Estimate: $10,000-$15,000

The reserve for this lot is available at HA.com/FineArt.

25137

ITALIAN SCHOOL
The Prayer
Oil on panel
15 x 11 inches (38.1 x 27.9 cm)
Initialed lower left: *MP*

Provenance:
Florence Art Gallery;
Private collection (New York)

Estimate: $9,000-$11,000

The reserve for this lot is available at HA.com/FineArt.

25138

JULIEN JOSEPH (JULIEN JOS) (Belgian 1890-1910)
Untitled (Peasant Farmers)
Oil on canvas
33-1/2 x 24-1/4 inches (85.1 x 61.6 cm)
Signed lower left: *Julian Jos*

Estimate: $6,000-$9,000

The reserve for this lot is available at HA.com/FineArt.

25139

CONTINENTAL SCHOOL
(Nineteenth Century)
Impressionistic Courtyard With Candlelit Table
Oil on canvas
30 x 36 inches (76.2 x 91.4 cm)
Unsigned

Estimate: $3,000-$5,000

The reserve for this lot is available at HA.com/FineArt.

25140

FRENCH SCHOOL (Early Twentieth Century)
Nun In A Courtyard Garden
Oil on canvas
30-1/4 x 20-1/8 inches (76.8 x 51.1 cm)
Signed and inscribed lower right: *"A Biri, souvenir de..."*(illegible)

Estimate: $800-$1,200

The reserve for this lot is available at HA.com/FineArt.

25141

HIPPOLYTE PETITJEAN (French 1824-1929)
Paysage
Oil on artist's board
8-1/2 x 5-5/8 inches (21.6 x 14.3 cm)
Unsigned

Provenance:
Hammer Galleries (New York);
Knoedler Galleries (New York);
Arkansas Arts Center

Estimate: $2,000-$4,000

The reserve for this lot is available at HA.com/FineArt.

25142

ALBERT ANDRÉ (French 1869-1954)
Roses dans un Verre
Oil on canvas
25-1/2 x 25-3/4 inches (64.8 x 65.4 cm)
Signed lower left: Albert André

Provenance:
David B. Findlay Galleries

Estimate: $12,000-$18,000
The reserve for this lot is available at HA.com/FineArt.

25143

OTAKAR (OTHON) COUBINE
(Czech 1883-1969)
Still Life, Vase Of Hollyhocks
Oil on canvas
36-1/2 x 28-7/8 inches (92.7 x 73.2 cm)
Signed lower right: *Coubine*

Estimate: $10,000-$15,000
The reserve for this lot is available at HA.com/FineArt.

25144

SIR DAVID YOUNG CAMERON (Scottish 1865-1945)
Seascape With Cliffs (possibly Aberdour, Scotland on the Firth of Forth), circa 1900-1903
Oil on canvas
55 x 45 inches (139.7 x 114.3 cm)

Sir David Young Cameron (1865-1945) was a British master of landscape and architectural views, both in paint and in etching. He was trained at the Edinburgh School of Art, became an Associate Engraver at the Royal Academy in London in 1911, where he was elected to the position of Academician in 1920. His landscapes and architectural views, though often devoid of human figures, nonetheless possess a strong human presence. He was tremendously influenced by the somber beauty of his native Scotland, and his prints and paintings have a rich, dark tone that reflects these topographical characteristics. His more famous works include views of British architecture and interior cathedral views, while his gargoyle etchings pay homage to the great French etcher Charles Meryon. Cameron spent his time traveling throughout the countryside in search of romantic subject matter, and he completed five hundred plates between 1892-1909. From 1887-1892 he was a member of the Royal Society of Painter-Etchers, and an important figure in the etching revival movement. In general both his prints and his paintings feature areas of inky darkness, offset by blistering highlights. After 1903, his paintings brighten up considerably, have a more colorful palette, and focus primarily on the Scottish Highlands.

Estimate: $15,000-$25,000

The reserve for this lot is available at HA.com/FineArt.

25145

ANTOINE BOUVARD (French 1870-1956)
A Venetian Canal Scene
Oil on canvas
25-1/2 x 19-1/2 inches (64.8 x 49.5 cm)
Signed at lower right: *Bouvard*

Provenance:
Private collection (Dallas, Texas)

Estimate: $8,000-$12,000
The reserve for this lot is available at HA.com/FineArt.

25146

PIETRO BARUCCI (Italian 1845-1917)
Fishing Boats, 1895
Oil on canvas
24 x 43 inches (61 x 109.2 cm)
Inscribed lower left: *P. Barucci / Roma 1895*

Estimate: $13,000-$15,000
The reserve for this lot is available at HA.com/FineArt.

25147

JOHN ROBERTSON REID (British 1851-1926)
Santa Maria de la Salute, Venecia Peace, 1919
Watercolor on panel
22 x 14 inches (55.9 x 35.6 cm)
Signed lower right: *John R. Reid*
Dated and titled lower left: *6 P.M. 28/6/19, Peace !!!*

Estimate: $1,000-$2,000

The reserve for this lot is available at HA.com/FineArt.

25148

CHARLES ROWNOTHAM
(British 1856-1921)
The Harbour Of Messina With The Shore Of Calabria In The Distance, 1901
Watercolor on paper
6-1/8 x 10-3/4 inches (15.6 x 27.3 cm)
Signed and dated lower right: *Chas Rownotham / 1901*

Exhibition:
The Lower Nupend Gallery,
Fine English Nineteenth Century Watercolors, September 1979
(Upper Montclair, New Jersey)

Estimate: $2,500-$5,000

The reserve for this lot is available at HA.com/FineArt.

25149

CHARLES ROWNOTHAM
(British 1856-1921)
The Castle Of Canero, Lake Maggiore, 1901
Watercolor on paper
6-1/8 x 10-3/4 inches (15.6 x 27.3 cm)
Signed and dated lower left: *Chas Rownotham / 1901*

Exhibited:
The Lower Nupend Gallery,
Fine English Nineteenth Century Watercolors, September 1979
(Upper Montclair, New Jersey)

Estimate: $2,500-$5,000

The reserve for this lot is available at HA.com/FineArt.

25150

FRANCISCO GONZALES DE ITURRINO (Spanish 1864-1924)
Nu Alangui
Oil on canvas
33-1/2 x 61-5/8 inches (85.1 x 156.5 cm)

Literature:
E. Benezit, *Dictionnaire des Peintres, Sculpteurs, Dessinateurs et Graveurs,* vol. 7, cited p.389 as *Nu Alangui*

Depicting a voluptuous woman laying on a bed of feathers with an almost staged gaze. Her physique subtly rendered in tones of pale cream and rose with strokes of umber added for contrast against the white background.

Estimate: $10,000-$15,000

The reserve for this lot is available at HA.com/FineArt.

25151

KAREL SPILLAR
(Czech 1871-1939)
Jeunes Femmes au Jardin, 1920
Oil on canvas
43-1/2 x 63-1/4 inches (110.5 x 160.7 cm)
Signed and dated at upper left: *K. Spillar 1920*

Provenance:
Private collection (New Orleans, Louisiana)

Karel Spillar was one of the foremost Czechoslovakian Post-Impressionist painters and leader of the Prague Secessionist Movement. Spillar depicts two nudes in a natural setting not unlike that of earlier and more traditional artists who painted nudes in a landscape, however, his loose brushwork and handling of light adopts more Post-Impressionist methods.

Estimate: $20,000-$30,000

The reserve for this lot is available at HA.com/FineArt.

25152

PIERRE-AUGUSTE RENOIR (French 1841-1919)
Gabrielle Nue, Assise sur un lit (Gabrielle Nude, Sitting on a Bed)
Oil on linen
8 x 7-1/2 inches (20.3 x 19.1 cm)
Signed upper left: *Renoir*

Gabrielle Nue, Assise sur un Lit is an intimate study of the nude female form, following in the tradition of Renoir's "Bathers." The painting offers a subdued palette of neutral tones blending muted greens with natural sand tones. The stylistically strong work is comprised of a simple composition of the lone figure against an abstract background.

This lot has been authenticated by the Wildenstein Institute (2001).

Estimate: $80,000-$120,000

The reserve for this lot is available at HA.com/FineArt.

25153

CAMILLE PISSARO
(French 1830-1903)
Portrait d'Alfred Isaacson,
circa 1883
Pastel on paper
20-1/2 x 16 inches
(52.1 x 40.6 cm)

Provenance:
Acquired from the artist by his nephew, Alfred Isaacson (London);
Hirschl & Adler Galleries (New York);
Henry Pearlman collection (New York)

Literature:
Ludovic-Rodolfe Pissarro and Lionello Venturi, *Camille Pissarro, Son Art-Son Oeuvre* (Paris, 1939), vol. 1, no. 1564, vol. 2, no. 1564, illus.;
Camille Pissarro, *Letters to His Son Lucien,* edited with the assistance of Lucien Pissarro by John Rewald, 3rd ed. (New York, 1972), pp. 49-51.

This lively sketch depicts Pissarro's nephew, his half-sister's son, Alfred Isaacson. The artist's own son, Lucien, stayed with Alfred and his family when in London. Writing to Lucien in a letter dated December 28, 1883, Pissarro mentions this portrait, stating that it is a good resemblance (see *Letters* in Literature above). The spirited letter mostly addresses popular philosophical matters, revealing the artist's passion for the groundbreaking liberal ideas of the day. Pissarro promises to send his son a copy of Baudelaire's *Les Fleurs du Mal* and also encourages Alfred to read books on socialism as well as the works of John Stuart Mill: "They are easy reading and should give him [Alfred] a general idea of the movement which points to the new road our society must take" (*Letters,* p. 50).

Estimate: $80,000-$120,000

The reserve for this lot is available at HA.com/FineArt.

25154

CAMILLE PISSARRO (French 1830-1903)
Personnages Assis Dans Une Foret
Pencil on paper
8-3/4 x 12 inches, sight (22.2 x 30.5 cm)
Signed with estate stamp, initials: *CP*, and pencil inscriptions

Provenance:
Pissarro Exhibition, Schonemnan, 1959 (New York);
Collection of Mrs. Alice Tully;
Spoleto Festival, May 8, 1973, Parke-Bernet [Lot33], donated by Mrs. Alice Tully;
Property from a New York Estate

Estimate: $5,000-$7,000

The reserve for this lot is available at HA.com/FineArt.

25155

FERNAND LEGER
(French 1881-1955)
Standing Figure, 1905
Pen drawing on paper
13 x 7 inches, sight (33 x 17.8 cm)
Dated lower right: *1905*
Inscribed verso: *Ferdinand Leger / figure (1905) / Suivant reproduction / "Leger" par Theriade / Edition Cahier d'Art / Paris*

Estimate: $9,000-$11,000

The reserve for this lot is available at HA.com/FineArt.

25156

PIERRE GEORGES JEANNIOT (French 1848-1934)
Barques en Automne, 1891
Pastel on paper laid on canvas
21-1/4 x 25-1/2 inches (54 x 64.8 cm)
Signed and dated at lower left: *Jeanniot/ 1891*

Provenance:
Sale, Christie's South Kensington, Nov. 29, 2001, Lot 2

Estimate: $6,000-$8,000
The reserve for this lot is available at HA.com/FineArt.

25157

JULES-JOSEPH LEFEBVRE (French 1834-1911)
Springtime
Oil on canvas
55-1/2 x 34 inches (140.6 x 86.4 cm)
Signed lower right: *Jules Lefebvre*

While elegant young women remained Lefebvre's preferred subject throughout his long and distinguished career, his beautiful sitters remained sensitive to the dominant esthetic tastes of the day. In the late 1880s and 1890s, as the Symbolist and Classicist mode of artists such as Puvis de Chavannes or Gustave Moreau supplanted the Naturalist or exotic tendencies of earlier decades, Lefebvre's work shifted accordingly. The present work, most likely of this period, presents an allegorical figure of *Springtime* crowned with a wreath of pale blossoms and carrying fresh stems in the folds of her classical gown. Despite the idealized, symbolist subject, Lefebvre's commitment to painting from life is evident in the very specific, crisply painted flowers and foliage and in the translucent tones of flesh and fabric.

Jules-Joseph Lefebvre is best known as a romantic allegorical painter who specialized in genre scenes, portraits, and nudes. His father, a baker, encouraged his sons artistic career and sent him to Paris at age sixteen. There he studied with Léon Cogniet and entered the Ecole des Beaux-Arts in 1852. He competed for the Prix de Rome, winning a second place in 1859 and first place in 1861 with his painting of *The Death of Priam.* While living in Rome he painted his first nude, a Bather, which was sent to Paris in 1863. During his stay in Italy he also painted many works with ancient subject matter, investing them with an elegant or amusing quality. When he returned to Paris, Lefebvre became disenchanted with the academic focus on working from memory and sought to paint directly from life. The result was a series of statuesque women, both nudes and draped, which passed from his studio under the guises of such characters as Pandora, Diana, Sappho, Mary Magdalene and Ophelia. *Ophelia,* a similar work of 1890, is in the permanent collection of the Springfield Museum of Fine Arts, Springfield, Massachusetts.

Lefebvre made a distinguished career as a painter of women. One reviewer wrote in 1881,

> *It is sufficient to just mention his name in order to immediately evoke the memory and the image of the thousand adorable creature of which he is the father.... An unusually skilled draughtsman, Jules Lefebvre better than anyone else caresses, with a brush both delicate and sure, the undulating contour of the feminine form.*

Lefebvre won medals at the Salons of 1865, 1868, and 1870. After the last, where he exhibited his famous nude *Truth,* now in the Musée d'Orsay, he was made a Chevalier of the Legion of Honor. His success only grew and he won a first class medal at the Exposition Universelle of 1878 and the grand prize in 1889. In 1891 he became a member of the Institute and in 1898 was made a Commander of the Legion of Honor.

Estimate: $80,000-$120,000

The reserve for this lot is available at HA.com/FineArt.

25158

PIERRE CARRIER BELLEUSE (French 1851-1932)
La Danseuse, 1906
Pastel on paper
37-12/16 x 15-3/8 inches (96 x 39 cm)
Signed and dated lower left: *P. Carrier-Belleuse. / 1906*

Provenance:
Stoppenbach & Delestre Ltd. (London);
Private collection (Connecticut)

Estimate: $10,000-$15,000
The reserve for this lot is available at HA.com/FineArt.

25159

GEORGE D'ESPAGNAT (French 1870-1950)
Portrait Of A Lady
Oil on canvas
18-1/2 x 15-1/8 inches (47 x 38.4 cm)
Signed upper left

Provenance:
Private collection (Connecticut)

Estimate: $3,000-$5,000
The reserve for this lot is available at HA.com/FineArt.

25160

FRANZ HEINRICH LOVIS CORINTH (German 1858-1925)
Walchensee, 1912
Oil on canvas
15-1/2 x 21-1/2 inches (39.4 x 31.8 cm)
Signed lower right: *Walchensee / Lovis Corinth / April 1912 pinxit*
On verso, faintly inscribed in black ink: *Staatliche Gemäldegalerie Dresden*

Lovis Corinth was one of the significant German artists of the modern era and is most often known as a founding member of German Secessionism, although he is sometimes called both a German Impressionist and German Expressionist. His earliest pictures are known for their naturalistic style, reflecting the influence of his studies at the Munich Academy in the early 1880s. After his period at the Académie Julian in France, Corinth's works reflect both Symbolist and Impressionist influences. With their bold colors, rough lines, and emotive sensibilities, his later works are often linked with Expressionism.

The Walchensee (Walchen Lake) in Bavaria was one of Corinth's favorite subjects, particularly during his mature career when he and his family spent each holiday there from 1919 until his death. As it was painted in April of 1912, the present work is one of the artist's earlier treatments of this subject. It also belongs to an important period in his career since, after suffering a stroke late in 1911, Corinth returned to painting in 1912 with a bold and vigorous style. As exemplified by *Walchensee,* Corinth's brushwork during this period becomes decisively urgent and his palette becomes brighter and stronger.

Estimate: $80,000-$120,000

The reserve for this lot is available at HA.com/FineArt.

25161

PIERRE AUGUSTE RENOIR
(French 1841-1919)
La Pendule, 1915
Bronze, dark brown patina with wood base
30 inches, high (76.2 cm)
Signed, dated and stamped: *C. Valsuani, cire perdue*

Provenance:
Edouard Jonas, Paris;
Sale, Sotheby Parke-Bernet (No. 3322), March 1, 1972, Lot 8;
Charles E. Slatkin, Inc. Galleries;
Private collector (New York)

The casting of *La Pendule* is to have been limited by the Renoir family to an edition of two casts, with the orignal plaster, from the Collection of Edouard Jonas, Paris, to be turned over to the permanent collection of the Museum of Fine Arts in Boston (*Model for Clock Case,* 1915).

Estimate: $60,000-$80,000
The reserve for this lot is available at HA.com/FineArt.

25162

MATHURIN MEHEUT
(French 1882-1958)
Untitled, circa 1929
Oil on canvas
24 x 84 inches (61 x 129.1 cm)
Signed lower right: *M. Meheut*

Provenance:
Jeffrey Basinger, family descent, grandson of Mr. and Mrs. Minton;
Mary Anne Minton, family descent, daughter of Mr. and Mrs. Minton;
Harriet and John Preston Minton

Painter and illustrator Maturing Meheut, is well known throughout France, and in particular in Normandy and the coast as he is noted for his depictions of the sea and marine life. Sea life fascinated Meheut, as did the traditional clothing of the local, which have since disappeared. Meheut was the official artist for the French Navy for a number of years and traveled and worked extensively in Japan and Crete. He also became recognized for ceramic designs and partnered with Henriot Quimper (Kempter), a well-known French ceramic designer and producer.

All the Meheut lots offered have a unique provenance and are accompanied by a letter of authenticity. The two sketches were gifted by the artist to Harriot and John Preston Minton in 1929, in appreciation of their friendship and patronage. Mr. Minton had a strong interest in the arts, as he was a direct descendant of Herbert Minton, who founded the Minton china/ceramic factories of Stoke-on-Trent England in 1793. Knowing of Meheut's dabbles in ceramic design; Minton became interested in Meheut's artwork purchasing a number of the artist's paintings. Meheut's have remained within the Minton family until know, their debut on the open art market.

Estimate: $20,000-$40,000
The reserve for this lot is available at HA.com/FineArt.

25163

MATHURIN MEHEUT
(French 1882-1958)
Untitled, circa 1929
Oil on canvas
24 x 84 inches (61 x 129.1 cm)
Signed lower right: *M. Meheut*

Provenance:
Jeffrey Basinger, family descent, grandson of Mr. and Mrs. Minton;
Mary Anne Minton, family descent, daughter of Mr. and Mrs. Minton;
Harriet and John Preston Minton

Estimate: $20,000-$40,000
The reserve for this lot is available at HA.com/FineArt.

25164

MATHURIN MEHEUT
(French 1882-1958)
Untitled, circa 1929
Oil on canvas
29 x 39 inches
(73.7 x 99.1 cm)
Unsigned

Provenance:
Jeffrey Basinger, family descent, grandson of Mr. and Mrs. Minton;
Mary Anne Minton, family descent, daughter of Mr. and Mrs. Minton;
Harriet and John Preston Minton

Estimate: $20,000-$40,000

The reserve for this lot is available at HA.com/FineArt.

25165

MATHURIN MEHEUT (French 1882-1958)
Le départ de marchands d'oignons pour l'Angleterre (The departure of onion merchants for England), 1929
Mixed media on paper (Ink, crayon, watercolor and varish)
10 x 7-3/4 inches (25.4 x 19.7 cm)
Inscribed upper right: *A Madame Minton./ respectueux hommage./ M-Mehuet (To Mrs. Minton/Respectful hommage./ M-Mehuet)*
Inscribed lower right: *Roscoff le 27 juillet 1929 (The departure of onion merchants for England/ Roscoff the 27th of July 1929)*
Inscribed with artist's monogram lower left

Provenance:
Jeffrey Basinger, family descent, grandson of Mr. and Mrs. Minton;
Mary Anne Minton, family descent, daughter of Mr. and Mrs. Minton;
Harriet and John Preston Minton

Estimate: $1,000-$2,000

This lot is being sold without reserve. Unreserved lots generally open at 50% of the low estimate.

25166

MATHURIN MEHEUT (French 1882-1958)
Rencontre à Roscoff (Meeting at Roscoff)
Graphite and crayon on paper
10 x 7-3/4 inches (25.4 x 19.7 cm)
Inscribed lower right: *A Monsieur et Madame Minton en souvenir de notre rencontre a Roscoff./leur cordialement dévoué/Mathurin Meheut (To Mr. and Mrs. Minton in remembrance of our meeting at Roscoff/ their cordially devoted/ Mathurin Meheut)*
Inscribed with artist's monogram lower left

Provenance:
Jeffrey Basinger, family descent, grandson of Mr. and Mrs. Minton;
Mary Anne Minton, family descent, daughter of Mr. and Mrs. Minton;
Harriet and John Preston Minton

Estimate: $1,000-$2,000

This lot is being sold without reserve. Unreserved lots generally open at 50% of the low estimate.

25167

LEON BAKST (Russian 1866-1924)
Medieval Prince and *Dame De La Cour*
10 x 7 inches, sheet (25.4 x 17.8 cm) and 11-1/2 x 8-1/2 inches, sheet (29.2 x 21.6 cm)
Watercolor and gouache on paper
Signed lower right, each: *BAKST*

Estimate: $8,000-$12,000

The reserve for this lot is available at HA.com/FineArt.

25168

VINCENT G. STIEPEVICH (Russian 1840-1911)
Seated Woman
Oil on canvas
21-1/2 x 15-1/2 inches (54.6 x 34.9 cm)
Signed lower right: *VG Stiepevich*

Estimate: $8,000-$10,000

The reserve for this lot is available at HA.com/FineArt.

25169

ALEXANDER NIKOLAYEVICH VIEZZHEV (Russian-Ukranian 1865-1918)
Portrait Of A Man, 1901
Oil on canvas
17 x 11-1/2 inches (43.2 x 29.2 cm)
Signed and dated verso, Cyrillic

Estimate: $5,000-$7,000

The reserve for this lot is available at HA.com/FineArt.

25170

LUIBOV POPOVA (Russian 1889-1924)
Untitled
Gouache on paper
8-1/2 x 6-1/2 inches (21.6 x 16.5 cm)
Initialed lower right

Estimate: $6,000-$8,000

The reserve for this lot is available at HA.com/FineArt.

25171

LUIBOV POPOVA (Russian 1889-1924)
Untitled
Mixed media on paper
9 x 7-1/4 inches (22.9 x 18.4 cm)
Signed lower right

Estimate: $6,000-$8,000

The reserve for this lot is available at HA.com/FineArt.

25172

LUIBOV POPOVA (Russian 1889-1924)
Untitled
Mixed media on paper
9 x 7-3/8 inches (27.9 x 21.6 cm)
Initialed lower right

Estimate: $6,000-$8,000

The reserve for this lot is available at HA.com/FineArt.

25173

LUIBOV POPOVA
(Russian 1889-1924)
Untitled
Oil and gouache on paper
11 x 8-7/8 inches (27.9 x 22.6 cm)
Initialed lower left
Stamped verso

Estimate: $6,000-$8,000

The reserve for this lot is available at HA.com/FineArt.

25174

IVAN KLIUN (Russian 1870-1942)
Untitled
Found object sculpture, mixed media
6-1/2 inches, high (16.5 cm)

Estimate: $5,000-$10,000

The reserve for this lot is available at HA.com/FineArt.

25175

IVAN KLIUN (Russian 1870-1942)
Untitled
Found object sculpture, mixed media
7 inches, high (17.8 cm)

Estimate: $5,000-$10,000

The reserve for this lot is available at HA.com/FineArt.

25176

IVAN KLIUN
(Russian 1870-1942)
Untitled
Oil on linen on board
21 x 15 inches (53.3 x 38.1 cm)
Signed lower right

Estimate: $25,000-$35,000

The reserve for this lot is available at HA.com/FineArt.

25177

IVAN KLIUN (Russian 1870-1942)
Untitled (Woman in Profile)
Oil and gouache on paper
11-3/4 x 10-1/2 inches (29.8 x 26.7 cm)
Signed lower left

Estimate: $4,000-$6,000

The reserve for this lot is available at HA.com/FineArt.

25178

IVAN KLIUN (Russian 1870-1942)
Untitled
Watercolor on paper
6-1/2 x 9-3/4 inches (16.5 x 24.8 cm)
Signed lower right and verso

Estimate: $4,000-$6,000

The reserve for this lot is available at HA.com/FineArt.

25179

LUIBOV POPOVA (Russian 1889-1924)
Untitled
Oil and gouache on paper
8-1/2 x 6-1/4 inches (21.6 x 15.9 cm)
Initialed lower right

Estimate: $6,000-$8,000

The reserve for this lot is available at HA.com/FineArt.

25180

LUIBOV POPOVA
(Russian 1889-1924)
Untitled
Oil and gouache on paper
6-1/4 x 8-1/2 inches (15.9 x 21.6 cm)
Initialed lower right

Estimate: $6,000-$8,000

The reserve for this lot is available at HA.com/FineArt.

25181

LUIBOV POPOVA (Russian 1889-1924)
Untitled
Oil and gouache on paper
8-1/2 x 6-1/4 inches (21.6 x 15.9 cm)

Estimate: $6,000-$8,000

The reserve for this lot is available at HA.com/FineArt.

25182

LUIBOV POPOVA (Russian 1889-1924)
Oil and gouache on paper
8-1/2 x 6-1/4 inches (21.6 x 15.9 cm)
Initialed lower right

Estimate: $6,000-$8,000

The reserve for this lot is available at HA.com/FineArt.

25183

LUIBOV POPOVA (Russian 1889-1924)
Untitled
Oil, gouache and collage on paper
9 x 7-3/8 inches (22.9 x 19.9 cm)
Initialed lower right

Estimate: $8,000-$10,000

The reserve for this lot is available at HA.com/FineArt.

25184

LUIBOV POPOVA (Russian 1889-1924)
Untitled
Oil and gouache on paper
9 x 7-3/8 inches (22.9 x 18.7 cm)
Initialed lower right

Estimate: $8,000-$10,000

The reserve for this lot is available at HA.com/FineArt.

25185

MSTISLAW DOBUZHINSKII (Russian 1875-1957)
Untitled
Gouache on paper
5-1/2 x 13 inches (14 x 33 cm)
Signed lower right

Estimate: $2,000-$3,000

This lot is being sold without reserve. Unreserved lots generally open at 50% of the low estimate.

25186

NATALIA SERGEEVNA GONCHAROVA (Russian 1881-1962)
The Mushroom Pickers
Oil on canvas
17-3/4 x 22-1/2 inches (45.1 x 57.2 cm)
Signed in Cyrillic lower left

This work will be included in the forthcoming catalogue raisonné of Goncharova by Dr. Anthony Parton. An art historical report by Dr. Parton accompanies this lot.

Estimate: $30,000-$50,000

The reserve for this lot is available at HA.com/FineArt.

25187

NIKOLAI IVANOVITCH VASIL'EV (Russian-American 1892-1970)
Portrait Of A Woman In Red, circa 1930
Oil on canvas
36 x 24 inches (91.4 x 61 cm)
Unsigned

Estimate: $12,000-$18,000

The reserve for this lot is available at HA.com/FineArt.

25188

KONSTANTIN ALEXEIEVITCH KOROVIN (Russian 1861-1939)
Russian Landscape With Houses
Gouache on cardboard
12-1/2 x 15-1/2 inches (31.8 x 39.4 cm)
Signed lower left: *Constant Korwine Russie*
Inscription in cursive Cyrillic verso, which describes the location depicted in the image.

Estimate: $10,000-$15,000

The reserve for this lot is available at HA.com/FineArt.

25189

DAVID BURLIUK (Russian-American 1882-1967)
I See The Artist
Impasto on wood
6-1/2 x 6-3/4 inches (16.5 x 17.1 cm)
Signed and titled lower margin: *Burliuk / I See The Artist*

Estimate: $3,000-$5,000

The reserve for this lot is available at HA.com/FineArt.

25190

JOACHIM WEINGART (Polish 1895-1942)
Girl At A Table With Flowers
Oil on canvas
28-3/4 x 23-3/4 inches (73 x 60.3 cm)
Signed lower right: *Weingart*

Estimate: $3,000-$6,000

The reserve for this lot is available at HA.com/FineArt.

25191

MARC CHAGALL
(Belarusian-French 1887-1985)
Femme au bouquet,
circa 1960s-70s
Colored crayons on Japon paper
26-3/4 x 20-1/2 inches (68 x 52 cm)
Signed at lower right in brown crayon: *Marc Chagall*
Accompanied by a letter of authenticity from the Chagall Committee.

Provenance:
Sale, Sotheby's, London, 24 March 1999, Lot 82, to the following;
Crow Art Partnership collection (Dallas, Texas)

In 1923, after witnessing the enormous toll Germany's aggression had taken on his native Vitebsk, Belarussia, Marc Chagall went into exile and settled in Paris where he was embraced by the avant-garde artists of the day. In Paris Chagall found a freedom of artistic expression that he would not have found in his country, yet he felt strongly that his work reflected his homeland. Chagall thrived in Paris during the 1920s and 30s.

After the war Chagall settled along the Cote d'Azur where he was inspired by the lush gardens and topography of the region. In 1952 Chagall married Russian-born Valentia Brodsky (Vada). She was his model for many of the subsequent floral bouquet and lover themed compositions.

Marc Chagall was a compulsive draftsman who was equally attracted to color and line. During the later decades of his career, drawing took on a new importance for him, and with it came a lighter and sparer line. Despite Chagall's tendency to work with a rather restricted set of imagery, it is possible nonetheless, to date his efforts on the basis of style, compositional arrangements of motifs, and choice of media and way of manipulating them. The present work, Femme au bouquet, has a nimbler touch in its use of materials. In contrast to his paintings, which the artist tended to work over at length, Chagall's late drawings are more spontaneous and playful. In Femme au Bouquet, his favorite motifs are present-the woman, the bouquet, the goat, and the embracing couple-but are sometimes superimposed upon one another in a childlike manner. The sumptuous bouquets found throughout his oeuvre are never still lifes but exuberant explosions of sweetly colored blossoms that no actual vase could ever contain. Chagall often explained that as he was developing a drawing, he would turn it sideways and even upside-down to see whether the image was more successful in another orientation. In this drawing, Chagall worked solely with colored crayons-a medium generally associated only with children's art. Very likely he seems to have drawn the central figure of a woman with a bouquet and the goat first, then to have reversed the sheet of paper to sketch the head at the bottom as well as the floating couple. A notable feature of this drawing is the use of a Japanese paper, which has a semi-translucent quality much like the ethereal image itself.

Estimate: $60,000-$80,000
The reserve for this lot is available at HA.com/FineArt.

25192

MARC CHAGALL (Belarusian-French 1887-1985)
Untitled
Lithograph
13-3/8 x 9-3/4 inches, sight (34 x 24.8 cm)
Edition: 28/75
Signed lower right in pencil: *Marc Chagall*

Estimate: $3,000-$5,000

The reserve for this lot is available at HA.com/FineArt.

25193

ZOLTAN L. SEPESHY
(Hungarian-American 1898-1974)
Seascape, 1924
Oil on masonite
7-3/4 x 10 inches (19.7 x 25.4 cm)
Signed and dated lower right:
To Mickey and Paul with hearty regards/ Zoltan Sepeshy/ 1924

Provenance:
Stephen Silagy Art Gallery (Los Angeles, California);
Private collection (Dallas, Texas)

Estimate: $800-$1,200

The reserve for this lot is available at HA.com/FineArt.

25194

ZOLTAN L. SEPESHY (Hungarian-American 1898-1974)
Sunbathers
Tempera on board
21-1/2 x 28 inches, framed (46 x 59.9 cm)
Signed at lower left: *L. Sepeshy*

Provenance:
Stephen Silagy Gallery (Los Angeles, California);
Private collection (Dallas, Texas)

Estimate: $2,000-$4,000
The reserve for this lot is available at HA.com/FineArt.

25195

CHANA ORLOFF (French-Ukrainian 1878-1968)
Maternité, 1924
Bronze
25 x 14-1/2 x 11-1/4 inches (63.5 x 36.8 x 28.6 cm)
Edition 2/8
Susse Fondeur Paris
Inscribed, *Ch Orloff 1924 2/8* and stamped

Provenance:
Crow Art Partnership collection (Dallas, Texas)

Russian born realist sculptor Chana Orloff lived the majority of her life in Paris where she trained and worked, while identifying strongly with her Eretz-Israel heritage. She ran in avant-garde circles, befriending artists such as Matisse, Picasso and Modigliani. In 1916 she married, but was widowed in 1918, left to raise her one year old son alone. When Paris was invaded during World War II Orloff fled to Switzerland with her son, returning to Paris after the war. She made many trips to Ertz-Israel and Israel throughout her life. Her first exhibition at the Tel Aviv Museum was held in 1935, followed by a number of subsequent exhibitions and retrospectives.

Her sculptures reflect her personal trials and triumphs evidenced by the reoccurring themes of women, children and motherhood through the mediums of wood, bronze and stone. She also favored the subject of animals. Her mannered sculptures such as the above offered work, won her acclaim and a sound flow of commissions for portraits and monuments.

Estimate: $40,000-$60,000
The reserve for this lot is available at HA.com/FineArt.

25196

ALEXANDRE IACOVLEFF (Russian 1887-1938)
Woman, Hue - French Indo-China, 1932
Sanguine and charcaol on paper
20-1/2 x 20 inches (52.1 x 50.8 cm)
Signed and dated lower right: *A Iacovleff, Hue, 1932*

Provenance:
Grand Central Galleries, Inc., 1939 (New York)

Exhibitions:
Explorer's Hall, National Geographic Society, Washington D.C., 1935;
Grand Central Art Galleries, Inc. (New York), *Memorial Exhibition of the work of Alexandre Iacovleff,* April 11 - 29, 1939, No. 64 as "Chinese Mother and Child"
Reproduced in catalogue, p. 10, with title: *Woman and Child, Hue - French, Indo-China.*

Literature:
Boston Sunday Herald, April 7, 1935, Section B, p. 8 (Reproduced);
National Geographic Magazine, January 1936, Plate XVI (Reproduced in color)

Estimate: $20,000-$25,000
The reserve for this lot is available at HA.com/FineArt.

25197

EMILE AUBRY (French 1880-1964)
La Calanque d'Emeraude
Oil on board
12-1/2 x 12 inches (31.8 x 30.5 cm)
Signed at lower left

Provenance:
Alain Sineau: Emile Aubry 1880/1964- L'Atelier du Peintre, Feb. 22, 1998, Lot 128

Estimate: $3,000-$5,000
The reserve for this lot is available at HA.com/FineArt.

25198

HENRI JEAN GUILLAUME MARTIN (French 1860-1943)
Goat, circa 1910-30
Oil on board
12-1/2 x 16 inches (31.8 x 41.2 cm)
Signed at lower right: *Henri Martin*

Provenance:
Chaite Gallery, 1950 (Paris);
Private collection (New York)

In 1900 Martin purchased a summer home, Marquayrol, in the village of Labastide-du-Vert in south-west France. This peaceful retreat from the city would influence many of Martin's paintings. Landscapes, for example, become his favorite subject matter and goats appeared in many of Martin's paintings between 1910 and 1930.

Estimate: $30,000-$50,000

The reserve for this lot is available at HA.com/FineArt.

25199

HENRI JEAN GUILLAUME MARTIN (French 1860-1943)
Boy With Sailboat, circa 1930
Oil on board
17-1/2 x 14-1/2 inches (44.5 x 36.8 cm)
Signed at lower right: *Henri Martin*

Provenance:
Chaite Gallery, 1950 (Paris);
Private collection (New York)

Martin moved to Paris in 1879 to study at the Ecole des Beaux-Arts under Jean-Paul Laurens. Under the influence of his contemporaries Georges Seurat and Paul Signac, Martin began experimenting with pointillism. Representative of his finest works produced in the latter half of his career, the present lot depicts a boy holding a sailboat with exuberant color and light.

Estimate: $50,000-$70,000

The reserve for this lot is available at HA.com/FineArt.

25200

ANDRE BAUCHANT
(French 1873-1958)
Figures Outside Castle Walls, 1949
Oil on panel
10-1/2 x 13-3/4 inches (26.7 x 34.9 cm)
Signed and dated lower center:
A Bauchant / 1949

Estimate: $3,000-$5,000

This lot is being sold without reserve. Unreserved lots generally open at 50% of the low estimate.

25201

SEI KOYANAGUI (Japanese b.1896)
Still Life With Roses In A Delft Jar
Oil on canvas
25-3/4 x 21-1/2 inches (65.4 x 54.6 cm)
Signed lower right: *(artist's monogram) / Koyanagui*

Estimate: $2,000-$4,000

This lot is being sold without reserve. Unreserved lots generally open at 50% of the low estimate.

25202

MARCEL CHARLES LAURENT SALINAS (French b.1913)
Still Life With Basket Of Pears And Grapes
Oil on canvas
15 x 18 inches (38.1 x 45.7 cm)
Signed upper left: *Salinas*

Estimate: $1,000-$2,000

The reserve for this lot is available at HA.com/FineArt.

25203

PIERRE ERNEST KOHL (French 1897-1985)
Reflection, 1931
Oil on canvas
25-3/4 x 19-3/4 inches (65.4 x 50.2 cm)
Signed lower right: *Pierre Ernest Kohl 1931 / Fer.*

Estimate: $1,200-$1,800

The reserve for this lot is available at HA.com/FineArt.

25204

LEON D'USSEAU (b.1947)
Modern Sailboats With Sun And Moon
Oil on board
24 x 35-1/2 inches (61 x 90.2 cm)
Signed lower right

Estimate: $1,500-$2,500

The reserve for this lot is available at HA.com/FineArt.

25205

NICHOLAAS MATHIEU EEKMAN
(Belgian 1889-1973)
Artiste et Modele, 1947
Oil on wood panel
11 x 18 inches (27.9 x 45.7 cm)
Signed upper left
Inscribed, titled and dated verso

Estimate: $1,000-$2,000

The reserve for this lot is available at HA.com/FineArt.

25206

FRANCOIS GALL
(French 1912-1987)
La Leçon de Danse
Oil on canvas
18 x 22 inches
(45.7 x 55.9 cm)
Signed lower left

Exhibited:
Salon des Indépendants, 1969

Estimate: $5,000-$8,000

The reserve for this lot is available at HA.com/FineArt.

25207

FRANCOIS GALL
(French 1912-1987)
Pont Solferino, 1954
Oil on canvas
8-3/4 x 10-3/4 inches
(22.2 x 27.3 cm)
Signed lower left and inscribed:
Paris, 1954

Estimate: $5,000-$8,000

The reserve for this lot is available at HA.com/FineArt.

25208

JAN LEBENSTEIN (Polish b.1930)
Girl At A Window, 1956
Ink and watercolor on paper
23 x 14 inches (58.4 x 35.6 cm)
Signed and dated lower left

Estimate: $3,000-$5,000

The reserve for this lot is available at HA.com/FineArt.

25209

JOSEPA COLE
(Italian Nineteenth Century)
Landscape With
Oil on canvas
16-3/4 x 24-3/8 inches
Signed lower left

Estimate: $2,000-$4,000

The reserve for this lot is available at HA.com/FineArt.

25210

HELENE GIROD DE L'AIN (French b.1926)
The Game
Oil on canvas
24 x 23-3/4 inches (61 x 60.3 cm)
Signed upper right: *girod de l'ain*

Estimate: $500-$800

The reserve for this lot is available at HA.com/FineArt.

25211

PHILIPPE HENRI NOYER (French 1917-1985)
La Petit Fille De L'Autobus, 1948
Oil on canvas
25-3/4 x 20 inches (65.4 x 50.8 cm)
Signed and dated lower right: *PR NOYER 48*

Estimate: $2,500-$3,500

The reserve for this lot is available at HA.com/FineArt.

25212

BRUNO KRAUSKOPF (German 1892-1960)
Three Figures
Oil on panel
39 x 31-1/2 inches (99.1 x 80 cm)
Signed lower left: *Krauskopf*
Inscribed verso: *Krauskopt / ogna / ..ren*

Estimate: $4,000-$6,000

The reserve for this lot is available at HA.com/FineArt.

25213

HANS WILHELM SCHMIDT (German 1859-1950)
Untitled
Oil on canvas
25-3/4 x 34-3/4 inches (64.4 x 88.3 cm)
Signed lower left: *W Schmidt*

Estimate: $1,000-$2,000

The reserve for this lot is available at HA.com/FineArt.

25214

EDOUARD LÉON CORTÈS
(French 1882-1969)
Marché aux Fleurs
Oil on canvas
13 x 18 inches (33 x 45.7 cm)
Signed at lower left:
Edouard.Cortès.

Provenace:
Galerie F. Clair, 1971 (Paris);
Private collection (Loop, Texas)

Estimate: $20,000-$30,000
The reserve for this lot is available at HA.com/FineArt.

25215

EDOUARD LÉON CORTÈS
(French 1882-1969)
Champs Elysées
Oil on board
18 x 21-1/2 inches
(45.7 x 54.6 cm)
Signed at lower right:
Edouard.Cortès.

Provenance:
Galerie F. Clair, circa 1970 (Paris);
Private collection (Loop,Texas)

Estimate: $20,000-$30,000
The reserve for this lot is available at HA.com/FineArt.

25216

EDOUARD LÉON CORTÈS
(French 1882-1969)
Rue Royale à Paris
Oil on board
17-1/2 x 21-1/2 inches
(44.5 x 54.6 cm)
Signed at lower right:
Edouard Cortès

Provenance:
Galerie F. Clair, circa 1970
(Paris);
Private collection (Loop,
Texas)

Estimate: $20,000-$30,000

The reserve for this lot is available at HA.com/FineArt.

25217

ANTOINE BLANCHARD
(French 1910-1988)
Porte Saint Denis à Paris
Oil on canvas
12 x 16 inches (30.5 x 40.6 cm)
Signed at lower right: *Antoine Blanchard*

Estimate: $4,000-$6,000

The reserve for this lot is available at HA.com/FineArt.

25218

EMILIO GRAU SALA (Spanish 1911-1975)
Untitled, 1969
Oil on canvas
23-3/4 x 28-3/4 inches (60.3 x 73 cm)
Signed lower right: *Grau Sala*
Inscribed verso: *Grau Sala / 1969*

Estimate: $45,000-$50,000

This lot is being sold without reserve. Unreserved lots generally open at 50% of the low estimate.

25219

FRANCOIS GALL (French 1912-1987)
Attente
Oil on canvas
13-3/4 x 10-3/4 inches (34.9 x 27.3 cm)
Signed lower right: *F. Gall*
Signed and titled verso

Provenance:
Dominion Gallery (Montreal)

Estimate: $5,000-$7,000
The reserve for this lot is available at HA.com/FineArt.

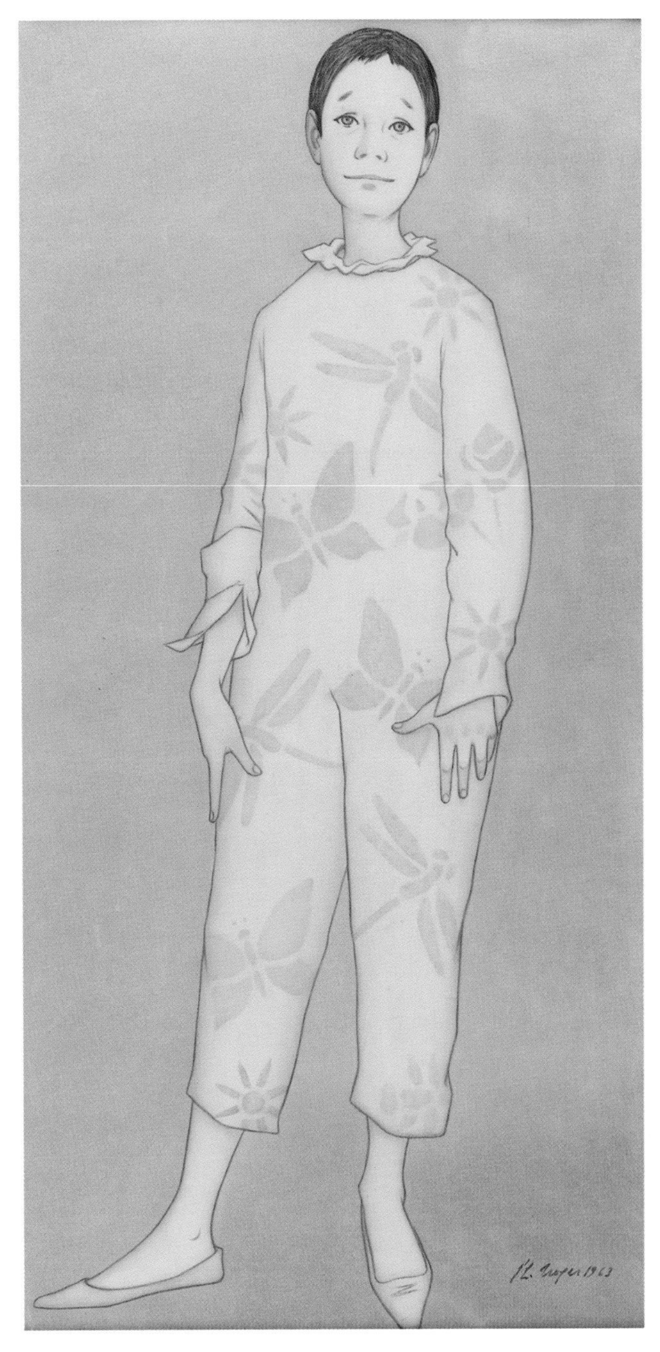

25220

PHILIPPE HENRI NOYER (French 1917-1985)
Clown, 1963
Oil on canvas
39-1/2 x 19-1/2 inches (100.3 x 49.5 cm)
Signed and dated lower right: *Ph. H. Noyer 1963*

Estimate: $2,500-$3,500
The reserve for this lot is available at HA.com/FineArt.

25221

GEORGE GROSZ (German-American 1893-1959)
Hanging, 1912
Charcoal on paper
11-1/8 x 8-3/8 inches, sheet (28.3 x 21.3 cm)
Signed lower right: *Grosz*

Provenance:
The Estate of George Grosz;
Property from a New York estate

Exhibition:
George Grosz 1893-1959 Retrospective Exhibition, Forum Gallery, 1963, illus. (Berlin, Germany)

Estimate: $8,000-$12,000

The reserve for this lot is available at HA.com/FineArt.

25222

TSUGUHARU FOUJITA (French-Japanese 1896-1968)
Seated Girl With Flowers
Watercolor on paper
12 x 9 inches (31 x 23 cm)
Signed lower center: *Foujita*

Provenance:
Ex-Waugh Collection (New York)

Estimate: $40,000-$60,000

The reserve for this lot is available at HA.com/FineArt.

25223

JEAN-PIERRE JOUFFROY
(French b.1933)
Sailboat, 1963
Oil on board
10 x 8 inches (25.4 x 20.3 cm)
Signed and dated lower left: *Jean-Pierre Jouffroy 63*

Estimate: $1,200-$1,800

The reserve for this lot is available at HA.com/FineArt.

25224

SALVADOR DALI (Spanish 1904-1989)
Alice's Adventures In Wonderland, 1969
One original engraving and twelve heliogravures
17 x 11-1/2 inches (43.2 x 29.2 cm)
Edition 2109/2500

Salvador Dali's Surrealist interpretation of Lewis Carols' *Alice's Adventures in Wonderland,* includes one original engraving and twelve heliogravures with woodcut remarque on Mandeure paper. Published by Maecenas Press-Random House, New York in 1969, the twelve heliogravures are after gouaches done in 1968-69 include *Down The Rabbit Hole; The Pool Of Tears; A Caucus Race And A Long Tale; The Rabbit Sends In A Little Bill; Advice From A Caterpillar; Pig And Pepper; A Mad Tea Party; The Queen's Croquet Ground The Mock Turtle's Story; The Lobster Quadrille; Who Stole The Tarts?;* and *Alice's Evidence.* The original colored etching *Alice,* signed in the plate by the artist complements the signed title page.

Estimate: $3,000-$5,000

This lot is being sold without reserve. Unreserved lots generally open at 50% of the low estimate.

25225

EUROPEAN SCHOOL
Seated Nude
Ink on paper
16 x 13 inches (40.6 x 33 cm)
Signed lower left (indecipherable)

Estimate: $500-$1,000

The reserve for this lot is available at HA.com/FineArt.

25226

JEAN JANSEM
(French b.1920)
Young Male Dancer, Seated
Ink and wash on paper
25-1/2 x 19-1/4 inches (64.8 x 48.9 cm)
Signed upper left: *Jansem*

Estimate: $1,500-$3,000

The reserve for this lot is available at HA.com/FineArt.

25227

KAREL APPEL (Dutch 1921-2006)
Untitled, 1974
Oil on canvas
19-1/2 x 15-1/2 inches (49.5 x 39.4 cm)
Signed and dated at lower right: *appeL.74*

Provenance:
Private collection (Detroit, Michigan)

Appel, a Dutch expressionist painter, studied at the Royal Academy of Fine Arts Amsterdam from 1940-1948. In 1948, he helped found CoBra, a post-War Eurpean avant-garde movement. By 1970, however, his surrealist-automatic technique gave way to a more decorative aesthetic, which is evident in this example.

Estimate: $20,000-$30,000

The reserve for this lot is available at HA.com/FineArt.

SESSION IV
PHOTOGRAPHY

26001

CARLETON E. WATKINS (American 1829-1916)
Mirror View of El Capitan
Image date circa 1872, printed by Isaiah West Taber circa 1880
Ablumen print mounted on board
8 x 12 inches (20.3 x 30.5 cm)

Provenance:
The Collection of Mrs. Rowena Nadig (San Antonio, Texas)

Estimate: $2,000-$4,000

This lot is being sold without reserve. Unreserved lots generally open at 50% of the low estimate.

26002

L.A. HUFFMAN (American 1879 - 1931)
Sunday Morning at the Mission
Printing-Out Paper mounted on board
20 x 16 inches (50.8 x 40.6 cm)
Inscribed on bottom edge: *Sunday Morning at the Mission/©L. A. Huffman*
Stamped on reverse: *L.A. Huffman/All rights reserved/Coffrin's Old West Gallery/1600 Main St.-Miles City, Mt. 59301*

L. A. Huffman (1879-1931) is recognized as a premier photographer of the early American West, providing significant historic documentation. He remains the only photographer to have been inducted into the Hall of Great Westerners at the National Cowboy and Western Heritage Center in Oklahoma City, Oklahoma. The photographs presented here were made by Huffman's noted successor Jack Coffin, circa 1950. These prints are rare collector items, not just because of their age but because they were made from L. A. Huffman's original glass plate negatives. The clarity of the prints is unexcelled.

Estimate: $300-$500

This lot is being sold without reserve. Unreserved lots generally open at 50% of the low estimate.

26003

L.A. HUFFMAN (American 1879-1931)
Portfolio of three photographs from Bronco Bustin at Bow Gun Ranch:
#300-1/2-11 - The First Pull of the Latigo
#300-1/2-13 - Bronco's First Slicker Lesson
Gelatin silver print
11 x 14 inches (27.9 x 35.6 cm)
Last known set of L.A. Huffman contact prints from the original negatives, printed by Jack Coffrin circa 1950
All prints are signed lower right: © *L.A. Huffman*

Estimate: $400-$600

This lot is being sold without reserve. Unreserved lots generally open at 50% of the low estimate.

26005

L.A. HUFFMAN (American 1879-1931)
Portfolio of three photographs of Native Americans:
#300-1/2-11 - The First Pull of the Latigo
#69 - Cheyenne "Brave Wolf" and Squaw Beside the Sweat Lodge - 1901
#133B - Fr. Berthold Reservation, N.D. - 1902
#111 - "Little Crow" and Brother
Gelatin silver print
11 x 14 inches (27.9 x 35.6 cm)
Last known set of L.A. Huffman contact prints from the original negatives, printed by Jack Coffrin circa 1950
All prints are signed lower right: © *L.A. Huffman*

Estimate: $400-$600

This lot is being sold without reserve. Unreserved lots generally open at 50% of the low estimate.

26004

L.A. HUFFMAN (American 1879-1931)
Portfolio of three photographs from Bronco Bustin at Bow Gun Ranch:
#300-1/2-14 - The Ear Twist
#300-1/12-16 - The Bronco Doges the Saddle Blanket
#300-1/2 17 - The Flying Noose Falls True
Gelatin silver print
11 x 14 inches (27.9 x 35.6 cm)
Last known set of L.A. Huffman contact prints from the original negatives, printed by Jack Coffrin circa 1950
All prints are signed lower right: © *L.A. Huffman*

Estimate: $400-$600

This lot is being sold without reserve. Unreserved lots generally open at 50% of the low estimate.

26006

L.A. HUFFMAN (American 1879-1931)
Portfolio of three photographs of Hunting Scenes:
#347 - My First Grizzly - 1181
#332 - Bullard and Big Whitetail - 212 lb. dressed - 1880
#340A - Shield's Hunting Part, Bennett Creek, Montana 1882
Gelatin silver print
11 x 14 inches (27.9 x 35.6 cm)
Last known set of L.A. Huffman contact prints from the original negatives, printed by Jack Coffrin circa 1950
All prints are signed lower right: © *L.A. Huffman*

Estimate: $400-$600

This lot is being sold without reserve. Unreserved lots generally open at 50% of the low estimate.

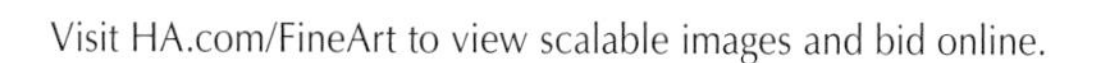

26007

L.A. HUFFMAN (American 1879-1931)
Portfolio of three photographs of Custer's Battlefield:
#201 A - Graves of Unknown- Custer Battlefield - 1877
#204 - The First Monument on Custer's Hill - 1877
#218 - Grave of Col. Keoch - Custer Battlefield - 1877
Gelatin silver print
11 x 14 inches (27.9 x 35.6 cm)
Last known set of L.A. Huffman contact prints from the original negatives, printed by Jack Coffrin circa 1950
All prints are signed lower right: © *L.A. Huffman*

Estimate: $400-$600

This lot is being sold without reserve. Unreserved lots generally open at 50% of the low estimate.

26008

L.A. HUFFMAN (American 1879-1931)
Portfolio of three photographs of life on the Cattle Drive:
#151 - Lubar Cook Making Bread - 1904
#247 - Bringing a Calf to the Branding Fire
#245 - XIT Roundup on the Move - 4:30 A.M. c. 1988
Gelatin silver print
11 x 14 inches (27.9 x 35.6 cm)
Last known set of L.A. Huffman contact prints from the original negatives, printed by Jack Coffrin circa 1950
All prints are signed lower right: © *L.A. Huffman*

Estimate: $400-$600

This lot is being sold without reserve. Unreserved lots generally open at 50% of the low estimate.

26009

L.A. HUFFMAN (American 1879-1931)
Porfolio of three photographs of Miles City, Montana:
#386 - Park St. Miles City, M.T. 1882, Looking North From "The Grey Mule"
#395 - Bull Train At Main and Park Streets - Miles City, 1881
#397 - Custer County Court House, Miles City, M.T. 1884
Gelatin silver print
11 x 14 inches (27.9 x 35.6 cm)
Last known set of L.A. Huffman contact prints from the original negatives, printed by Jack Coffrin circa 1950
All prints are signed lower right: © *L.A. Huffman*

Estimate: $400-$600

This lot is being sold without reserve. Unreserved lots generally open at 50% of the low estimate.

26010

L.A. HUFFMAN (American 1879-1931)
Portfolio of three photographic Western Portraits:
#154-1/2 - Granville Stuart 1883
#122 - Yellowstone Kelly, 1878
#423 - Only and Original Calamity Jane - Miles City - 1880
Gelatin silver print
11 x 14 inches (27.9 x 35.6 cm)
Last known set of L.A. Huffman contact prints from the original negatives, printed by Jack Coffrin circa 1950
All prints are signed lower right: © *L.A. Huffman*

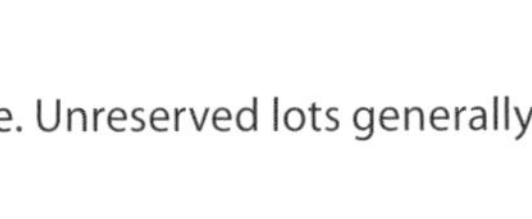

Estimate: $400-$600

This lot is being sold without reserve. Unreserved lots generally open at 50% of the low estimate.

26011

L.A. HUFFMAN (American 1879-1931)
Portfolio of three photographs of cowboys:
#152 - Conrad Kohrs (right) and Ranch Foreman
#307A - Dunn - The Hat X - Horse Wrangler - 1904
#421 - Two Montana Cowboys (c. 1985)
Gelatin silver print
11 x 14 inches (27.9 x 35.6 cm)
Last known set of L.A. Huffman contact prints from the original negatives, printed by Jack Coffrin circa 1950
All prints are signed lower right: © *L.A. Huffman*

Estimate: $400-$600

This lot is being sold without reserve. Unreserved lots generally open at 50% of the low estimate.

26012

EDWARD WESTON (American 1886-1958)
Juniper at Lake Tenayu, 1937
Gelatin silver print, mounted
9-1/2 x 7-1/2 inches (24.1 x 19.1 cm)
Original negative by Edward Weston
Printed by Cole Weston

Provenance:
The Collection of Mrs. Rowena Nadig (San Antonio, Texas)

Estimate: $1,500-$2,000

This lot is being sold without reserve. Unreserved lots generally open at 50% of the low estimate.

26013

ANSEL ADAMS
(American 1902-1984)
Upper Yosemite Falls, Spring
Vintage photograph
9-5/8 x 7-3/8 inches
(24.4 x 18.7 cm)
Edition 13/90
Signed in ink lower right (beneath mat): *Ansel Adams*

Estimate: $3,000-$5,000

This lot is being sold without reserve. Unreserved lots generally open at 50% of the low estimate.

26014

ANSEL ADAMS (American 1902-1984)
Mt. LeConte, Autumn, Great Smokey Mountain National Park,
Negative made circa 1948, printed 1960s
Gelatin silver print
15 x 19 inches (38.1 x 48.3 cm)
Signed lower right on matte: *Ansel Adams*

Estimate: $8,000-$12,000

This lot is being sold **without reserve. Unreserved lots generally open at 50% of the low estimate.**

26015

ANSEL ADAMS (American 1902-1984)
Moon and Half Dome, Yosemite National Park, California
Negative made 1960, printed by Alan Ross from Ansel Adams' original negative under his supervision 1975-79
Gelatin silver print, mounted
9-1/2 x 7-1/4 inches (24.1 x 18.4 cm)
Special edition of photographs of Yosemite by Ansel Adams

Provenance:
The Collection of Mrs. Rowena Nadig (San Antonio, Texas)
The Ansel Adams Gallery (Yosemite Park, California)

Estimate: $800-$1,200

This lot is being sold without reserve. Unreserved lots generally open at 50% of the low estimate.

26016

ANSEL ADAMS (American 1902-1984)
Fern Spring, Dusk, Yosemite Valley, California, circa 1961
Gelatin silver print
12 x 9 inches (30.5 x 22.9 cm)
Signed, print number 420
Original print to accompany the De Luxe Edition of *Ansel Adams: Images, 1923-1974*

Provenance:
The Collection of Mrs. Rowena Nadig (San Antonio, Texas)

Estimate: $2,000-$3,000

This lot is being sold without reserve. Unreserved lots generally open at 50% of the low estimate.

26017

E.O. GOLDBECK
(American 1892-1986)
Galveston's 5th Annual Bathing Girl Revue- May 17 - 18 - 19th '24, 1924
Gelatin silver panoramic contact print
32 x7-1/2 inches (81.3 x 19.1 cm)
Signed lower right: *E.O. Goldbeck*

Provenance:
The Collection of Mrs. Rowena Nadig (San Antonio, Texas)

A native of San Antonio, Texas, photographer Eugene Omar Goldbeck is highly regarded for his panoramic photographs of large groups of people, vast landscapes and cityscapes. Known as the "unofficial photographer of America's military", Goldbeck toured all of the major military bases in and outside of the United States. Utilizing a specialized panoramic Cirkut camera that revolved on a tripod while the film advanced at the same speed, Goldbeck created negatives as large as 10 by 60 inches. All of his images are contact printed—no enlargements were made. Goldbeck established the National Photo Service in 1921, the first and only independent news-photograph supplier headquartered in Texas.

Estimate: $800-$1,200

This lot is being sold without reserve. Unreserved lots generally open at 50% of the low estimate.

26018

E.O. GOLDBECK
(American 1892-1986)
The New York Yankees as Seen in San Antonio, Texas - March 31st 1924 - Babe Ruth in Center of Photo , 1924
Gelatin silver panoramic contact print
24 x 9 inches (61 x 22.9 cm)
Signed lower right: *E.O. Goldbeck*
Inscription lower right: *Goldbeck Foto #199/ For National Photo Service/787 E. Houston St./San Antonio, Texas.*

Provenance:
The Collection of Mrs. Rowena Nadig (San Antonio, Texas)

Estimate: $800-$1,200

This lot is being sold without reserve. Unreserved lots generally open at 50% of the low estimate.

26019

E.O. GOLDBECK (American 1892-1986)
Set of two panoramic photographs of Galveston Beauty Revues

Photograph #1:
Galveston's 5th Annual Bathing Girl Revue - May 17 - 18 - 19th- 24, 1924
Gelatin silver panoramic contact print
32-1/2 x 8-1/2 inches (82.6 x 21.6cm)

Photograph #2:
3rd Annual Bathing Girl Revue, Galveston, Tex., May 14th 1922
Gelatin silver panoramic contact print
27-3/4 x 9 inches (70.5x 22.9 cm)
Inscribed lower center: © *E.O. Goldbeck/S.A. Texas.*

Estimate: $1,500-$2,000

This lot is being sold without reserve. Unreserved lots generally open at 50% of the low estimate.

26020

E.O. GOLDBECK
(American 1892-1986)
Set of two panoramic landscape photographs

Photograph #1:
The Great Pyramid & Sphinx - Cairo, Egypt, 1971
Gelatin silver panoramic contact print
40-1/2 x 9 inches (102.9 x 22.9 cm)
Signed and inscribed lower right: *E.O. Goldbeck/ © Goldbeck/National Photo Service/San Antonio, Texas*

Photograph #2:
The Long Hidden City of the Incas - Machu Picchu, Peru, 1972
Gelatin silver panoramic contact print
55-1/2 x 9 inches (141 x 22.9 cm)
Signed and inscribed lower right: *E.O. Goldbeck/© Goldbeck/Photo 11018721/National Photo Service/San Antonio, Texas*

Estimate: $2,000-$2,500

This lot is being sold without reserve. Unreserved lots generally open at 50% of the low estimate.

26021

E.O. GOLDBECK
(American 1892-1986)
In the "Needles," Black Hills of So.Dakota circa 1925-1930
Gelatin silver panoramic contact print
61 x 8-1/2 inches (154.9 x 21.6 cm)
Signed lower right: *E.O. Goldbeck*

Provenance:
The Collection of Mrs. Rowena Nadig (San Antonio, Texas)

Estimate: $800-$1,200

This lot is being sold without reserve. Unreserved lots generally open at 50% of the low estimate.

26022

E.O. GOLDBECK (American 1892-1986)
Set of three panoramic landscape photographs of American National Parks

Photograph #1:
The Maripos Grove of Big Trees (Sequoia Giganticus), circa 1925-1930
Gelatin silver panoramic contact print
63-1/2 x 9 inches (163.1 x 22.9 cm)
Inscribed lower right: *Goldbeck Foto 977-11/ National Photo Service/San Antonio, Tex.*

Photograph #2:
MT. McKinley and the Alaskan Range - Mt. McKinley National Park, Alaska, circa 1925-1930
Gelatin silver panoramic contact print
44-1/4 x 9 inches (112.4 x 22.9 cm)
Inscribed lower right: *© Goldbeck/Photo No. 1825/National Photo Service/San Antonio, Tex. (partial)*

Photograph #3:
Mirror Lake - Yosemite National Park, circa 1925-1930
Gelatin silver panoramic contact print
22-3/4 x 9 inches (57.8 x 22.9 cm)
Inscribed lower right: *© E.O. Goldbeck Photo -975-B/National Photo & News Service/San Antonio, Tex.*

Estimate: $3,000-$3,500

This lot is being sold without reserve. Unreserved lots generally open at 50% of the low estimate.

26023

E.O. GOLDBECK (American 1892-1986)
Set of seven color panoramic landscape photographs

Photograph #1:
Tower of London and Tower Bridge, London England, circa 1980
Color C-print
17-3/4 x 8-3/4 inches (45.1 x 22.2 cm)
Inscribed lower left: *Goldbeck Co.*

Photograph #2:
El Capitan, Bridal Veil Falls, The Merced River Etc. Yosemite National Park, 1981
Color C-Print
44 x 8-1/2 inches (111.8 x 21.6 cm)
Inscribed lower right: © *Goldbeck/ Photo 1981*

Photography #3:
Grand Canyon, Arizonia, circa 1980
Color C-Print
51 x 9 inches (129.5 x 22.9 cm)
Inscribed lower right: *Goldbeck*

Photograph #4:
Yosemite National Park, circa 1980
Color C-print
53-1/2 x 9 inches (135.9 x 22.9 cm)
Inscribed lower right: *E.O.Goldbeck Photo/San Antonio, Texas*
Photograph #5
Niagra Falls, circa 1980
Color C-print
34 x 9 inches (86.4 x22.9 cm)
Inscribed lower right: *Copyright Goldbeck Co*

Photograph #6:
View from Glacier Point - Yosemite National Park, 1980
Color C-Print
52 x 9 inches (132.1 x 22.9 cm)
Inscribed lower right: *© Goldbeck 1980/E.O. Goldbeck (signature)*

Photograph #7
Mariposa Grove - California, 1981
Color C-Print
52 x 9 inches (132.1 x 22.9 cm)
Inscribed lower right: © *Goldbeck Photo 1981*

Estimate: $2,000-$3,000

This lot is being sold without reserve. Unreserved lots generally open at 50% of the low estimate.

26024

MICHAEL A. SMITH (American b.1942)
Oregon Coast, 1975
Gelatin silver print, mounted
9-1/2 x 7-1/2 inches (24.1 x 19.1 cm)
Signed on matte: *Michael A. Smith*

Provenance:
The Collection of Mrs. Rowena Nadig (San Antonio, Texas)

Estimate: $500-$700

This lot is being sold without reserve. Unreserved lots generally open at 50% of the low estimate.

26025

MICHAEL A. SMITH
(American b.1942)
New Orleans, 1985
Gelatin silver print, mounted.
19-1/2 x 7-1/2 inches (49.5 x 19.1 cm)
Signed and dated on matte:
Michael A. Smith / 1985

Provenance:
The Collection of Mrs. Rowena Nadig (San Antonio, Texas)

Estimate: $800-$1,200

This lot is being sold without reserve. Unreserved lots generally open at 50% of the low estimate.

26026

MICHAEL A. SMITH (American b.1942)
East side of the Siennas (from Bristlecone Pine National Forest, California), 1982
Gelatin silver print, mounted.
19-1/2 x 7-1/2 inches (49.5 x 19.1 cm)
Signed and dated on matte:
Michael A. Smith / 1982

Provenance:
The Collection of Mrs. Rowena Nadig (San Antonio, Texas)

Estimate: $800-$1,200

This lot is being sold without reserve. Unreserved lots generally open at 50% of the low estimate.

26027

MICHAEL A. SMITH
(American b.1942)
Toroweap Overlook, Grand Canyon, Arizona 1978
Gelatin silver print
19-1/2 x 7-1/2 inches (49.5 x 19.1 cm)
Signed and dated on matte:
Michael A. Smith / 1978

Provenance:
The Collection of Mrs. Rowena Nadig (San Antonio, Texas)

Estimate: $800-$1,200

This lot is being sold without reserve. Unreserved lots generally open at 50% of the low estimate.

26028

MICHAEL A. SMITH
(American, b.1942)
New Orleans, 1984
Gelatin silver print, mounted.
Signed and dated on matte:
Michael A. Smith / 1984

Provenance:
The Collection of Mrs. Rowena Nadig (San Antonio, Texas)

Estimate: $500-$700

This lot is being sold without reserve. Unreserved lots generally open at 50% of the low estimate.

26029

ARTHUR ROTHSTEIN (American 1915-1985)
Plantation, Owner's Daughter Checks the Weight of Cotton, Kaufman County, Texas
Negative made 1936, printed by the Library of Congress in 1976,
archivally washed and selenium toned by Steve Satterwhite who initialed on reverse
Gelatin silver print
9-1/2 x 7 inches (24.1 x 17.8 cm)
Signed on matte: *Arthur Rothstein*

Provenance:
The Collection of Mrs. Rowena Nadig (San Antonio, Texas)

Exhibition:
The Witkin Gallery Inc., New York, New York

Estimate: $1,000-$1,200

This lot is being sold without reserve. Unreserved lots generally open at 50% of the low estimate.

26030

FARM SECURTIY ADMINISTRATION PHOTOGRAPHS
Portfolio of seven photographs selected and printed under the supervision of Arthur Rothstein
Gelatin silver prints
11 x 14 inches (27.9 x 35.6 cm)

ARTHUR ROTHSTEIN (American 1915 - 1985)
The Bleached Skull of a Steer on the Dry Sun-baked Earth of the South Dakota Badlands, 1936;
Farmer and Sons Walking in the Face of a Dust Storm. Cimarron County, Oklahoma, 1936;
Mr. and Mrs. Andy Bahain, FSA (Farm Security Administration) borrowers, on their Farm near Kersey, Colorado, 1939

DOROTHEA LANGE (American 1895 - 1965)
Hoe culture. Alabama Tenant Farmer near Anniston, 1936

WALKER EVANS (American 1903 - 1975)
Bethlehem Graveyard and Steel Mill. Pennsylvania, 1935

BEN SHAHN (Lithuanian-born American 1898-1969)
A Deputy with a Gun on his Hip During the September 1935 Strike in Morgantown, West Virginia, 1935:
Pastor Greeting his Parishioners, Linworth, Ohio, 1938

To view all items in this lot please visit HA.com/FIneArt.

Estimate: $3,000-$5,000

This lot is being sold without reserve. Unreserved lots generally open at 50% of the low estimate.

26031

EDWARD STEICHEN (American 1879-1973)
Steeplechase Day, Paris, 1903
Photo grauvre for Camera Work
8 x 6 inches (20.3 x 15.2 cm)

Provenance:
The Collection of Mrs. Rowena Nadig (San Antonio, Texas)

Exhibition:
San Antonio Museum of Art, San Antonio, Texas, *American Photography: A History in Pictures,* 1994

Estimate: $2,000-$4,000

This lot is being sold without reserve. Unreserved lots generally open at 50% of the low estimate.

26032

ERNEST WATLER HISTED (British-American 1862-1947)
A Photgraph of George Bernard Shaw, circa 1905
4 x 6-3/4 inches (10.2 x 17.1 cm)
Platinum print, vintage

Provenance:
The Collection of Mrs. Rowena Nadig (San Antonio, Texas);
Archibald Henderson (1877-1963), Shaw biographer and Mathematics professor, University of North Carolina (Chapel Hill, North Carolina)

Estimate: $600-$900

This lot is being sold without reserve. Unreserved lots generally open at 50% of the low estimate.

26033

EDWARD STEICHEN (American 1879 - 1973)
La Cigale, 1906
Photo grauvre for *Camera Work*
6-1/2 x 7 inches (16.5 x 17.8 cm)

Estimate: $1,500-$2,500

This lot is being sold without reserve. Unreserved lots generally open at 50% of the low estimate.

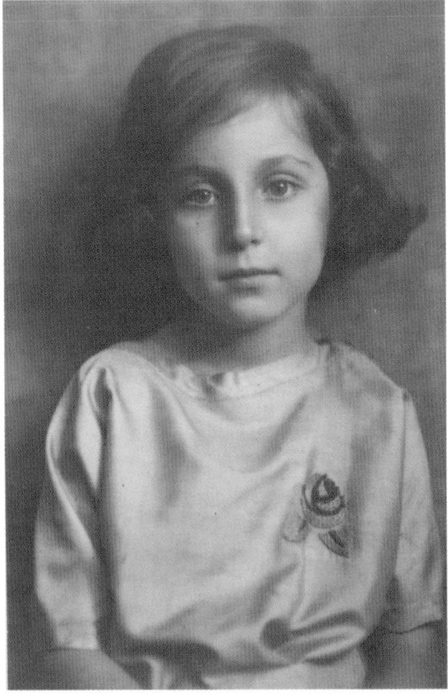

26034

NICKOLAS MURAY (Hungarian American 1892 - 1965)
Two portraits of a young girl, 1922
Silver bromide print mounted on board
9-1/2 x 6 inches (24.1 x 15.2 cm)
Signed and dated on matte:*1922/Muray*
9-1/2 x 7-1/4 inches (24.1 x 18.4 cm)
Signed and dated on matte:*1922/Muray*
Embossed on image lower left:*Nickolas Muray/New York*

Estimate: $400-$600

This lot is being sold without reserve. Unreserved lots generally open at 50% of the low estimate.

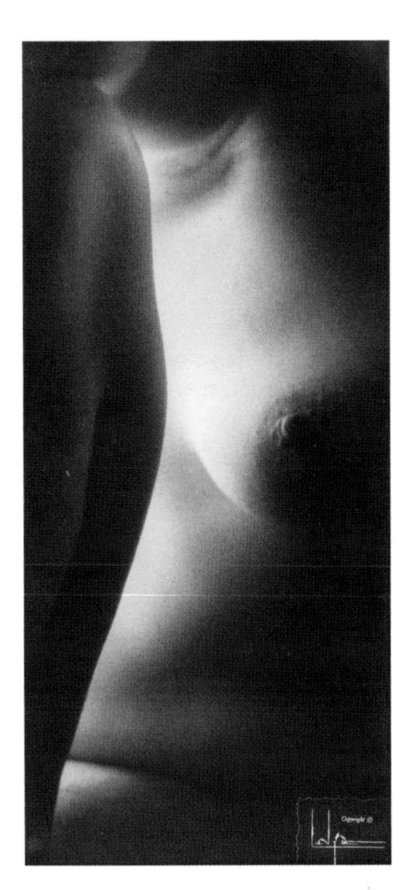

26035

LEE NYE (American 1926 - 1999)
Untitled (Nude from Black Series)
Gelatin silver print
10 x 5 inches (24.4 x 12.7 cm)
Imprinted lower right: *Copyright © Lee Nye*

Estimate: $400-$600
This lot is being sold without reserve. Unreserved lots generally open at 50% of the low estimate.

26036

LEE FRIEDLANDER
(American b.1934)
*Kyoto,*1977
Photo grauvre
13 x 8-3/4 inches
(20.3 x 19.7cm)
Edition 2/50
Signed and numbered:
2/50 / Lee Friedlander

Provenance:
The Collection of
Mrs. Rowena Nadig
(San Antonio, Texas)

Exhibition:
San Antonio Museum of Art, San Antonio, Texas, *American Photography: A History in Pictures,* 1994

Estimate: $3,000-$5,000
This lot is being sold without reserve. Unreserved lots generally open at 50% of the low estimate.

26037

ELEANOR PARKE CUSTIS (American 1897-1983)
Mechanics and Man, 1938
Vintage bromide print
16-1/2 x 14 inches (41.9 x 35.6 cm)
Signed on fragment of a vintage overmat: *Eleanor Parke Custis*

Estimate: $1,000-$1,500

*The reserve for this l*ot is available at HA.com/FineArt.

26038

ARTHUR SMITH GRAY
(American 1884-1976)
Refinery I and *Refinery II,* circa 1937
Two vintage gelatin silver prints
13-1/4 x 10-1/4 inches (33.7 x 26 cm);
10-1/2 x 13-1/2 inches (26.7 x 34.3 cm)
Artist's estate stamp verso

Provenance:
Estate of the artist

Estimate: $500-$700

*The reserve for this l*ot is available at HA.com/FineArt.

26039

WILLY RONIS (French b. 1910)
Rue Rambuteau, 1946
Gelatin silver print
16 x12 inches (40.6 x 30.5 cm)
Inscribed on reverse:*rue Rambuteau/1946 - P16/232 - tirage/1994*
Stamped on reverse: *©WILLY RONIS/46, Rue de Lagny/75020 PARIS/(1) 43.70.39.30*

Estimate: $2,000-$2,500

This lot is being sold without reserve. Unreserved lots generally open at 50% of the low estimate.

26040

ALFRED EISENSTAEDT (American 1898-1995)
Sailor, 1954
Gelatin silver print
9-3/8 x 7-1/2 inches (23.8 x 19.1 cm)
Photographer's stamp on reverse

American photographer, Alfred Eisenstaedt, is renowned for his captivating iconic images of American life featured on over 90 covers of Life magazine from 1936 to 1972. He is most famous for his photograph, *VJ Day in Times Square,* capturing an American sailor kissing a young woman on August 15, 1945.

Estimate: $2,000-$3,000

This lot is being sold without reserve. Unreserved lots generally open at 50% of the low estimate.

26041

BORIS IGNATOVITCH (Russian 1899 - 1976)
Monument to Ferdinand Lassalle, Leningrad, 1930
Gelatin silver print
11-1/2 x 8 inches (29.2 x 20.3 cm)
Stamped and signed on reverse: *B. Ignatovitch*

Estimate: $700-$900

This lot is being sold without reserve. Unreserved lots generally open at 50% of the low estimate.

26042

UMBO (OTTO UMBEHR) (German 1902 - 1980)
Untitled (Portrait of an artist)
Image date 1927-1930, Print date 1980
Gelatin silver print
9 x 7 inches (22.9 x 17.8 cm)
Signed lower right: *Umbo*
Stamped on reverse:*UMBO Portfolio lo Photographien 1927-1930/ Galerie RUDOLF KICKEN und Photograph, Klion 1980/PRINT NR 46/50*

German photographer Umbo (Otto Umbehr), along with contemporary Moholy- Nagy, is one of the most important photographers to emerge from the Bauhaus where he studied from 1921 - 1923. Moreover, Umbo was a pioneer in German photojournalism working for the notable German photo agency, Dephot.

Estimate: $600-$800

This lot is being sold without reserve. Unreserved lots generally open at 50% of the low estimate.

26043

ANDRÉ KERTÉSZ (Hungarian-American 1894 - 1985)
Chez Mondrian, 1926
Gelatin silver print, mounted.
9-3/4 x 7-1/2 inches (24.8 x 19.1 cm)
Signed on matte: *A. Kertesz*
Titled and dated on reverse: *Chez Mondrian/Paris/1926*

Photographer Andre Kertész is known for his extended study of Washington Square Park and his distorted nudes of the 1930s. Working as an aritist for over seventy years, Kertész created images with minimal poetic compositions. *Chez Mondrian,* one of his most celebrated photographs, juxtaposes a uniquely lit interior with a simple still life.

Estimate: $8,000-$10,000

This lot is being sold without reserve. Unreserved lots generally open at 50% of the low estimate.

26044

ANDRÉ KERTÉSZ (Hungarian-American 1894- 1985)
Melancholic Tulip, 1939
Gelatin silver print
14 x 11 inches (35.6 x 27.9 cm)
Signed lower right: *A. Kertesz*
Numbered lower left: *32/150*
Titled and dated on reverse: *Melanchonic Tulip/Feb. 10 - 1939*

Kertész's widely diverse oeuvre ranges from cityscapes to still life studies. In *Melancholic Tulip,* Kertész transforms ordinary still life subject matter into an extraordinary composition. Delicate yet dramatic lighting projects an emotive atmosphere that permits the tulip to behave as a metaphor of human condition.

Estimate: $5,000-$7,000

This lot is being sold without reserve. Unreserved lots generally open at 50% of the low estimate.

26045

RUTH BERNHARD (American 1905 - 2006)
In the Box, 1962
Gelatin silver print, mounted.
5-2/8 x 9-1/2 inches (13.4 x 24.2 cm)
Signed and numbered on matte: *Ruth Bernhard - 56/76*
Stamped on reverse: *Ruth Bernhard: The Eternal Body/ Title: In the Box-horizontal/ Date photographed: 1962/ Number: 56/75 / Special Edition Print 1984*

This item includes a monograph of Ruth Bernhard's nudes *The Eternal Body,* in which *In the Box* is featured. The monograph published by Photography West, received recognition as the Photography Book of the Year, earning Bernhard widespread acclaim as a photographer of the nude.

Estimate: $6,000-$8,000

This lot is being sold without reserve. Unreserved lots generally open at 50% of the low estimate.

26046

TIM GIDAL (German 1909-1996)
Munich, 1929
Gelatin silver print
6-1/2 x 9-1/2 inches (16.5 x 24.1 cm)
Titled, dated and signed: *Munich 1929/ Tim Gidal*

Provenance:
The Collection of Mrs. Rowena Nadig (San Antonio, Texas)

Estimate: $1,000-$1,500

This lot is being sold without reserve. Unreserved lots generally open at 50% of the low estimate.

26047

IMOGEN CUNNINGHAM (American 1883-1976)
My Father at 90, 1936
Gelatin silver print, mounted
9-1/2 x 7-1/2 inches (24.1 x 19.1 cm)
Signed and dated on matte: *Imogen Cunningham, 1936*

Provenance:
The Collection of Mrs. Rowena Nadig (San Antonio, Texas)

Estimate: $2,000-$4,000

This lot is being sold without reserve. Unreserved lots generally open at 50% of the low estimate.

26048

AARON SISKIND
Providence, 1972
Gelatin silver print
6 x 6 inches (15.2 x 15.2 cm)
Signed on matte

Provenance:
The Collection of Mrs. Rowena Nadig (San Antonio, Texas)

Exhibition:
McNay Art Museum, San Antonio, Texas, *Ray Metzker Photographs from the Collection of Perry and Rowena Nadig: December 10, 1996 - February 9, 1997;*
San Antonio Museum of Art, San Antonio, Texas, *American Photography: A History in Pictures,* 1994

Estimate: $2,000-$3,000

This lot is being sold without reserve. Unreserved lots generally open at 50% of the low estimate.

26049

MINOR WHITE

Essence of a Boat, circa 1960
Gelatin silver print, mounted.
7 x 9 inches (17.8 x 22.9 cm)

Provenance:
The Collection of Mrs. Rowena Nadig (San Antonio, Texas)

Estimate: $2,000-$3,000

This lot is being sold without reserve. Unreserved lots generally open at 50% of the low estimate.

26050

MINOR WHITE
(American 1908-1976)
Untitled (Rock Abstraction)
Vintage silver print
6 x 7-1/2 inches (15.2 x 19.1 cm)
Unsigned

Estimate: $2,000-$3,000

The reserve for this lot is available at HA.com/FineArt.

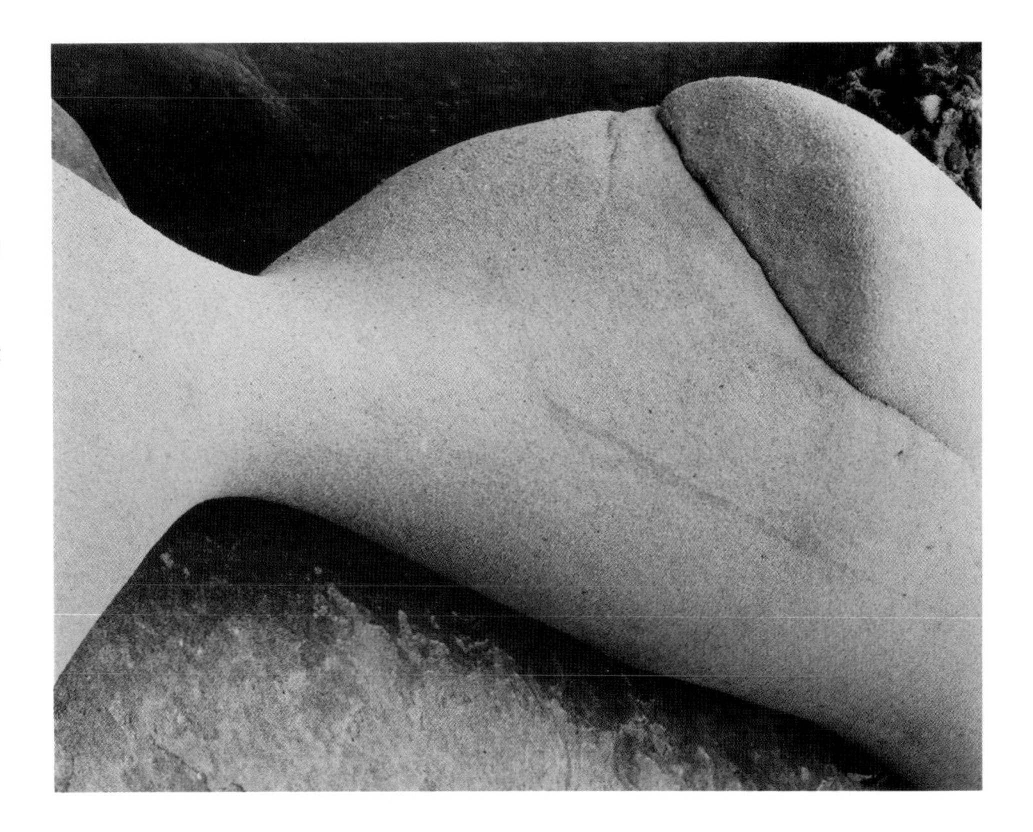

26051

MINOR WHITE
(American 1908-1976)
Untitled (Portrait of a Woman with Rock Abstraction)
Vintage silver print
10-1/2 x 13 inches (26.7 x 33 cm)
Unsigned

Estimate: $2,500-$3,500

The reserve for this lot is available at HA.com/FineArt.

26052

BARBARA MORGAN (American 1900-1992)
Martha Graham
Vintage silver print
6 x 11-1/4 inches (15.2 x 28.6 cm)
Unsigned

Estimate: $1,000-$1,500

*The reserve for this l*ot is available at HA.com/FineArt.

26053

WILLIAM M. RITTASE (American 1887-1968)
Untitled (Dance)
Vintage silver print
10-1/2 x 13-3/4 inches (26.7 x 34.9 cm)
Signed lower right: *Rittase*

Estimate: $500-$700

*The reserve for this l*ot is available at HA.com/FineArt.

26054

RAY METZKER (American b.1931)
75 DQ-23 II, circa 1970-1980
Gelatin silver print, unique solarization process
11 x 14 inches (27.9 x 35.6 cm)
Signed verso

Provenance:
The Collection of Mrs. Rowena Nadig (San Antonio, Texas)

Exhibited:
McNay Art Museum, San Antonio, Texas, *Ray Metzker Photographs from the Collection of Perry and Rowena Nadig: December 10, 1996 - February 9, 1997*

Estimate: $1,200-$1,800

This lot is being sold without reserve. Unreserved lots generally open at 50% of the low estimate.

26055

RAY METZKER (American b.1931)
64 CS-8, circa 1960
Gelatin silver print
9 x 6-1/2 inches (22.9 x 16.5 cm)
Edition 6/85
Signed verso

Provenance:
The Collection of Mrs. Rowena Nadig (San Antonio, Texas)

Exhibition:
McNay Art Museum, San Antonio, Texas, *Ray Metzker Photographs from the Collection of Perry and Rowena Nadig: December 10, 1996 - February 9, 1997*

Estimate: $1,000-$1,500

This lot is being sold without reserve. Unreserved lots generally open at 50% of the low estimate.

26056

RAY METZKER (American b.1931)
Sand Creatures, Atlantic City, 1968
Gelatin silver print
6-3/4 x 4-3/4 inches (17.1 x 12.1 cm)
Edition 2/20
Signed verso

Provenance:
The Collection of Mrs. Rowena Nadig (San Antonio, Texas)

Exhibition:
McNay Art Museum, San Antonio, Texas, *Ray Metzker Photographs from the Collection of Perry and Rowena Nadig: December 10, 1996 - February 9, 1997*

Estimate: $4,000-$6,000

This lot is being sold without reserve. Unreserved lots generally open at 50% of the low estimate.

26057

RAY METZKER (American b.1931)
Chicago, 1981
Gelatin silver print
7-1/2 x 11 inches (19.1 x 27.9 cm)
Edition 5/20
Signed verso

Provenance:
The Collection of Mrs. Rowena Nadig (San Antonio, Texas)

Exhibition:
McNay Art Museum, San Antonio, Texas, *Ray Metzker Photographs from the Collection of Perry and Rowena Nadig: December 10, 1996 - February 9, 1997*

Estimate: $2,000-$3,000

This lot is being sold without reserve. Unreserved lots generally open at 50% of the low estimate.

26058

RAY METZKER (American b.1931)
City Whispers, Philadelphia, 1983
Gelatin silver print
9-1/2 x 9-1/2 inches (24.1 x 24.1 cm)
Edition 7/30
Signed verso

Provenance:
The Collection of Mrs. Rowena Nadig (San Antonio, Texas)

Exhibitions:
McNay Art Museum, San Antonio, Texas, *Ray Metzker Photographs from the Collection of Perry and Rowena Nadig: December 10, 1996 - February 9, 1997;*
San Antonio Museum of Art, San Antonio, Texas, *American Photography: A History in Pictures,* 1994

Estimate: $2,000-$4,000

This lot is being sold without reserve. Unreserved lots generally open at 50% of the low estimate.

26059

JUDY DATER (American b.1941)
Untitled, 1979
Color C-print
8 x 8 inches (20.3 x 20.3 cm)
Signed lower right: *Judy Dater*

Provenance:
The Collection of Mrs. Rowena Nadig (San Antonio, Texas)

Estimate: $700-$900

This lot is being sold without reserve. Unreserved lots generally open at 50% of the low estimate.

26060

ROBERT CAPA
(American 1913-1954)
Attack Pictures Sequence
D-Day Invasion-Images of War (Sequence B), 1944
Gelatin silver print
11 x 14 inches (27.9 x 35.6 cm)
One of the ten photos selected from the eleven surviving negatives and published by LIFE on June 19, 1944.

Provenance:
The Collection of Mrs. Rowena Nadig (San Antonio, Texas)

Estimate: $3,000-$5,000

This lot is being sold without reserve. Unreserved lots generally open at 50% of the low estimate.

26061

MARY ELLEN MARK (American b.1941)
Mother Teresa, Calcutta, 1980
Gelatin silver print
12 x 8-1/2 inches (30.5 x 21 cm)
Signed, titled, and dated verso:*Mary Ellen Mark/ Mother Theresa Calcutta/1980*

Provenance:
The Collection of Mrs. Rowena Nadig (San Antonio, Texas)

Estimate: $1,000-$1,500

This lot is being sold without reserve. Unreserved lots generally open at 50% of the low estimate.

26062

MARY ELLEN MARK
(American b. 1941)
Marlon Brando: On the set of "Apocalypse Now", 1977
Gelatin silver print
8-1/2 x 12 inches
(21.6 x 30.5 cm)
Stamped on reverse

Estimate: $500-$800

This lot is being sold without reserve. Unreserved lots generally open at 50% of the low estimate.

26063

MARY ELLEN MARK
(American b. 1941)
Marlon Brando: On the set of "Apocalypse Now", 1977
Gelatin silver print
8-1/2 x 12 inches
(21.6 x 30.5 cm)
Stamped on reverse

Estimate: $500-$800

This lot is being sold without reserve. Unreserved lots generally open at 50% of the low estimate.

26064

MARY ELLEN MARK (American b. 1941)
Marlon Brando: On the set of "Apocalypse Now", 1977
Gelatin silver print
8-1/2 x 12 inches (21.6 x 30.5 cm)
Stamped on reverse

Estimate: $500-$800

This lot is being sold without reserve. Unreserved lots generally open at 50% of the low estimate.

26065

MARY ELLEN MARK (American b. 1941)
Marlon Brando: On the set of "Apocalypse Now", 1977
Gelatin silver print
8-1/2 x 12 inches (21.6 x 30.5 cm)
Stamped on reverse

Estimate: $500-$800

This lot is being sold without reserve. Unreserved lots generally open at 50% of the low estimate.

26066

STAN HEALY (American 1918 - 1996)
Untitled (Boy with Rifle)
Gelatin silver print
14 x 11 inches (35.6 x 27.9 cm)
Stamped on reverse: *#2 in an Edition of 100/© Stan Healy Collection/Timothy Gordon/ Missoula, MT*

Estimate: $200-$400

This lot is being sold without reserve. Unreserved lots generally open at 50% of the low estimate.

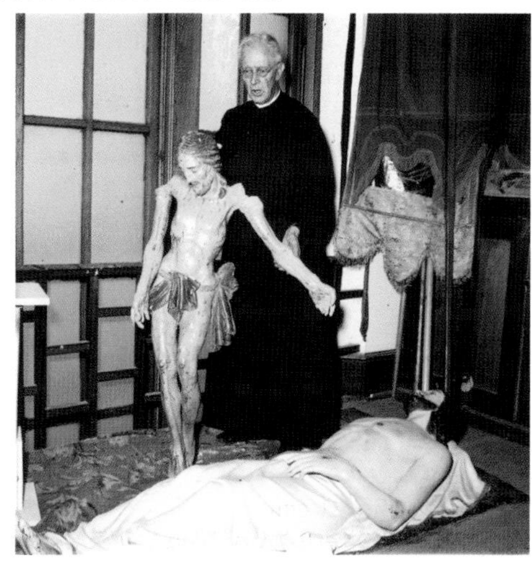

26067

STAN HEALY (American 1918 - 1996)
Untitled (Priest)
Gelatin silver print
14 x 11 inches (35.6 x 27.9 cm)
Stamped on reverse: *#2 in an Edition of 100/© Stan Healy Collection/Timothy Gordon/ Missoula, MT*

Estimate: $200-$400

This lot is being sold without reserve. Unreserved lots generally open at 50% of the low estimate.

26068

STAN HEALY (American 1918 - 1996)
Untitled (Lost Child at Police Station)
Gelatin silver print
14 x 11 inches (35.6 x 27.9 cm)
Stamped on reverse: *#2 in an Edition of 100/© Stan Healy Collection/Timothy Gordon/ Missoula, MT*

Estimate: $200-$400

This lot is being sold without reserve. Unreserved lots generally open at 50% of the low estimate.

26070

STAN HEALY (American 1918 - 1996)
Untitled (Woman with Gun)
Gelatin silver print
14 x 11 inches (35.6 x 27.9 cm)
Stamped on reverse: *Stan Healy Collection/© T.G. 2000/#13 of 100*

Estimate: $200-$400

This lot is being sold without reserve. Unreserved lots generally open at 50% of the low estimate.

26069

STAN HEALY (American 1918 - 1996)
Untitled (Mirror reflection)
Gelatin silver print
14 x 11 inches (35.6 x 27.9 cm)
Stamped on reverse: *Stan Healy Collection/© T.G. 2000/#13 of 100*

Estimate: $200-$400

This lot is being sold without reserve. Unreserved lots generally open at 50% of the low estimate.

26071

STAN HEALY
(American 1918 -1996)
Untitled (Native American)
Gelatin silver print
14 x 11 inches (35.6 x 27.9 cm)
Stamped on reverse: *Stan Healy Collection/© T.G. 2000/ # 13 of 100*

Estimate: $200-$400

This lot is being sold without reserve. Unreserved lots generally open at 50% of the low estimate.

26072

STAN HEALY (American 1918 - 1996)
Untitled (Diner Crime Scene)
Gelatin silver print
14 x 11 inches (35.6 x 27.9 cm)
Stamped on reverse: *Stan Healy Collection/© T.G. 2000/#13 of 100*

Estimate: $200-$400

This lot is being sold without reserve. Unreserved lots generally open at 50% of the low estimate.

26073

STAN HEALY (American 1918 -1996)
Untitled (Native American Child in Train Station)
Gelatin silver print
14 x 11 inches (35.6 x 27.9 cm)
Stamped on reverse: *Stan Healy Collection/© T.G. 2000/ # 13 of 100*

Estimate: $200-$400

This lot is being sold without reserve. Unreserved lots generally open at 50% of the low estimate.

26074

STAN HEALY (American 1918 - 1996)
Untitled (Car Crash)
Gelatin silver print
14 x 11 inches (35.6 x 27.9 cm)
Stamped on reverse: *#2 in an Edition of 100/© Stan Healy Collection/Timothy Gordon/Missoula, MT*

Estimate: $200-$400

This lot is being sold without reserve. Unreserved lots generally open at 50% of the low estimate.

26075

SALLY MANN
(American b.1951)
Jessie in the Wind, 1989
Gelatin silver print
7-1/2 x 9-1/2 inches
(19.1 x 24.1 cm)
Signed, titled and dated verso: *Jesse in the Wind/ © 1989 Sally Mann/ 4/25*

Estimate: $6,000-$8,000
This lot is being sold without reserve. Unreserved lots generally open at 50% of the low estimate.

26076

NIC NICOSIA (American b. 1951)
Untitled #9, 1992
Gelatin silver print
36 x 36 inches (91.4 x 91.4 cm)

Provenance:
Dallas Collection, acquired directly from the artist
Dallas native, Nic Nicosia, captures the emotion of contemporary American life, blending humor with taboo issues such as lust and violence that pervade many aspects of modern society. Dramatic lighting and compositional choices add mystery to typically mundane backgrounds of everyday life: kitchens, bedrooms, backyards. Nicosia's photographs have been exhibited internationally and are in the collections of numerous museums including the Museum of Modern Art and the Guggenheim Museum.

Estimate: $3,500-$4,000
This lot is being sold without reserve. Unreserved lots generally open at 50% of the low estimate.

26077

NIC NICOSIA (American b. 1951)
Untitled #1, 1991
Gelatin silver print
36 x 36 inches (91.4 x 91.4 cm)

Provenance:
Dallas Collection, acquired directly from the artist

Estimate: $3,500-$4,000

This lot is being sold without reserve. Unreserved lots generally open at 50% of the low estimate.

26078

NIC NICOSIA (American b. 1951)
Untitled #10, 1992
Gelatin silver print
36 x 36 inches (91.4 x 91.4 cm)

Provenance:
Dallas Collection, acquired directly from the artist

Estimate: $3,500-$4,000

This lot is being sold without reserve. Unreserved lots generally open at 50% of the low estimate.

26079

NIC NICOSIA (American b. 1951)
Untitled #3, 1991
Gelatin silver print
36 x 36 inches (91.4 x 91.4 cm)

Provenance:
Dallas Collection, acquired directly from the artist

Estimate: $3,500-$4,000

This lot is being sold without reserve. Unreserved lots generally open at 50% of the low estimate.

26080

NIC NICOSIA (American b. 1951)
Untitled #8, 1992
Gelatin silver print
36 x 36 inches (91.4 x 91.4 cm)

Provenance:
Dallas Collection, acquired directly from the artist

Estimate: $3,500-$4,000

This lot is being sold without reserve. Unreserved lots generally open at 50% of the low estimate.

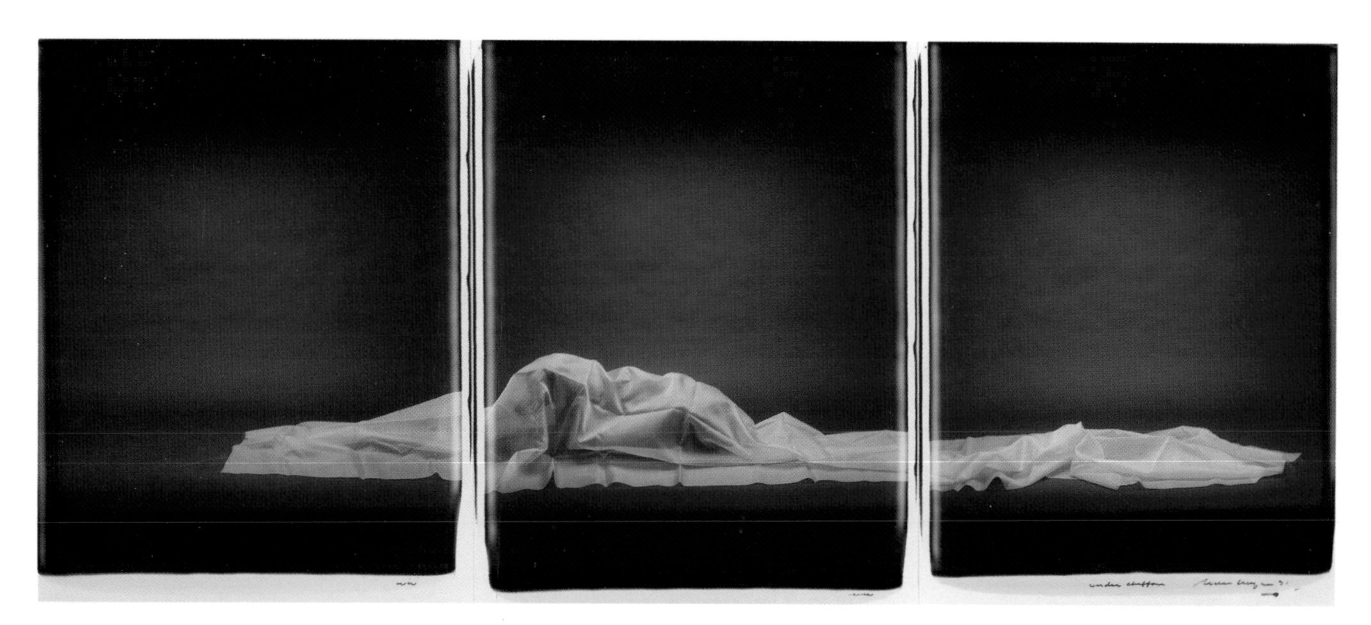

26081

WILLIAM WEGMAN (American b. 1943)
Under Chiffon (Triptych), circa 1989
Polaroid
24 x 20 inches each (61 x 50.8 cm)
Titled and signed on lower right of third image: *Under Chiffon/ William Wegman*

Provenance:
Private collector (Dallas, Texas);
Gerald Peters Gallery (Dallas, Texas)

Photographer William Wegman graduated from both the Massachusetts College of Art, Boston, and the University of Illinois, Champaign-Urbana, with a BFA and MFA in painting respectively. After teaching at various universities, Wegman's interests in areas beyond painting ultimately led him to photography. Wegman is famous for his compositions involving his Weimaraner dogs in various costumes and poses. Wegman's most prominent photographs were made on a large format Polaroid camera, the method implemented in *Under Chiffon,* unlike his more recent works which are shot in digital format.

While living in Long Beach, California, Wegman acquired Man Ray, his first Weimaraner which signaled the start of his now famous oeuvre. In 1972, Wegman and Man Ray moved to New York and in 1986, a new dog, Fay Ray, came into Wegman's life, and soon thereafter a new series of portraits emerged, marked by Wegman's use of the Polaroid 20 x 24 camera. Fay Ray is the subject of *Under Chiffon.* Wegman's artwork has been exhibited in museums and galleries internationally, including a traveling retrospective of his work that included an exihibition at the renowned Whitney Museum of American Art in New York.

Estimate: $15,000-$20,000

This lot is being sold without reserve. Unreserved lots generally open at 50% of the low estimate.

End of Auction

ARTIST INDEX

Heritage Auction #652 – Index to Artists by Lot Number

Please note: This auction is comprised of two separate catalogs. If you are interested in a particular artist not included in the catolog(s) you received, you may view additional lots online at HA.com or request a printed catalog by calling 866-835-3243 and reference code FLY6757.

Artists listed in green have works featured in a separate volume, Art of the American West.
Artists listed in brown have works featured in this volume, which includes Sessions I, III, and IV of Heritage Fine Art auction #652.
Those in black have works in both volumes.

A

ACHENBACH, ANDREAS 25086
ADAMS, ANSEL 26013, 26014, 26015, 26016
ADOMEIT, GEORGE GUSTAV 23173
AMERICAN 19TH CENTURY 23001, 23020, 23047
AMERICAN SCHOOL 23001, 23005, 23010
AMERICAN TONALIST SCHOOL 23116
ANDRE, ALBERT 25142
ANGUIANO, RAUL 23198
APPEL, KAREL 25227
ARANDA, JOSÉ JIMÉNEZ Y 25129
AUBRY, EMILE 25197
AVERY, MARCH 23203
AVERY, MILTON 23185, 23186, 23187

B

BACON, CHARLES ROSWELL 23142
BAIRD, WILLIAM BAPTISTE 23037
BAKST, LEON 25167
BALINK, HENRY CORNELIUS 24025
BARRETT, BILL 23232
BARUCCI, PIETRO 25146
BASKIN, LEONARD 23221
BAUCHANT, ANDRE 25200
BEARD, WILLIAM HOLBROOK 23018
BELLEUSE, PIERRE CARRIER 25158
BELLUSCI, GUSTAVO 25134
BENSON, FRANK WESTON 23098
BENTON, THOMAS HART 24070, 24071
BERANGER, ANTOINE 25059
BERG, JOAN 25115
BERNHARD, RUTH 26045
BERTHELSEN, JOHANN 23162, 23163
BEST, ARTHUR WILLIAM 23082
BIGG, WILLIAM REDMORE 25057
BISSOLO, Ascribed to PIER FRANCESCO 25001
BISTTRAM, EMIL 23175, 23176, 23177, 23178, 23179, 23180, 23181, 23182
BLACK, LAVERNE NELSON 24004
BLANCHARD, ANTOINE 25217
BLANKE, MARIA ELSA 23092
BLUM, ROBERT FREDERICK 23030
BOILLY, Attributed to LOUIS-LÉOPOLD 25047
BOSA, LOUIS 23195
BOSTON, FREDERICK JAMES 23066
BOUAT, H. 25023
BOUVARD, ANTOINE 25145
BOWDOIN, HARRIETTE 23208
BOYD, RUTHERFORD 23102
BRAUN, MAURICE 24037
BRECKENRIDGE, HUGH H. 23096
BRONZINO, After AGNOLO 25002
BROWNE, BYRON 23194
BROWNE, GEORGE ELMER 23155
BRUSH, GEORGE DE FOREST 23103
BUFF, CONRAD 24046, 24047
BURCHFIELD, CHARLES EPHRAIM 23107, 23108
BURLIUK, DAVID 25189
BURNS, MILTON JAMES 23053

C

CALDER, ALEXANDER 23213
CAMERON, SIR DAVID YOUNG 25144
CAPA, ROBERT 26060
CAPONE, GAETANO 25109
CARISS, HENRY T. 23029
CARLES, ARTHUR BEECHER 23125
CARLSEN, EMIL 23112
CARRIER-BELLEUSE, ALBERT ERNEST 25012
CHAGALL, MARC 25191, 25192
CHAMBERLAIN, SAMUEL 23154
CHAMBERS, Attributed to GEORGE CHAMBERS, JR. 25089
CHARPENTIER, School of JEAN BAPTISTE 25032
CHASE, Manner of WILLIAM MERRITT 23244
CHEFFETZ, ASA 23154
CHENEY, PHILIP 23154
CLAIRIN, GEORGES JULES VICTOR 23243
CLYMER, JOHN 23209
COLE, JOSEPA 25209
COLEMAN, CHARLES CARYL 23019
COLSON, PIERRIE THEODORE 25060
CONNOLLY, HOWARD 24051
CONSTABLE, R.A., Attributed to JOHN 25043, 25044, 25045
CONSTANT, BENJAMIN 23240
CONTINENTAL SCHOOL 25005, 2502, 25042, 25058, 25090, 25110, 25118, 25139
CORINTH, FRANZ HEINRICH LOVIS 25160
CORNOYER, PAUL 23114
CORTES, EDOUARD LEON 25215, 25216, 25214
COSWAY, Manner of RICHARD 25077
COUBINE, OTAKAR 25143
COURBET, GUSTAVE 25092, 25093
COUSE, EANGER IRVING 24021
CRANE, WALTER 23237
CRAWFORD, RALSTON 23145
CROSS, HENRY H. 24028
CUNNINGHAM, IMOGEN 26047
CUSTIS, ELEANOR PARKE 26037

D

DALI, SALVADOR 25224
DATER, JUDY 26059
DAUGHTERS, ROBERT A. 24060
DAVIS, STUART 23138
DAWSON-WATSON, DAWSON 24043
de ANDREIS, ALEX 25075
de BREANSKI, SR., A.R.C.A., ALFRED 25106
de CONDAMY, CHARLES FERNAND 25125
de DREUX, ALFRED 25074
de HAAS, WILLIAM FREDERICK 23052
de ITURRINO, FRANCISCO GONZALES 25150
de JONGERE, MARIUS 23131
de KOONING, ELAINE MARIE 23205, 23206
de la COUPERIE, MARIE-PHILIPPE COUPIN 25038
de la PENA, NARCISSE VIRGILE DIAZ 25094
de L'AIN, HELENE GIROD 25210
de MARTELLY, JOHN STOCKTON 23151
de SYSZLO, FERNANDO 23189
DELACROIX, EUGÈNE 25066
DELCOURT, DELCOURT 25070
DEMUTH, CHARLES 23111

DENNIS, MORGAN 23150
DENNY, GIDEON JACQUES 23050, 23051
DESMOULINS, FRANCOIS BARTHÉLÉMY AUGUSTIN 25049
D'ESPAGNAT, GEORGE 25159
DIXON, MAYNARD 24023
DOBUZHINSKII, MSTISLAW 25185
DODGE, WILLIAM DE LEFTWICH 23084
DOSAMANTES, FRANCISCO 23155
DOUGHERTY, PAUL 24044
D'OUVILLY, BALTHAZAR GERBIER 25007
DOYLE, JOHN 23222
DRAKE, WILLIAM HENRY 23117
DUFEU, EDOUARD JACQUES 25068
DUNNING, ROBERT SPEAR 23042
DUNOUY, ALEXANDRE-HYACINTHE 25041
DUNTON, WILLIAM HERBERT (BUCK) 24001, 24064, 24066, 24067, 24068
DUPUY, PAUL MICHEL 25121
DURAND, After ASHER B. 23068
DURCK, FRIEDRICH 25076
D'USSEAU, LEON 25204
DUTCH or CONTINENTAL SCHOOL 25072
DUVENECK, FRANK DUVENECK 23026
DVORAK, FRANZ 25130

E

EARLE, LAWRENCE CARMICHAEL 23027
EDWARDS, LIONEL DALHOUISE ROBERTSON 25127
EEKMAN, NICHOLAAS MATHIEU 25205
EILSHEMIUS, LOUIS MICHAEL 23087
EISENSTAEDT, ALFRED 26040
ELLIS, FREMONT F. 24061, 24062, 24063
ENGLISH SCHOOL 25097, 25101, 25122
ETNIER, STEPHEN MORGAN 23201
EUPOPEAN SCHOOL 25056, 25025, 25040, 25083, 25098, 25102, 25103, 25225
EUWER, ANTHONY HENDERSON 23136
EVANS, WALKER 26030

F

FARASYN, EDGARD 25113
FARM SECURTIY ADMINISTRATION PHOTOGRAPHS 26030
FARNY, HENRY FRANCOIS 24026
FERRERS, BENJAMIN 25022
FERRIS, JEAN LEON GEROME 23043
FISHER, Attributed to ALVAN 23006
FLEMISH SCHOOL 25028, 25029
FLORENTINE SCHOOL 25015
FOUJITA, TSUGUHARU 25222
FRANCIS, JOHN F. 23023
FRANCKEN II, FRANS 25008
FRENCH SCHOOL 25004, 25026, 25063, 25140
FRIEDLANDER, LEE 26036
FRISHMUTH, HARRIET WHITNEY 23110

G

GAINSBOROUGH, Attributed to THOMAS 25034
GAINSBOROUGH R.A., Attributed to THOMAS 25033
GALEOTTI, A. 25027
GALL, FRANCOIS 25206, 25207, 25219
GAMBOGI, FANNY 25107
GASPARD, LEON 24056, 24057, 24058, 24059
GAUDEZ, ADRIEN ÉTIENNE 25099
GAW, WILLIAM ALEXANDER 24055
GIBSON, CHARLES DANA 23167
GIDAL, TIM 26046
GILBERT, CHARLES ALLAN 23097
GISSON, ANDRE 23225
GLACKENS, WILLIAM 23140, 23141, 24065
GLENDENING, ALFRED AUGUSTUS 25084
GOLDBECK, E.O. 26017, 26018, 26019, 26020, 26021, 26022, 26023
GONCHAROVA, NATALIA SERGEEVNA 25186
GOODACRE, GLENNA 24007
GORSLINE, DOUGLAS 23155
GRANT, DONALD 25126
GRANT, FRANCIS 25100
GRANT, GORDON 23155
GRAY, ARTHUR SMITH 26038
GREACEN, EDMUND WILLIAM 23101, 23130
GREUZE, Attributed to JEAN BAPTISTE 25031
GRILL, OSWALD 25111
GRIMM 23028
GRISSON 23199
GROSZ, GEORGE 25221
GRUPPE, CHARLES PAUL 23090, 23091
GRUPPE, EMILE ALBERT 23146

H

HACKAERT, Circle of JAN 25016
HAIR, THOMAS H. 25087
HAMILTON, JAMES 23049
HARDING, Attributed to (CHARLES) CHESTER 23004
HARE, DENNIS 23230, 23231
HARNETT, WILLIAM MICHAEL 23024
HASSAM, CHILDE 23063
HAWTHORNE, CHARLES W. 23094
HEALY, GEORGE PETER ALEXANDER 23015
HEALY, STAN 26066, 26067, 26068, 26069, 26070, 26071, 26072, 26073, 26074
HENNER, JEAN-JACQUES 25104
HENNINGS, ERNEST MARTIN 23093
HENRI, ROBERT 23064, 23065, 23104
HILL, JOHN WILLIAM 23021
HILLS, ANNA ALTHEA 23077
HISTED, ERNEST WATLER 26032
HITCHCOCK, DAVID HOWARD 23113
HOEBER, ARTHUR 23038
HOFFMAN, MALVINA 24041
HOGARTH, Circle of WILLIAM 25018
HOLDREDGE, RANSOM GILLET 23012
HOLTY, CARL ROBERT 23193
HOWE, HARRY HARLOW 23056
HUFFMAN, L.A. 23035, 26002, 26003, 26004, 26005, 26006, 26007, 26008, 26009, 26010, 26011
HUMPHRISS, CHARLES H. 24029
HUNTER, FREDERICK LEO 23120, 23121
HUNTINGTON, DANIEL 23046
HURD, PETER 24049, 24073
HUTTY, ALFRED HEBER 23132, 23133

I

IACOVLEFF, ALEXANDRE 25196
IGNATOVITCH, BORIS 26041
INNESS, GEORGE 23017
IRISH SCHOOL 25079
ITALIAN SCHOOL 25137

J

JACOBSEN, ANTONIO JACOBSEN 23058, 23059, 23060, 23061
JACQUET, GUSTAVE JEAN 25053
JANSEM, JEAN 25226

INDEX BY LOT NUMBER

JEANNIOT, PIERRE GEORGES 25156
JOHNSON, FRANK TENNEY 24002
JOHNSON, RAYMOND 23214
JOSEPH, JULIEN 25138
JOUFFROY, JEAN-PIERRE 25223

K

KAPLAN, S. 23183
KASIMIR, LUIGI 23148
KASIMIR-HOERNES, TANNA 23148
KAUFMANN, THEODORE 24054
KEELHOFF, FRANS 25095
KELLY, RAMON 24006
KERTÉSZ, ANDRÉ 26043, 26044
KEVER, After JACOB SIMON HENDRICK 25091
KEVER, JACOB SIMON HENDRIK 25082
KING, PAUL BERNARD 23119
KINGMAN, DON 23215
KLIUN, IVAN 25174, 25175, 25176, 25177, 25178
KLOSS, GENE 24072
KNATHS, KARL 23190
KNÉBEL the Younger, FRANZ 25105
KOCH, JOHN 23164, 23165
KOHL, PIERRE ERNEST 25203
KOROVIN, KONSTANTIN ALEXEIEVITCH 25188
KOST, FREDERICK WILLIAM 25119
KOYANAGUI, SEI 25201
KRAFFT, CARL R. KRAFFT 23127, 23128, 23129
KRAUSKOPF, BRUNO 25212
KRONBERG, LOUIS 23168
KUHNERT, WILLIAM 23235

L

LACROIX, PAUL 23022
LAMBDIN, JAMES REID 23014
LAMI, EUGENE-LOUIS 25051
LANGE, DOROTHEA 26030
LARWIN, HANS 25085
LAURENCE, SYDNEY MORTIMER 24042
LAURENT, EUGÈNE 25133
LAWRENCE, Studio of THOMAS 25037
LAWRENCE, Style of THOMAS 25036
LEBDUSKA, LAWRENCE H. 23002, 23003
LEBENSTEIN, JAN 25208
LEE, CHEE CHIN S. CHEUNG 23122, 23123
LEFEBVRE, JULES-JOSEPH 25157
LEGER, FERNAND 25155
LEIGH, WILLIAM ROBINSON 24008
LEMASLE, LOUIS-NICOLAS 25024
LEVER, HAYLEY 23072, 23073, 23074, 23075, 23076
LIBERTE, JEAN 23174
LINDSAY, THOMAS CORWIN 23011
LINK, CARL 24069
LINUS, AXEL 24045
LLOYD, WALTER STUART 25120
LOCKE, WALTER RONALD 23155
LOCKWOOD, ROBERT WILTON 23045
LONE WOLF 24052
LONGFELLOW, ERNEST WADSWORTH 23031
LOVELL, TOM 24036
LUBIENIECKI, BOGDAN THEODOR 25019
LUCIONI, LUIGI 23134, 23153
LUKS, GEORGE BENJAMIN 23109
LUMPKINS, WILLIAM THOMAS 23126, 23191
LUNY, School of THOMAS 25088

M

MACLEAN, WILLIAM 23154
MACRAE, ELMER LIVINGSTON 23095
MAES, EUGÉNE RÉMY 25073
MALACREA, FRANCESCO 25064
MALTINO, A. 25108
MANN, SALLY 26075
MARCHETTI, Attributed to LUDOVICO 25054
MARK, MARY ELLEN 26061, 26062, 26063, 26064, 26065
MARTIN, HENRI JEAN GUILLAUME 25198, 25199
MAUVE, ANTON 25114
McAULIFFE, JAMES J. 23007
MCCARTER, HENRY 23124
McHURON, GREG 23226
MEHEUT, MATHURIN 25162, 25163, 25164, 25165,25166
MELLOR, WILLIAM 25116
METZKER, RAY 26054, 26055, 26056, 26057, 26058
MEUCCI, MICHAELANGELO 25123
MEYERHEIM, PAUL FRIEDRICH 23238
MIRA, ALFRED S. 23143
MOESSEL, JULIUS 23188
MOORE, FRANK MONTAGUE 23086
MORAN, PERCY 23044
MORAN, THOMAS 23057
MORGAN, BARBARA 26052
MORGAN, MARY DENEALE 23085
MORRIS, GEORGE FORD 23149
MURAY, NICKOLAS 26034

N

NAKIAN, REUBEN 23204
NERLY, FREDERICO 25136
NEUHUIJS, ALBERT, NEUHUYS or 25080
NEUHUIJS, JOHANN ALBERT NEUHUYS or 25081
NEVELSON, LOUISE 23220
NICHOLSON, GEORGE WASHINGTON 23048
NICOSIA, NIC 26076, 26077, 26078, 26079,26080
NISBET, POLLOCK SINCLAIR 25112
NORDFELDT, BROR JULIUS OLSSON 23105
NOYER, PHILIPPE HENRI 25211, 25220
NYE, LEE 26035

O

ORIENTALIST SCHOOL 23242
ORLOFF, CHANA 25195
OSTHAUS, EDMUND HENRY 23034
OUTIN, PIERRE 25096

P

PARADISE, PHILLIP HERSCHEL 23147
PARKER, JOHN ADAMS 23013
PARRISH, MAXFIELD 23157
PARTON, ARTHUR 23033
PASKELL, WILLIAM FREDERICK 23056
PASSAROTTI, BARTOLOMEO 25003
PAVIS, ELIE ANATOLE 23137
PAYNE, EDGAR ALWIN 24003
PAYNE, Style of EDGAR ALWIN 23088
PEARCE, CHARLES SPRAGUE 23036
PENNOYER, ALBERT SHELDON 23083
PERKINS, GRANVILLE 23032
PETERSON, JANE 23079, 23080, 23081, 23241
PETITJEAN, HIPPOLYTE 25141
PHILIPP, ROBERT 23169, 23170, 23171
PHILLIPS, BERT GREER 24020
PHILLIPS, TOM 24050
PICASSO, PABLO 23212

INDEX BY LOT NUMBER

PISSARO, CAMILLE 25153, 25154
POONS, LARRY 23227
POPOVA, LUIBOV 25170, 25171, 25172, 25173, 25179, 25180, 25181, 25182, 25183, 25184
POTTHAST, EDWARD HENRY 23062
POWERS, HIRAM 23016

R

RAMSEY, MILNE 23041
REID, JOHN ROBERTSON 25147
REISMAN, PHILIP 23172
REMINGTON, FREDERIC 24030
RENOIR, PIERRE AUGUSTE 25161, 25152
RESTOUT II, Circle of JEAN 25020
RIDER, CHAUNCEY 23154
RITTASE, WILLIAM M. 26053
ROLLINS, WARREN ELIPHALET 24024
ROLSHOVEN, JULIUS 24022
ROMAN SCHOOL 25039
RONIS, WILLY 26039
ROSELAND, HARRY HERMAN 23099
ROTHSTEIN, ARTHUR 26029, 26030
ROWNOTHAM, CHARLES 25148, 25149
RUBENS, School of SIR PETER PAUL 25006
RUMPH, ALICE EDITH 23154
RUSSELL, CHARLES MARION 24031, 24032, 24033, 24034, 24035
RYDER, CHAUNCY FOSTER 23070

S

SALA, EMILIO GRAU 25218
SALINAS, MARCEL CHARLES LAURENT 25202
SANI, ALESSANDRO 25065
SCAFFAI, LUIGI 25061
SCHIEFER, JOHANNES 23144
SCHIOTT, ELISABETH 25124
SCHMIDT, HANS WILHELM 25213
SEPESHY, ZOLTAN L. 25193, 25194
SHAHN, BEN 26030
SHARP, JOSEPH HENRY 24009, 24010, 24011, 24012, 24013, 24014, 24015, 24016, 24017, 24018, 24019
SHAYER, WILLIAM JOSEPH 25128
SHEARER, CHRISTOPHER H. 23069
SHEPPARD, School of WARREN 23055
SHEPPARD, WARREN W. 23054
SHIKLER, AARON , A.N.A. 23135
SHINN, EVERETT 23139
SIQUEIROS, DAVID ALFARO 23192
SISKIND, AARON 26048
SLOAN, HELEN FARR 23200
SLOAN, JOHN 23106
SLOANE, ERIC 23156
SMITH, MICHAEL A. 26024, 26025, 26026, 26027, 26028
SMITH, T.HUDSON 23115
SOYER, RAPHAEL 23166
SPANISH SCHOOL 25011
SPAT, GABRIEL 23207
SPILLAR, KAREL 25151
SPULAK, A. 25055
STEICHEN, EDWARD 26031, 26033
STEVENS, ALFRED 23025
STEVENS JR., EDWARD JOHN 23202
STEWART, JULIUS 23245
STIEPEVICH, VINCENT G. 25168
STOBBE, MARIE 23100
SULTAN, DONALD 23228
SUSTERMANS, Circle of JUSTUS 25009

T

TAIT, ARTHUR FITZWILLIAM TAIT 23039, 23040
TAYLOR, EDGAR 23008
THAL, SAM 23154
THERIAT, CHARLES JAMES 23239
TIFFANY, LOUIS COMFORT 23071
TOMASO, RICO 23210
TOMINZ, Circle of GIUSEPPE 25048
TOURIER, ALFRED HOLST 25062
TROUILLEBERT, PAUL DÉSIRÉ 25069

U

UMBEHR, UMBO 26042
UNGEWITTER, HUGO 25131

V

van DER MEULEN, ADAMS FRANS 25017
van HONTHORST, Studio of GERRIT 25010
van RIJN, REMBRANDT 25013, 25014
van RYSSELBERGHE, THEO 25132
van STARKENBORG, JACOBUS NICOLAS TJARDA 25117
VANDEVERDONK, FRANCOIS 25071
VARILLAZ, V. 25050
VASIL'EV, NIKOLAI IVANOVITCH 25187
VELÁSQUEZ, Circle of EUGENIO LUCAS 25067
VERNET, EMILE JEAN HORACE 23236
VERNON, EMILE 25078
VIAUD, EMILIO BAZ 23196
VIEZZHEV, ALEXANDER NIKOLAYEVICH 25169
VIGÉE-LEBRUN, Follower of ELISABETH LOUISE 25046
VILLAMIL, EUGENE LUCAS Y 25052
von MOELLER, REINHOLD 23234

W

WACKERNAGEL, OTTO 23148
WALTERS, CURT 24048
WARHOL, ANDY 23211
WATKINS, CARLETON E. 26001
WATSON, ROBERT 23223, 23224
WEEKS, EDWIN LORD 23233
WEGMAN, WILLIAM 26081
WEIN, ALBERT W. 23184
WEINGART, JOACHIM 25190
WEIR, ROBERT WALTER 24027
WESTON, EDWARD 26012
WHEATLEY, FRANCIS 25030
WHITE, MINOR 26049, 26050, 26051
WHITTREDGE, WORTHINGTON 23067
WHORF, JOHN 23118
WIGGINS, GUY CARELTON 23158, 23159, 23160, 23161
WIGGINS, KIM DOUGLAS 23219, 23229
WILLIAMSON, JOHN 23009
WILLIS, JOSEPH ROY 24005
WINTER, ALICE BEACH 23089
WIRE, MELVILLE 23154
WOOD, GRANT 23152
WOOD, ROBERT 24038, 24039, 24040
WYETH, ANDREW WYETH 23216, 23217, 23218

Y

YENS, KARL JULIUS HEINRICH 24053

Z

ZALCE, ALFREDO 23197
ZAMPIGHI, EUGENIO 25135
ZOFFANY, Attributed JOHANN JOSEPH 25035

World Headquarters
3500 Maple Avenue, 17th Floor
Dallas, Texas 75219-3941
800-872-6467

CORPORATE OFFICERS

R. Steven Ivy, Co-Chairman
James L. Halperin, Co-Chairman
Gregory J. Rohan, President
Paul Minshull, Chief Operating Officer

HA.com/FineArt

Edmund P. Pillsbury, Ph.D.
Chairman, Fine Arts
Ext. 533 • EPP@HA.com

Norma Gonzalez, Vice President Operations
Ext. 242 • Norma@HA.com

UNITED STATES COINS

HA.com/Coins

U.S. Coins

Leo Frese, Ext. 294
Leo@HA.com

Charles Clifford, Ext. 477
CharlesC@HA.com

Sam Foose, Ext. 227
SamF@HA.com

Jim Jelinski, Ext. 257
JimJ@HA.com

Katherine Kurachek, Ext. 389
KKurachek@HA.com

David Lewis, Ext. 520
DLewis@HA.com

David Lisot, Ext. 303
DavidL@HA.com

Bob Marino, Ext. 374
BobMarino@HA.com

David Mayfield, Ext. 277
DavidM@HA.com

Bob Phillips, Ext. 588
BobP@HA.com

Mike Sadler, Ext. 332
MikeS@HA.com

UNITED STATES COINS PRIVATE TREATY SALES

HA.com/Coins

Todd Imhof, Ext. 313
Todd@HA.com

CURRENCY

HA.com/Currency

Paper Money

Len Glazer, Ext. 390
Len@HA.com

Allen Mincho, Ext. 327
Allen@HA.com

Dustin Johnston, Ext. 302
Dustin@HA.com

Jim Fitzgerald, Ext. 348
JimF@HA.com

Michael Moczalla, Ext. 481
MichaelM@HA.com

WORLD COINS

HA.com/Coins

World Coins & Currencies

Warren Tucker, Ext. 287
WTucker@HA.com

Scott Cordry, Ext. 369
ScottC@HA.com

Harvey Gamer, Ext. 676
HarveyG@HA.com

COMICS

HA.com/Comics

Comics, Original Comic Art and Related Memorabilia

Ed Jaster, Ext. 288
EdJ@HA.com

Lon Allen, Ext. 261
LonA@HA.com

MUSIC & ENTERTAINMENT MEMORABILIA

HA.com/Entertainment

Stage-Worn Costumes, Records, Signed Photos & Memorabilia

Doug Norwine, Ext. 452
DougN@HA.com

John Hickey, Ext. 264
JohnH@HA.com

Jim Steele, Ext. 328
JimSt@HA.com

POLITICAL MEMORABILIA & AMERICANA

HA.com/Americana

Historical & Pop Culture Americana, Vintage Toys, Presidential & Political Memorabilia, Buttons & Medals, Books & Manuscripts, First Editions and Collectible Autographs

Tom Slater, Ext. 441
TomS@HA.com

Marsha Dixey, Ext. 455
MarshaD@HA.com

John Hickey, Ext. 264
JohnH@HA.com

Sandra Palomino, Ext. 107
SandraP@HA.com

Michael Riley, Ext. 467
MichaelR@HA.com

SPORTS COLLECTIBLES

HA.com/Sports

Sports Cards, Artifacts, Game-Used Jerseys & Equipment

Chris Ivy, Ext. 319
CIvy@HA.com

Stephen Carlisle, Ext. 292
StephenC@HA.com

Jonathan Scheier, Ext. 314
JonathanS@HA.com

Mark Jordan, Ext. 187
MarkJ@HA.com

Mike Gutierrez, Ext. 183
MikeG@HA.com

VINTAGE MOVIE POSTERS

HA.com/MoviePosters

Posters, Lobby Cards, and Hollywood Ephemera

Grey Smith, Ext. 367
GreySm@HA.com

Bruce Carteron, Ext. 551
BruceC@HA.com

TRUSTS AND ESTATES

HA.com/Estates

Steven Roach, Ext. 694
Roach@HA.com

FINE ART

HA.com/FineArt

Impressionist, Old Masters and Contemporary Drawings, Paintings, Sculpture and Photography

Edmund P. Pillsbury, Ph.D., Ext. 533
EPP@HA.com

Kathleen Guzman, Ext. 672
KathleenG@HA.com

Ed Jaster, Ext. 288
EdJ@HA.com

Christine Carmody, Ext. 521
ChristineC@HA.com

Lindsay Davis, Ext. 542
LindsayD@HA.com

TEXAS ART

HA.com/TexasArt

Early Texas Art, Drawings and Paintings

Larry Boettigheimer, Ext. 523
LarryB@HA.com

ILLUSTRATION ART/PHOTOGRAPHY

HA.com/FineArt

Pinups and Illustration Art

Ed Jaster, Ext. 288
EdJ@HA.com

DECORATIVE ARTS

HA.com/FineArt

Art Glass, European & American Silver, Pottery & Ceramics

Michael Wolf, Ext. 541
MWolf@HA.com

Tim Rigdon, Ext. 119
TimR@HA.com

Courtney Case, Ext. 293
CourtneyC@HA.com

JEWELRY & TIMEPIECES

HA.com/Jewelry

Jewelry & Timepieces

Jill Burgum, Ext. 697
JillB@HA.com

Ghislain d'Humières, Ext. 157
GDH@HA.com

MEDIA RELATIONS

Marketing and Public Relations

Kelley Norwine, Ext. 583
KelleyN@HA.com

John Petty, Ext. 283
JohnP@HA.com

CREDIT DEPARTMENT

Marti Korver, Ext 248
Marti@HA.com

WIRING INSTRUCTIONS

Bank Information: JP Morgan Chase Bank, N.A.
270 Park Avenue, New York, NY 10017
Account Name: Heritage Numismatic Auctions Master Account
ABA Number: 021000021
Account Number: 1884827674
Swift Code: CHASUS33

FOR THE EXTENSIONS ABOVE, PLEASE CALL 800-872-6467
FOR TOLL-FREE DIRECT CLIENT SERVICES, CALL 866-835-3243

Upcoming Auctions

HERITAGE HA.com Auction Galleries

HA.com/Consign
Call Our Consignment Hotline
Toll Free: 800-872-6467 Ext. 222

Over 275,000 Online Registered Bidder-Members • Annual Sales Exceeding $500 Million

United States Coin Auctions	*Location*	*Auction Dates*	*Consignment Deadline*
Central States Numismatic Society (CSNS)	St. Louis, MO	May 9-12, 2007	Closed
Long Beach Coin, Stamp & Collectibles Expo	Long Beach, CA	May 30 - June 2, 2007	Closed
West Palm Beach (Summer F.U.N.)	West Palm Beach, FL	July 11-14, 2007	May 31, 2007
Milwaukee ANA	Milwaukee, WI	August 8-12, 2007	June 29, 2007
Long Beach	Long Beach, CA	September 26-29, 2007	August 16, 2007
World Coin Auctions	*Location*	*Auction Dates*	*Consignment Deadline*
Long Beach	Long Beach, CA	May 31-June 1, 2007	Closed
Long Beach	Long Beach, CA	September 26-29, 2007	August 9, 2007
Currency Auctions	*Location*	*Auction Dates*	*Consignment Deadline*
Central States Numismatic Society (CSNS)	St. Louis, MO	May 10-12, 2007	Closed
Long Beach	Long Beach, CA	September 28-29, 2007	August 9, 2007
Fine & Decorative Arts Auctions	*Location*	*Auction Dates*	*Consignment Deadline*
Texas Art	Dallas, TX	May 19, 2007	Closed
Fine Art	Dallas, TX	May 25, 2007	Closed
African & Oceanic Art	Dallas, TX	June 7, 2007	Closed
Pre Columbian/Native American Art	Dallas, TX	October 4-5, 2007	July 26, 2007
Decorative Arts	Dallas, TX	October 25-26, 2007	August 16, 2007
Fine Art	Dallas, TX	November 7-8, 2007	August 29, 2007
Jewelry & Timepieces Auction	*Location*	*Auction Dates*	*Consignment Deadline*
Estate Jewelry & Timepieces	Dallas, TX	May 21, 2007	Closed
Estate Jewelry & Timepieces	Dallas, TX	Dec 3, 2007	October 11, 2007
Vintage Movie Posters Auctions	*Location*	*Auction Dates*	*Consignment Deadline*
Vintage Movie Posters	Dallas, TX	July 13, 2007	May 21, 2007
Comics Auctions	*Location*	*Auction Dates*	*Consignment Deadline*
Comics & Original Comic Art	Dallas, TX	May 3-4, 2007	Closed
Illustration Art	Dallas, TX	June 14, 2007	April 29, 2007
Comics & Original Comic Art	Dallas, TX	August 2-4, 2007	June 19, 2007
Music & Entertainment Memorabilia Auctions	*Location*	*Auction Dates*	*Consignment Deadline*
Music Celebrity & Hollywood Memorabilia	Dallas, TX	October 12-13, 2007	August 20, 2007
Political Memorabilia & Americana Grand Format Auctions	*Location*	*Auction Dates*	*Consignment Deadline*
Important Historical Manuscripts & Autographs	Dallas, TX	June 9, 2007	Closed
Civil War Auction	Gettysburg, PA	June 24, 2007	April 20, 2007
Grand Format Autographs Auction	Dallas, TX	October 18-19, 2007	August 26, 2007
Sports Collectibles Auctions	*Location*	*Auction Dates*	*Consignment Deadline*
Dallas	Dallas, TX	May 5, 2007	Closed
Dallas	Dallas, TX	October 20, 2007	August 28, 2007

HERITAGE TUESDAY INTERNET COIN AUCTIONS • HERITAGE SUNDAY INTERNET COIN AUCTIONS • Begin and end every Tuesday and Sunday at 10 PM CT.
HERITAGE TUESDAY INTERNET CURRENCY AUCTIONS • Begin and end every Tuesday at 10 PM CT.
HERITAGE WEEKLY INTERNET COMICS AUCTIONS • Begin and end every Sunday of each month at 10 PM CT.
HERITAGE WEEKLY INTERNET MOVIE POSTER AUCTIONS • Begin and end every Sunday at 10 PM CT.
HERITAGE MONTHLY MARKETPLACE AUCTIONS • Wednesdays/Thursdays between 4 PM and 10 PM CT. This Auction has a combination of lots consisting of Americana, Sports, Comics, Fine Art/Decorative Arts, Texas Art and Music Memorabilia lots.
HERITAGE MONTHLY INTERNET SPORTS AUCTIONS • Begin and end, on the last Sunday of each month at 10 PM CT.

Heritage Numismatic Auctions, Inc.: California 3S 3062 16 63, Florida AB0000665, Ohio 2006000050. Currency Auctions of America: Florida AB 2218. Auctioneers: Leo Frese: Florida AU 0001059. California 3S 3062 16 64, NewYork City; Day 1094965, Night 1094966; Samuel Foose: North Carolina 8363, Texas 00011727, California 3S 3062 16 65, Florida AU3244, Ohio 2006000048, and New York City; Day 0952360, Night 0952361.Jim Fitzgerald: Texas Associate 16130. Mike Sadler: Texas Associate 16129. Scott Peterson: Texas 00013256, Florida AU3021. Robert Korver: North Carolina 8363, Ohio 2006000049, Texas 13754, Wisconsin 2412-52, and New York City; Day 1096338 and Night 1096340.

4/14/07

Choose Your Bidding Method

Interactive Internet™ Bidding

You can now bid with Heritage's exclusive *Interactive Internet*™ program, available only at our web site: HA.com. It's fun, and it's easy!

1. Register online at: HA.com
2. View the full-color photography of every single lot in the online catalog!
3. Construct your own personal catalog for preview.
4. View the current opening bids on lots you want; review the prices realized archive.
5. Bid and receive immediate notification if you are the top bidder; later, if someone else bids higher, you will be notified automatically by e-mail.
6. The *Interactive Internet*™ program opens the lot on the floor at one increment over the second highest bid. As the high bidder, your secret maximum bid will compete for you during the floor auction, and it is possible that you may be outbid on the floor after Internet bidding closes. Bid early, as the earliest bird wins in the event of a tie bid.
7. After the sale, you will be notified of your success. It's that easy!

Interactive Internet™ Bidding Instructions

1. **Log Onto Website**
   Log onto HA.com and chose the portal you're interested in (i.e., coins, comics, movie posters, fine arts, etc.).

2. **Search for Lots**
   Search or browse for the lot you are interested in. You can do this from the home page, from the Auctions home page, or from the home page for the particular auction in which you wish to participate.

3. **Select Lots**
   Click on the link or the photo icon for the lot you want to bid on.

4. **Enter Bid**
   At the top of the page, next to a small picture of the item, is a box outlining the current bid. Enter the amount of your secret maximum bid in the textbox next to "Secret Maximum Bid." The secret maximum bid is the maximum amount you are willing to pay for the item you are bidding on (for more information about bidding and bid increments, please see the section labeled "Bidding Increments" elsewhere in this catalog). Click on the button marked "Place Absentee Bid." A new area on the same page will open up for you to enter your username (or e-mail address) and password. Enter these, then click "Place Absentee Bid" again.

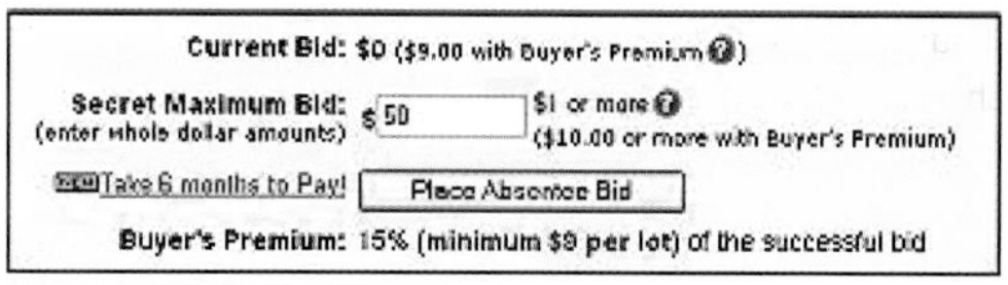

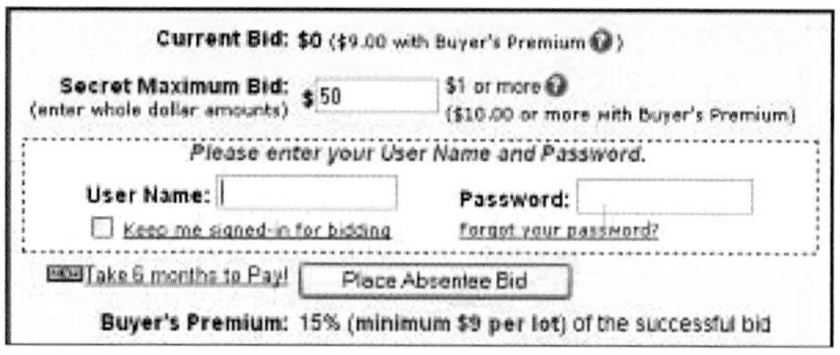

5. **Confirm Absentee Bid**
   You are taken to a page labeled, "Please Confirm Your Bid." This page shows you the name of the item you're bidding on, the current bid, and the maximum bid. When you are satisfied that all the information shown is correct, click on the button labeled, "Confirm Bid."

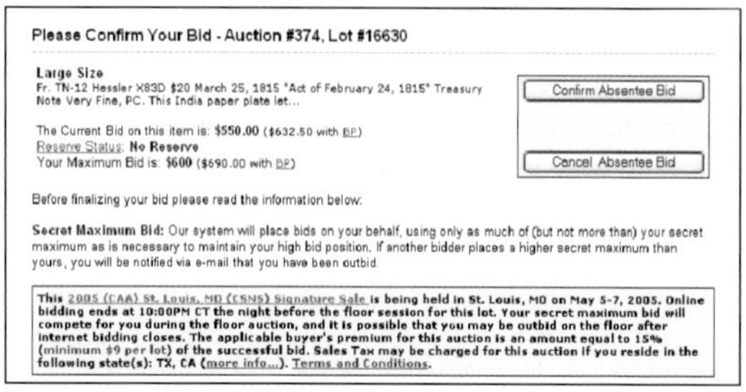

6. **Bidding Status Notification**
   One of two pages is now displayed.

   a. If your bid is the current high bid, you will be notified and given additional information as to what might happen to affect your high bidder status over the course of the remainder of the auction. You will also receive a Bid Confirmation notice via email.

   b. If your bid is not the current high bid, you will be notified of that fact and given the opportunity to increase your bid.

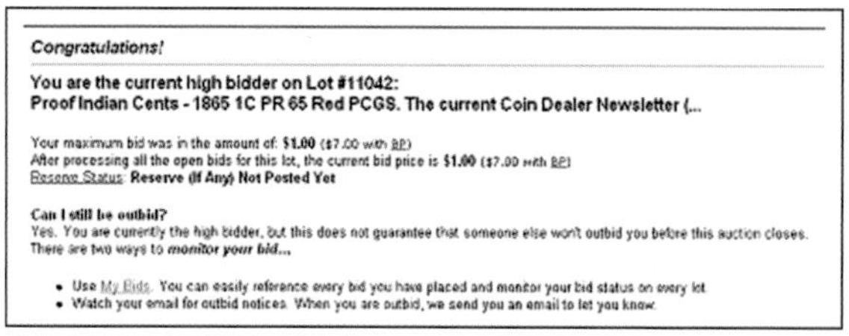

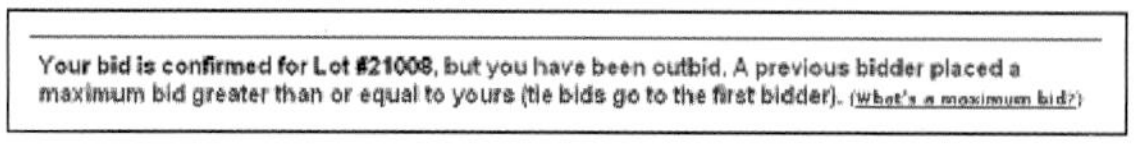

Choose Your Bidding Method, (Cont'd.)

Mail Bidding at Auction

Mail bidding at auction is fun and easy and only requires a few simple steps.

1. Look through the catalog, and determine the lots of interest.
2. Research their market value by checking price lists and other price guidelines.
3. Fill out your bid sheet, entering your maximum bid on each lot.
4. Verify your bids!
5. Mail Early. Preference is given to the first bids received in case of a tie. When bidding by mail, you frequently purchase items at less than your maximum bid.

Bidding is opened at the published increment above the second highest mail or Internet bid; we act on your behalf as the highest mail bidder. If bidding proceeds, we act as your agent, bidding in increments over the previous bid. This process is continued until you are awarded the lot or you are outbid.

An example of this procedure: You submit a bid of $100, and the second highest mail bid is at $50. Bidding starts at $51 on your behalf. If no other bids are placed, you purchase the lot for $51. If other bids are placed, we bid for you in the posted increments until we reach your maximum bid of $100. If bidding passes your maximum: if you are bidding through the Internet, we will contact you by e-mail; if you bid by mail, we take no other action. Bidding continues until the final bidder wins.

Telephone Bidding

To participate by telephone, please make arrangements at least one week before the sale date with Customer Service, 1-800-872-6467, Ext. 150.

We strongly recommend that you place preliminary bids by mail, fax, or Internet, even if you intend to participate by telephone. On many occasions this dual approach has helped reduce disappointments due to telephone problems, unexpected travel, late night sessions and time zone differences, etc. We will make sure that you do not bid against yourself.

Mail Bidding Instructions

1. **Name, Address, City, State, Zip**
   Your address is needed to mail your purchases. We need your telephone number to communicate any problems or changes that may affect your bids.

2. **References**
   If you have not established credit with us from previous auctions, you must send a 25% deposit, or list dealers with whom you have credit established.

3. **Lot Numbers and Bids**
   List all lots you desire to purchase. On the reverse are additional columns; you may also use another sheet. Under "Amount" enter the maximum you would pay for that lot (whole dollar amounts only). We will purchase the lot(s) for you as much below your bids as possible.

4. **Total Bid Sheet**
   Add up all bids and list that total in the appropriate box.

5. **Sign Your Bid Sheet**
   By signing the bid sheet, you have agreed to abide by the Terms of Auction listed in the auction catalog.

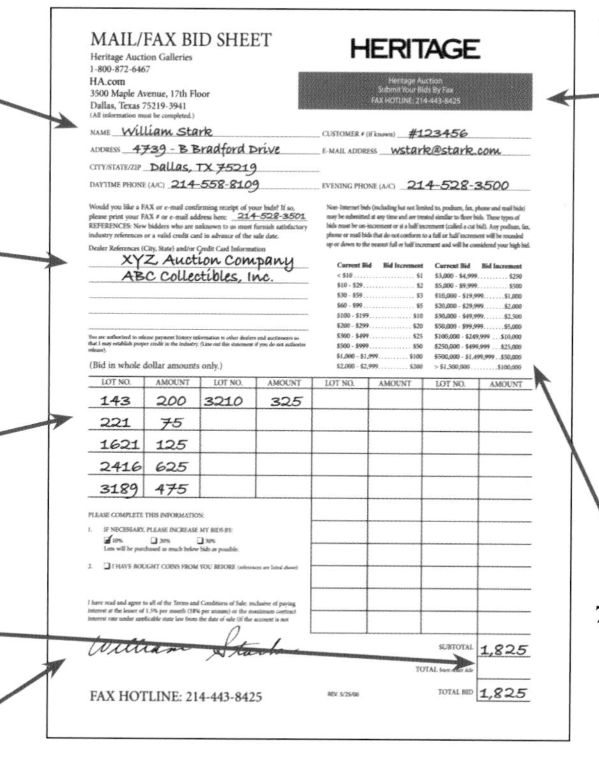

MAIL/FAX BID SHEET

Heritage Auction Galleries
1-800-872-6467
HA.com
3500 Maple Avenue, 17th Floor
Dallas, Texas 75219-3941
(All information must be completed.)

HERITAGE

Heritage Auction
Submit Your Bids By Fax
FAX HOTLINE: 214-443-8425

NAME William Stark — CUSTOMER # (if known) #123456
ADDRESS 4739 - B Bradford Drive — E-MAIL ADDRESS wstark@stark.com
CITY/STATE/ZIP Dallas, TX 75219
DAYTIME PHONE (A/C) 214-558-8109 — EVENING PHONE (A/C) 214-528-3500

Would you like a FAX or e-mail confirming receipt of your bids? If so, please print your FAX # or e-mail address here: 214-528-3501
REFERENCES: New bidders who are unknown to us must furnish satisfactory industry references or a valid credit card in advance of the sale date.

Dealer References (City, State) and/or Credit Card Information
XYZ Auction Company
ABC Collectibles, Inc.

Non-Internet bids (including but not limited to, podium, fax, phone and mail bids) may be submitted at any time and are treated similar to floor bids. These types of bids must be on-increment or at a half increment (called a cut bid). Any podium, fax, phone or mail bids that do not conform to a full or half increment will be rounded up or down to the nearest full or half increment and will be considered your high bid.

Current Bid	Bid Increment	Current Bid	Bid Increment
< $10	$1	$3,000 - $4,999	$250
$10 - $29	$2	$5,000 - $9,999	$500
$30 - $59	$3	$10,000 - $19,999	$1,000
$60 - $99	$5	$20,000 - $29,999	$2,000
$100 - $199	$10	$30,000 - $49,999	$2,500
$200 - $299	$20	$50,000 - $99,999	$5,000
$300 - $499	$25	$100,000 - $249,999	$10,000
$500 - $999	$50	$250,000 - $499,999	$25,000
$1,000 - $1,999	$100	$500,000 - $1,499,999	$50,000
$2,000 - $2,999	$200	> $1,500,000	$100,000

You are authorized to release payment history information to other dealers and auctioneers so that I may establish proper credit in the industry. (Line out this statement if you do not authorize release).

(Bid in whole dollar amounts only.)

LOT NO.	AMOUNT	LOT NO.	AMOUNT	LOT NO.	AMOUNT	LOT NO.	AMOUNT
143	200	3210	325				
221	75						
1621	125						
2416	625						
3189	475						

PLEASE COMPLETE THIS INFORMATION:

1. IF NECESSARY, PLEASE INCREASE MY BIDS BY:
   ☑ 10% ☐ 20% ☐ 30%
   Lots will be purchased as much below bids as possible.
2. ☐ I HAVE BOUGHT COINS FROM YOU BEFORE (references are listed above)

I have read and agree to all of the Terms and Conditions of Sale: inclusive of paying interest at the lesser of 1.5% per month (18% per annum) or the maximum contract interest rate under applicable state law from the date of sale (if the account is not

SUBTOTAL 1,825
TOTAL from other side
TOTAL BID 1,825

FAX HOTLINE: 214-443-8425

REV. 5/25/06

The official prices realized list that accompanies our auction catalogs is reserved for bidders and consignors only. We are happy to mail one to others upon receipt of $1.00. Written requests should be directed to Customer Service.

6. **Fax Your Bid Sheet**
   When time is short submit a Mail Bid Sheet on our exclusive Fax Hotline. There's no faster method to get your bids to us *instantly*. Simply use the **Heritage Fax Hotline number: 214-443-8425.**

When you send us your original after faxing, mark it "Confirmation of Fax" (preferably in red!)

7. **Bidding Increments**
   To facilitate bidding, please consult the following chart. Bids will be accepted on the increments or on the half increments.

Terms and Conditions of Auction

Auctioneer and Auction:

1. This Auction is presented by Heritage Auction Galleries, a d/b/a/ of Heritage Auctions, Inc., or their affiliates Heritage Numismatic Auctions, Inc. or Currency Auctions of America, Inc., d/b/a as identified with the applicable licensing information on the title page of the catalog or on the HA.com Internet site (the "Auctioneer"). The Auction is conducted under these Terms and Conditions of Auction and applicable state and local law. Announcements and corrections from the podium and those made through the Terms and Conditions of Auctions appearing on the Internet at HA.com supersede those in the printed catalog.

Buyer's Premium:

2. On bids placed through Heritage, a Buyer's Premium of fifteen percent (15%) will be added to the successful hammer price bid on lots in Coin and Currency auctions, or nineteen and one-half percent (19.5%) on lots in all other auctions. If your bid is placed through eBay Live, a Buyer's Premium equal to the normal Buyer's Premium plus an additional five percent (5%) of the hammer price will be added to the successful bid up to a maximum Buyer's Premium of Twenty Two and one-half percent (22.5%). There is a minimum Buyer's Premium of $9.00 per lot. In Gallery Auctions only, a ten percent (10%) handling fee is applied to all lots based upon the total of the hammer price plus the 15% Buyer's Premium.

Auction Venues:

3. The following Auctions are conducted solely on the Internet: Heritage Weekly Internet Coin, Currency, Comics, and Vintage Movie Poster Auctions; Heritage Monthly Internet Sports and Marketplace Auctions; OnLine Sessions. Signature Auctions and Grand Format Auctions accept bids on the Internet first, followed by a floor bidding session; bids may be placed prior to the floor bidding session by Internet, telephone, fax, or mail.

Bidders:

4. Any person participating or registering for the Auction agrees to be bound by and accepts these Terms and Conditions of Auction ("Bidder(s)").
5. All Bidders must meet Auctioneer's qualifications to bid. Any Bidder who is not a customer in good standing of the Auctioneer may be disqualified at Auctioneer's sole option and will not be awarded lots. Such determination may be made by Auctioneer in its sole and unlimited discretion, at any time prior to, during, or even after the close of the Auction. Auctioneer reserves the right to exclude any person it deems in its sole opinion is disruptive to the Auction or is otherwise commercially unsuitable.
6. If an entity places a bid, then the person executing the bid on behalf of the entity agrees to personally guarantee payment for any successful bid.

Credit References:

7. Bidders who have not established credit with the Auctioneer must either furnish satisfactory credit information (including two collectibles-related business references) well in advance of the Auction or supply valid credit card information. Bids placed through our Interactive Internet program will only be accepted from pre-registered Bidders; Bidders who are not members of HA.com or affiliates should pre-register at least two business days before the first session to allow adequate time to contact references.

Bidding Options:

8. Bids in Signature Auctions or Grand Format Auctions may be placed as set forth in the printed catalog section entitled "Choose your bidding method." For auctions held solely on the Internet, see the alternatives on HA.com. Review at HA.com/common/howtobid.php.
9. Presentment of Bids: Non-Internet bids (including but not limited to podium, fax, phone and mail bids) are treated similar to floor bids in that they must be on-increment or at a half increment (called a cut bid). Any podium, fax, phone, or mail bids that do not conform to a full or half increment will be rounded up or down to the nearest full or half increment and this revised amount will be considered your high bid.
10. Auctioneer's Execution of Certain Bids. Auctioneer cannot be responsible for your errors in bidding, so carefully check that every bid is entered correctly. When identical mail or FAX bids are submitted, preference is given to the first received. To ensure the greatest accuracy, your written bids should be entered on the standard printed bid sheet and be received at Auctioneer's place of business at least two business days before the Auction start. Auctioneer is not responsible for executing mail bids or FAX bids received on or after the day the first lot is sold, nor Internet bids submitted after the published closing time; nor is Auctioneer responsible for proper execution of bids submitted by telephone, mail, FAX, e-mail, Internet, or in person once the Auction begins. Internet bids may not be withdrawn until your written request is received and acknowledged by Auctioneer (FAX: 214-443-8425); such requests must state the reason, and may constitute grounds for withdrawal of bidding privileges. Lots won by mail Bidders will not be delivered at the Auction unless prearranged.
11. Caveat as to Bid Increments. Bid increments (over the current bid level) determine the lowest amount you may bid on a particular lot. Bids greater than one increment over the current bid can be any whole dollar amount. It is possible under several circumstances for winning bids to be between increments, sometimes only $1 above the previous increment. Please see: "How can I lose by less than an increment?" on our website.

The following chart governs current bidding increments.

Current Bid	Bid Increment	Current Bid	Bid Increment
< $10	$1	$3,000 - $4,999	$250
$10 - $29	$2	$5,000 - $9,999	$500
$30 - $59	$3	$10,000 - $19,999	$1,000
$60 - $99	$5	$20,000 - $29,999	$2,000
$100 - $199	$10	$30,000 - $49,999	$2,500
$200 - $299	$20	$50,000 - $99,999	$5,000
$300 - $499	$25	$100,000 - $249,999	$10,000
$500 - $999	$50	$250,000 - $499,999	$25,000
$1,000 - $1,999	$100	$500,000 - $1,499,999	$50,000
$2,000 - $2,999	$200	> $1,500,000	$100,000

12. If Auctioneer calls for a full increment, a floor/phone bidder may request Auctioneer to accept a bid at half of the increment ("Cut Bid") which will be that bidders final bid; if the Auctioneer solicits bids other the expected increment, they will not be considered Cut Bids, and bidders accepting such increments may continue to participate.

Conducting the Auction:

13. Notice of the consignor's liberty to place reserve bids on his lots in the Auction is hereby made in accordance with Article 2 of the Texas Uniform Commercial Code. A reserve is an amount below which the lot will not sell. THE CONSIGNOR OF PROPERTY MAY PLACE WRITTEN RESERVE BIDS ON HIS LOTS IN ADVANCE OF THE AUCTION; ON SUCH LOTS, IF THE HAMMER PRICE DOES NOT MEET THE RESERVE, THE CONSIGNOR MAY PAY A REDUCED COMMISSION ON THOSE LOTS. Reserves are generally posted online several days prior to the Auction closing. Any successful bid placed by a consignor on his Property on the Auction floor or by telephone during the live session, or after the reserves for an Auction have been posted, will be considered an Unqualified Bid, and in such instances the consignor agrees to pay full Buyer's Premium and Seller's Commissions on any lot so repurchased.
14. The highest qualified Bidder shall be the buyer. In the event of any dispute between floor Bidders at a Signature Auction, Auctioneer may at his sole discretion reoffer the lot. Auctioneer's decision and declaration of the winning Bidder shall be final and binding upon all Bidders.
15. Auctioneer reserves the right to refuse to honor any bid or to limit the amount of any bid which, in his sole discretion, is not submitted in "Good Faith," or is not supported by satisfactory credit, numismatic references, or otherwise. A bid is considered not made in "Good Faith" when an insolvent or irresponsible person, or a person under the age of eighteen makes it. Regardless of the disclosure of his identity, any bid by a consignor or his agent on a lot consigned by him is deemed to be made in "Good Faith".
16. Nominal Bids. The Auctioneer in its sole discretion may reject nominal bids, small opening bids, or very nominal advances. If a lot bearing estimates fails to open for 40 –60% of the low estimate, the Auctioneer may pass the item or may place a protective bid on behalf of the consignor.
17. Lots bearing bidding estimates shall open at Auctioneer's discretion (approximately 50% of the low estimate). In the event that no bid meets or exceeds that opening amount, the lot shall pass as unsold.
18. All items are to be purchased per lot as numerically indicated and no lots will be broken. Bids will be accepted in whole dollar amounts only. No "buy" or "unlimited" bids will be accepted. Off-increment bids may be accepted by the Auctioneer at Signature Auctions and Grand Format Auctions. Auctioneer reserves the right to withdraw, prior to the close, any lots from the Auction.
19. Auctioneer reserves the right to rescind the sale in the event of nonpayment, breach of a warranty, disputed ownership, auctioneer's clerical error or omission in exercising bids and reserves, or otherwise.
20. Auctioneer occasionally experiences Internet and/or Server service outages during which Bidders cannot participate or place bids. If such outage occurs, we may at our discretion extend bidding for the auction. This policy applies only to widespread outages and not to isolated problems that occur in various parts of the country from time to time. Auctioneer periodically schedules system downtime for maintenance and other purposes, which may be covered by the Outage Policy. Bidders unable to place their Bids through the Internet are directed to bid through Client Services at 1-800-872-6467.
21. The Auctioneer or its affiliates may consign items to be sold in the Auction, and may bid on those lots or any other lots. Auctioneer or affiliates expressly reserve the right to modify any such bids at any time prior to the hammer based upon data made known to the Auctioneer or its affiliates. The Auctioneer may extend advances, guarantees, or loans to certain consignors, and may extend financing or other credits at varying rates to certain Bidders in the auction.
22. The Auctioneer has the right to sell certain unsold items after the close of the Auction; Such lots shall be considered sold during the Auction and all these Terms and Conditions shall apply to such sales including but not limited to the Buyer's Premium, return rights, and disclaimers.

Payment:

23. All sales are strictly for cash in United States dollars. Cash includes: U.S. currency, bank wire, cashier checks, travelers checks, and bank money orders, all subject to reporting requirements. Checks may be subject to clearing before delivery of the purchases. Credit Card (Visa or Master Card only) and PayPal payments may be accepted up to $10,000 from non-dealers at the sole discretion of the auctioneer, subject to the following limitations: a) sales are only to the cardholder, b) purchases are shipped to the cardholder's registered and verified address, c) Auctioneer may pre-approve the cardholder's credit line, d) a credit card transaction may not be used in conjunction with any other financing or extended terms offered by the Auctioneer, and must transact immediately upon invoice presentation, e) rights of return are governed by these Terms and Conditions, which supersede those conditions promulgated by the card issuer, f) floor Bidders must present their card.

24. Payment is due upon closing of the Auction session, or upon presentment of an invoice. Auctioneer reserves the right to void an invoice if payment in full is not received within 7 days after the close of the Auction.
25. Lots delivered in the States of Texas, California, or other states where the Auction may be held, are subject to all applicable state and local taxes, unless appropriate permits are on file with us. Bidder agrees to pay Auctioneer the actual amount of tax due in the event that sales tax is not properly collected due to: 1) an expired, inaccurate, inappropriate tax certificate or declaration, 2) an incorrect interpretation of the applicable statute, 3) or any other reason. Lots from different Auctions may not be aggregated for sales tax purposes.
26. In the event that a Bidder's payment is dishonored upon presentment(s), Bidder shall pay the maximum statutory processing fee set by applicable state law.
27. If any Auction invoice submitted by Auctioneer is not paid in full when due, the unpaid balance will bear interest at the highest rate permitted by law from the date of invoice until paid. If the Auctioneer refers any invoice to an attorney for collection, the buyer agrees to pay attorney's fees, court costs, and other collection costs incurred by Auctioneer. If Auctioneer assigns collection to its in-house legal staff, such attorney's time expended on the matter shall be compensated at a rate comparable to the hourly rate of independent attorneys.
28. In the event a successful Bidder fails to pay all amounts due, Auctioneer reserves the right to resell the merchandise, and such Bidder agrees to pay for the reasonable costs of resale, including a 10% seller's commission, and also to pay any difference between the resale price and the price of the previously successful bid.
29. Auctioneer reserves the right to require payment in full in good funds before delivery of the merchandise.
30. Auctioneer shall have a lien against the merchandise purchased by the buyer to secure payment of the Auction invoice. Auctioneer is further granted a lien and the right to retain possession of any other property of the buyer then held by the Auctioneer or its affiliates to secure payment of any Auction invoice or any other amounts due the Auctioneer or affiliates from the buyer. With respect to these lien rights, Auctioneer shall have all the rights of a secured creditor under Article 9 of the Texas Uniform Commercial Code, including but not limited to the right of sale. In addition, with respect to payment of the Auction invoice(s), the buyer waives any and all rights of offset he might otherwise have against the Auctioneer and the consignor of the merchandise included on the invoice. If a Bidder owes Auctioneer or its affiliates on any account, Auctioneer and its affiliates shall have the right to offset such unpaid account by any credit balance due Bidder, and it may secure by possessory lien any unpaid amount by any of the Bidder's property in their possession.
31. Title shall not pass to the successful Bidder until all invoices are paid in full. It is the responsibility of the buyer to provide adequate insurance coverage for the items once they have been delivered.

Delivery; Shipping and Handling Charges:

32. Shipping and handling charges will be added to invoices. Please refer to Auctioneer's website www.HA.com/common/shipping.php for the latest charges or call Auctioneer. Auctioneer is unable to combine purchases from other auctions or affiliates into one package for shipping purposes.
33. Successful overseas Bidders shall provide written shipping instructions, including specified customs declarations, to the Auctioneer for any lots to be delivered outside of the United States. NOTE: Declaration value shall be the item(s) hammer price together with its buyer's premium.
34. All shipping charges will be borne by the successful Bidder. Any risk of loss during shipment will be borne by the buyer following Auctioneer's delivery to the designated common carrier or third-party shipper, regardless of domestic or foreign shipment.
35. Due to the nature of some items sold, it shall be the responsibility for the successful bidder to arrange pick-up and shipping through third-parties; as to such items Auctioneer shall have no liability.
36. Any request for shipping verification for undelivered packages must be made within 30 days of shipment by Auctioneer.

Cataloging, Warranties and Disclaimers:

37. NO WARRANTY, WHETHER EXPRESSED OR IMPLIED, IS MADE WITH RESPECT TO ANY DESCRIPTION OR CONDITION REPORT CONTAINED IN THIS AUCTION OR ANY SECOND OPINE. Any description of the items or second opine contained in this Auction is for the sole purpose of identifying the items for those Bidders who do not have the opportunity to view the lots prior to bidding, and no description of items has been made part of the basis of the bargain or has created any express warranty that the goods would conform to any description made by Auctioneer.
38. Auctioneer is selling only such right or title to the items being sold as Auctioneer may have by virtue of consignment agreements on the date of auction and disclaims any warranty of title to the Property. Auctioneer disclaims any warranty of merchantability or fitness for any particular purposes.
39. Translations of foreign language documents may be provided as a convenience to interested parties. Heritage makes no representation as to the accuracy of those translations and will not be held responsible for errors in bidding arising from inaccuracies in translation.
40. Auctioneer disclaims all liability for damages, consequential or otherwise, arising out of or in connection with the sale of any Property by Auctioneer to Bidder. No third party may rely on any benefit of these Terms and Conditions and any rights, if any, established hereunder are personal to the Bidder and may not be assigned. Any statement made by the Auctioneer is an opinion and does not constitute a warranty or representation. No employee of Auctioneer may alter these Terms and Conditions, and, unless signed by a principal of Auctioneer, any such alteration is null and void.
41. Auctioneer shall not be liable for breakage of glass or damage to frames (patent or latent); such defects, in any event, shall not be a basis for any claim for return or reduction in purchase price.

Release:

42. In consideration of participation in the Auction and the placing of a bid, Bidder expressly releases Auctioneer, its officers, directors and employees, its affiliates, and its outside experts that provide second opines, from any and all claims, cause of action, chose of action, whether at law or equity or any arbitration or mediation rights existing under the rules of any professional society or affiliation based upon the assigned description, or a derivative theory, breach of warranty express or implied, representation or other matter set forth within these Terms and Conditions of Auction or otherwise. In the event of a claim, Bidder agrees that such rights and privileges conferred therein are strictly construed as specifically declared herein; e.g., authenticity, typographical error, etc. and are the exclusive remedy. Bidder, by non-compliance to these express terms of a granted remedy, shall waive any claim against Auctioneer.

Dispute Resolution and Arbitration Provision:

43. By placing a bid or otherwise participating in the auction, Bidder accepts these Terms and Conditions of Auction, and specifically agrees to the alternative dispute resolution provided herein. Arbitration replaces the right to go to court, including the right to a jury trial.
44. Auctioneer in no event shall be responsible for consequential damages, incidental damages, compensatory damages, or other damages arising from the auction of any lot. In the event that Auctioneer cannot deliver the lot or subsequently it is established that the lot lacks title, provenance, authenticity, or other transfer or condition issue is claimed, Auctioneer's liability shall be limited to rescission of sale and refund of purchase price; in no case shall Auctioneer's maximum liability exceed the high bid on that lot, which bid shall be deemed for all purposes the value of the lot. After one year has elapsed, Auctioneer's maximum liability shall be limited to any commissions and fees Auctioneer earned on that lot.
45. In the event of an attribution error, Auctioneer may at its sole discretion, correct the error on the Internet, or, if discovered at a later date, to refund the buyer's purchase price without further obligation.
46. If any dispute arises regarding payment, authenticity, grading, description, provenance, or any other matter pertaining to the Auction, the Bidder or a participant in the Auction and/or the Auctioneer agree that the dispute shall be submitted, if otherwise mutually unresolved, to binding arbitration in accordance with the commercial rules of the American Arbitration Association (A.A.A.). A.A.A. arbitration shall be conducted under the provisions of the Federal Arbitration Act with locale in Dallas, Texas. Any claim made by a Bidder has to be presented within one (1) year or it is barred. The prevailing party may be awarded his reasonable attorney's fees and costs. An award granted in arbitration is enforceable in any court of competent jurisdiction. No claims of any kind (except for reasons of authenticity) can be considered after the settlements have been made with the consignors. Any dispute after the settlement date is strictly between the Bidder and consignor without involvement or responsibility of the Auctioneer.
47. In consideration of their participation in or application for the Auction, a person or entity (whether the successful Bidder, a Bidder, a purchaser and/or other Auction participant or registrant) agrees that all disputes in any way relating to, arising under, connected with, or incidental to these Terms and Conditions and purchases, or default in payment thereof, shall be arbitrated pursuant to the arbitration provision. In the event that any matter including actions to compel arbitration, construe the agreement, actions in aid or arbitration or otherwise needs to be litigated, such litigation shall be exclusively in the Courts of the State of Texas, in Dallas County, Texas, and if necessary the corresponding appellate courts. The successful Bidder, purchaser, or Auction participant also expressly submits himself to the personal jurisdiction of the State of Texas.
48. These Terms & Conditions provide specific remedies for occurrences in the auction and delivery process. Where such remedies are afforded, they shall be interpreted strictly. Bidder agrees that any claim shall utilize such remedies; Bidder making a claim in excess of those remedies provided in these Terms and Conditions agrees that in no case whatsoever shall Auctioneer's maximum liability exceed the high bid on that lot, which bid shall be deemed for all purposes the value of the lot..

Miscellaneous:

49. Agreements between Bidders and consignors to effectuate a non-sale of an item at Auction, inhibit bidding on a consigned item to enter into a private sale agreement for said item, or to utilize the Auctioneer's Auction to obtain sales for non-selling consigned items subsequent to the Auction, are strictly prohibited. If a subsequent sale of a previously consigned item occurs in violation of this provision, Auctioneer reserves the right to charge Bidder the applicable Buyer's Premium and consignor a Seller's Commission as determined for each auction venue and by the terms of the seller's agreement.
50. Acceptance of these Terms and Conditions qualifies Bidder as a Heritage customer who has consented to be contacted by Heritage in the future. In conformity with "do-not-call" regulations promulgated by the Federal or State regulatory agencies, participation by the Bidder is affirmative consent to being contacted at the phone number shown in his application and this consent shall remain in effect until it is revoked in writing. Heritage may from time to time contact Bidder concerning sale, purchase, and auction opportunities available through Heritage and its affiliates and subsidiaries.

State Notices:

Notice as to an Auction in California. Auctioneer has in compliance with Title 2.95 of the California Civil Code as amended October 11, 1993 Sec. 1812.600, posted with the California Secretary of State its bonds for it and its employees, and the auction is being conducted in compliance with Sec. 2338 of the Commercial Code and Sec. 535 of the Penal Code.

Notice as to an Auction in New York City. These Terms and Conditions are designed to conform to the applicable sections of the New York City Department of Consumer Affairs Rules and Regulations as Amended. This is a Public Auction Sale conducted by Auctioneer. The New York City licensed Auctioneers are Kathleen Guzman, No.0762165-Day, and Samuel W. Foose, No.0952360-Day, No.0952361-Night, who will conduct the Auction on behalf of Heritage Auctions, Inc. ("Auctioneer"). All lots are subject to: the consignor's right to bid thereon in accord with these Terms and Conditions of Auction, consignor's option to receive advances on their consignments, and Auctioneer, in its sole discretion, may offer limited extended financing to registered bidders, in accord with Auctioneer's internal credit standards. A registered bidder may inquire whether a lot is subject to an advance or reserve. Auctioneer has made advances to various consignors in this sale.

Additional Terms and Conditions of Auction

FINE AND DECORATIVE ARTS TERM A: Auctioneer warrants authorship, period or culture of each lot sold in this catalog is as set out in the BOLD faced type heading in the catalogue description of the lot, with the following exclusions. This warranty does not apply to:

i. authorship of any paintings, drawings or sculpture created prior to 1870, unless the lot is determined to be a counterfeit which has a value at the date of the claim for rescission which is materially less than the purchase price paid for the lot; or
ii. any catalog description where it was specifically mentioned that there is a conflict of specialist opinion on the authorship of a lot; or
iii. authorship which on the date of sale was in accordance with the then generally accepted opinion of scholars and specialists, despite the subsequent discovery of new information, whether historical or physical, concerning the artist or craftsman, his students, school, workshop or followers; or
iv. the identification of periods or dates of execution which may be proven inaccurate by means of scientific processes not generally accepted for use until after publication of the catalog, or which were unreasonably expensive or impractical to use at the time of publication of the catalog.

The term counterfeit is defined as a modern fake or forgery, made less than fifty years ago with the intent to deceive. The authenticity of signatures, monograms, initials or other similar indications of authorship is expressly excluded as a controlling factor in determining whether a work is a counterfeit under the meaning of these Terms and Conditions of Auction.

FINE AND DECORATIVE ARTS TERM B: GLOSSARY OF TERMS

Terms used in this catalog have the following meanings. Please note that all statements in this catalog regarding authorship, attribution, origin, date, age, provenance and condition are statements of opinion and are not treated a statement of fact. Special rules apply to the Warranty and are covered in to the Fine Arts Terms and Conditions of Auction.

1. THOMAS MORAN
In our opinion, the work is by the artist.

2. ATTRIBUTED TO THOMAS MORAN
In our opinion, the work is of the period of the artist which may be whole or in part the work of the artist.

3. STUDIO, (CIRCLE OR WORKSHOP) OF THOMAS MORAN
In our opinion, the work is of the period and closely relates to his style.

4. SCHOOL OF THOMAS MORAN
In our opinion, the work is by a pupil or a follower of the artist.

5. MANNER OF THOMAS MORAN
In our opinion, the work is in the style of the artist and is of a later period.

6. AFTER THOMAS MORAN
In our opinion, this work is a copy of the artist.

7. ASCRIBED TO THOMAS MORAN
In our opinion, this work is not by the artist, however, previous scholarship has noted this to be a work by the artist.

8. SIGNED (OR DATED)
The work has a signature (or date) which is in our opinion is genuine.

9. BEARS SIGNATURE (OR DATE)
The work has a signature (or date) which in our opinion is not authentic.

FINE AND DECORATIVE ARTS TERM C: WARRANTY: The warranty as to authorship is provided for a period of one (1) year from the date of the auction and is only for the benefit of the original purchaser of record and is not transferable. To obtain a claim of Authorship, you must provide us with written notice within the claim period and two written letters by independent and authorized appraisers in support of the claim. It is specifically understood that any refund agreed to by the Auctioneer would be limited to the purchase price.

FINE AND DECORATIVE ARTS TERM D: The Auction is not on approval. Under extremely limited circumstances not including authenticity (e.g. gross cataloging error), a purchaser who did not bid from the floor may request Auctioneer to evaluate voiding a sale; such request must be made in writing detailing the alleged gross error, and submission of the lot to Auctioneer must be pre-approved by Auctioneer. A bidder must notify the appropriate department head (check the inside front cover of the catalog or our website for a listing of department heads) in writing of the purchaser's request within three (3) days of the non-floor bidder's receipt of the lot. Any lot that is to be evaluated for return must be received in our offices within 30 days after Auction. AFTER THAT 30 DAY PERIOD, NO LOT MAY BE RETURNED FOR ANY REASONS. Lots returned must be in the same condition as when sold and must include any Certificate of Authenticity. No lots purchased by floor bidders may be returned (including those bidders acting as agents for others). Late remittance for purchases may be considered just cause to revoke all return privileges.

FINE AND DECORATIVE ARTS TERM E: The catalog descriptions are provided for identification purposes only. Bidders who intend to challenge a bold-faced provision in the description of a lot must notify Auctioneer in writing within thirty (30) days of the Auction's conclusion. In the event Auctioneer cannot deliver the lot or subsequently it is established that the lot lacks title or the bold faced section of description is incorrect, or other transfer or condition issue is claimed, Auctioneer's liability shall be limited to rescission of sale and refund of purchase price; in no case shall Auctioneer's maximum liability exceed the high bid on that lot, which bid shall be deemed for all purposes the value of the lot. After one year has elapsed, Auctioneer's maximum liability shall be limited to any commissions and fees Auctioneer earned on that lot.

FINE AND DECORATIVE ARTS TERM F: Any claim as to provenance or authenticity must be first transmitted to Auctioneer by credible and definitive evidence or the opine of a qualified third party expert and there is no assurance after such presentment that Auctioneer will validate the claim. Authentication is not an exact science and contrary opinions may not be recognized by Auctioneer. Even if Auctioneer agrees with the contrary opinion of such authentication, our liability for reimbursement for such service shall not exceed $500.

FINE AND DECORATIVE ARTS TERM G: Provenance and authenticity are guaranteed by neither the consignor nor Auctioneer. While every effort is made to determine provenance and authenticity, it is the responsibility of the Bidder to arrive at their own conclusion prior to bidding.

FINE AND DECORATIVE ARTS TERM H: On the fall of Auctioneer's hammer, Buyers of Fine Arts and Decorative Arts lots assumes full risk and responsibility for lot, including shipment by common carrier or third-party shipper, and must provide their own insurance coverage for shipments.

FINE AND DECORATIVE ARTS TERM I: Auctioneer complies to all Federal and State rules and regulations relating to the purchasing, registration and shipping of firearms. A purchaser is required to provide appropriate documents and the payment of associated fees, if any. Purchaser is responsible for providing a shipping address that is suitable for the receipt of a firearm.

WIRING INSTRUCTIONS:
Bank Information: JP Morgan Chase Bank, N.A., 270 Park Avenue, New York, NY 10017
Account Name: HERITAGE NUMISMATIC AUCTIONS MASTER ACCOUNT
ABA Number: 021000021
Account Number: 1884827674
Swift Code: CHASUS33